MACHINE SHOP THEORY

MACHINE SHOP THEORY

Editor
Samual Rodrigues

DPH

DISCOVERY PUBLISHING HOUSE
INDIA

Published by:

DISCOVERY PUBLISHING HOUSE
4383/4B, Ansari Road, Darya Ganj
New Delhi-110 002 (India)
Phone : +91-11-23279245; 23253475; 43596065
+91 9811179893 / +91 9871656464
E-mail : discoverybooksindia@gmail.com
orderdphbooks@gmail.com
namitwasan9@gmail.com
web : www.discoverypublishinggroup.com

***First Published:* 2024**

ISBN: 978-81-19205-63-9

Machine Shop Theory

Printed at:
Infinity Imaging Systems
Delhi

PREFACE

A machine shop is a facility equipped with various tools and machines for machining, which is the process of cutting, fabricating, and finishing parts to make them usable. Machine shops are used for creating new parts and repairing existing ones. Personnel working in a machine shop may have specialized training depending on the type of work done there, as certain machining tasks require specific skills and knowledge of how the finished parts will be used.

Many types of equipment, such as cars, aircraft, large engines, and manufacturing equipment, require parts that are created or repaired in a machine shop. Manufacturing companies often have a machine shop on site for fabricating new, custom, and test parts. Machine shops are also found in educational and research facilities where people learn about machining in the context of repair and developing equipment for custom applications. Traditionally, machine shops have relied on physical equipment and human labor for machining tasks. However, over the last decade, there has been a shift towards the digitalization of manufacturing, which aims to overcome the challenges of unexpected fluctuations in demand, increased quality requirements, and flexible supply chains.

Digitalization introduces an ecosystem of technologies, including sensing, communication, data modeling, and decision-making, among others. Recent advances in the semiconductor industry have enabled the installation of numerous sensors in production with low installation costs. Communication networks and mechanisms, such as Wireless Sensor Networks (WSN), Industrial Networks, and Web services, facilitate continuous information flow among different systems.

However, despite the benefits of digitalization, more than 90% of manufacturing resources are not integrated into the industrial communication network. Therefore, traditional machine shops are being transformed into Machine Shops 4.0, following the main directions of Industry 4.0. Machine Shops 4.0 incorporate digital technologies, such as the Internet of Things (IoT), to enable intelligent and connected machines that can communicate with each other and with the operators, thereby increasing efficiency and reducing costs.

This book focuses on the principles of machine shop theory, with an emphasis on both conventional and CNC machining operations. It is a reference work that highlights recent developments, covers the latest research results, and reflects current areas of emphasis in industrial practice.

The book covers a range of topics related to machine shop theory, including the fundamentals of machining processes, tool geometry, cutting tool materials, machine tool design and construction, CNC programming and operations, and safety practices. The contributors of the book are experts in the field of machine shop theory and have extensive experience in both academic and industrial settings. They provide detailed explanations of the fundamental principles of machine shop theory, along with practical examples and applications to real-world situations.

The editor of the book has gathered information from trustworthy and scientifically backed sources to give readers the most up-to-date and accurate information possible. The book is a collection of articles written by experts from all over the world, and the editor is grateful for their valuable input. The knowledge and expertise shared by these experts are insightful and will be beneficial for the readers.

Editor

CONTENTS

1

Multi-Task Multi-Agent Reinforcement Learning for Real-Time Scheduling of a Dual-Resource Flexible Job Shop with Robots

Xiaofei Zhu[1], Jiazhong Xu[1], Jianghua Ge[1], Yaping Wang[1] and Zhiqiang Xie[2]

[1]Key Laboratory of Advanced Manufacturing and Intelligent Technology, Ministry of Education, Harbin University of Science and Technology, Harbin 150080, China

[2]College of Computer Science and Technology, Harbin University of Science and Technology, Harbin 150080, China

ABSTRACT

In this paper, a real-time scheduling problem of a dual-resource flexible job shop with robots is studied. Multiple independent robots and their supervised machine sets form their own work cells. First, a mixed integer programming model is established, which considers the scheduling problems of jobs and machines in the work cells, and of jobs between work cells, based on the process plan flexibility. Second, in order to make real-time scheduling decisions, a framework of multi-task multi-agent reinforcement learning based on centralized training and decentralized execution is proposed. Each agent interacts with the environment and completes three decision-making tasks: job sequencing, machine selection, and process planning. In the process of centralized training, the value network is used to evaluate and optimize the policy network to achieve multi-agent cooperation, and the attention mechanism is introduced into the policy network to realize information sharing among multiple tasks. In the process of decentralized execution, each agent performs multiple task decisions through local observations according to the trained policy network. Then, observation, action, and reward are designed. Rewards include global and local rewards, which are decomposed into sub-rewards corresponding to tasks. The reinforcement learning training algorithm is designed based on a double-deep Q-network. Finally, the scheduling simulation environment is derived from benchmarks, and the experimental results show the effectiveness of the proposed method.

Keywords: *Real-Time Scheduling, Dual-Resource Constraint, Multi-Task Multi-Agent Reinforcement Learning, Flexible Job Shop Scheduling, Flexible Process Planning*

INTRODUCTION

The intelligent factory focuses on integrating advanced technologies such as the Internet, big data, and artificial intelligence with enterprise resource planning, a manufacturing execution system, and production process control [1]. The intelligent factory has self-perception, analysis, reasoning, decision, and control abilities [2]. In the rapid development of large-scale personalized manufacturing, workshop management and control systems in intelligent factories can learn independently to adapt to dynamic changes in the production process [3]. Industrial robots and artificial intelligence play a key role in improving workshop intelligence and realizing the intelligent workshop. The industrial robot, which is a resource that can transfer materials flexibly and quickly, is one of the elements in the process of intelligent transformation and is also a driver of intelligent manufacturing. At the same time, deep integration of artificial intelligence with the manufacturing system, and fast, intelligent real-time analysis based on production data effectively improve the decision ability and execution efficiency of the workshop management and control system. At the core of workshop management and control, production is directly involved in information transmission and task coordination. Its real-time optimization provides greater flexibility for the operation of the intelligent workshop, and it plays a positive role in optimizing resource allocation, improving production efficiency, and reducing costs [4].

In general, the intelligent workshop is a flexible manufacturing system composed of industrial robots, machines, and other hardware, and information acquisition and control software. In the intelligent workshop, the robot is the executor of scheduling schemes, such as the loading and unloading of jobs on the machine [5]. At the same time, the robot is also an element to be considered in scheduling optimization. The machines and robots are regarded as limited resources, and the production capacity of the workshop is constrained by both of them at the same time, which is a dual-resource constraint [6]. In addition, in a flexible manufacturing system, due to the diversification of processing methods, a job may have multiple alternative process plans. Scheduling decisions should consider not only the process plan flexibility of the job, but also the machine flexibility of the operation [7]. Therefore, in the complex and dynamically changing intelligent workshop, the workshop scheduling problem, which takes robots and machines as production resources and considers high flexibility, is a more complex flexible job shop scheduling problem (FJSP).

Extensive research has been carried out on the FJSP [8,9,10], providing possibilities for diversified and differentiated personalized mass manufacturing. At present, a large number of mathematical and metaheuristic algorithms have been developed, such as the evolutionary algorithm, ant colony algorithm, and particle swarm algorithm [11]. With scheduling application in actual production, researchers have expanded the scheduling problem according to different scenarios. Among them, the integration of process planning and scheduling issues has received a great deal of attention [12,13]. The FJSP with flexible process planning is a more complex decision problem. Özgüven et al. [14] developed a mixed integer programming model for FJSP with flexible process planning, which created an effective mathematical model. Phanden et al. [15] summarized three solutions for process planning and scheduling integration: non-chain, closed-loop, and distributed. In the above research, the scheduling problems mostly focused on the machines. However, the operation process requires not only machines, but also other types of resources, such as robots, workers, logistics equipment, and fixtures. Brucker et al. [16] studied the cyclic job–shop problem with transportation for optimization problems in fully automated manufacturing systems or assembly lines. They characterized feasible solutions based on the route of the robot and their properties. To optimally minimize the cycle time, a tree search method was developed to construct feasible solutions. Fatemi-Anaraki et al. [17] investigated a dynamic scheduling problem within a job shop robotic cell, wherein multiple robotic arms are responsible for material handling in a U-shaped arrangement. They also designed a mixed integer linear programming model and solution method for this problem. Ham [18] studied the simultaneous scheduling of production and material transfer in a FJSP environment. Two different constraint programming formulations are proposed for the FJSP with a robotic mobile fulfillment system. Analysis results show significant outperformance of all other benchmark approaches in the literature. The above literature shows that in intelligent workshops, machines and robots have gradually become the main production resources. This is more complex than the scheduling problem of a single resource [19].

The existing literature has studied different FJSPs with dual-resource constraints. Wu et al. [20] considered fixtures and machines as two kinds of resources and studied the FJSP with dual-resource constraints considering fixture loading and unloading. The research results showed that the scheduling scheme with multiple resources had a greater guiding role in production than the scheduling scheme with a single resource. He et al. [21] constructed a dual-resource constrained FJSP model with machine and worker. An improved African vulture optimization algorithm is developed such that the makespan and total delay are minimized. Jiang et al. [22] presented a discrete animal migration optimization to solve the dual-resource constrained energy-saving FJSP to minimize the total energy consumption in the workshop. Results demonstrate that the proposed algorithm has advantages against other compared algorithms in terms of the solving accuracy for solving the studied scheduling problem. Hongyu et al. [23] focused on three kinds of indicators of sustainable development—that is, economy, environment, and society—and schedule two types of resource—that is, machines and workers—simultaneously in the classical FJSP. An improved survival duration-guided NSGA-III algorithm is proposed to solve the problem. These studies assume that each worker can only operate one machine; that is, the dual-resource constraint problem with a single task and simultaneous supervision. However, in an intelligent workshop, robots generally serve multiple machines at the same time, which is called the dual-resource constraint problem with multiple tasks and simultaneous supervision (MTSSDRC). This can effectively improve productivity [24]. In this kind of scheduling problem, completing a job operation involves at least three activities: loading, processing, and unloading. The loading and unloading are carried out by the robot before and after processing, and the processing is completed by the machine.

At present, the literature on the MTSSDRC scheduling problem is limited. Costa et al. [25] and Akbar et al. [26,27] proposed a dual-resource constrained parallel machine scheduling problem, in which workers execute activities between machines. It makes up for the multi-worker supervision problem, which is usually ignored in traditional dual-resource scheduling, and establishes a mixed integer linear programming mathematical model. Later, Akbar et al. [28] improved several metaheuristic algorithms for the proposed model, making it suitable for solving MTSSDRC scheduling problems. The above literature laid a foundation for the MTSSDRC, and the algorithms are all suitable for solving the parallel machine scheduling problem. Research on the FJSP considering the MTSSDRC is scarce, which made it difficult to solve the scheduling problem proposed in this paper.

In the mass customization environment, the changing order and machine state are highly flexible, and the scheduling decision system needs to conduct adaptive self-optimization for such a dynamically changing workshop environment [29]. Therefore, the real-time generation of scheduling schemes becomes very important. Scheduling solutions based on mathematical modeling, the heuristic algorithm, the metaheuristic algorithm, and other algorithms [30,31,32] require iterative calculation and show poor real-time performance. Priority-based scheduling rules can effectively improve real-time decision-making. Choosing different priority rules according to dynamic changes is usually better than using a single priority rule. Therefore, the current related studies are focused on scheduling policies involving the dynamic selection of priority rules. This type of scheme completes the development of the scheduling policy through offline training, and then carries out high-quality and real-time scheduling online. Commonly used methods include genetic programming, machine learning (ML), and reinforcement learning (RL). The genetic programming method is carried out through iteration and population evolution. The disadvantage of this method is that it takes time to check the performance of candidate rule sets, which reduces the real-time scheduling. ML is used as a data mining tool to mine the historical data of the workshop. Based on the supervised learning method of classified tasks, appropriate scheduling rules are selected according to the real-time state of the workshop [33,34,35]. Different from ML, RL can establish direct mapping from environmental states to actions. Furthermore, deep reinforcement learning (DRL) using neural networks as value or policy functions can also handle complex tasks. These characteristics make DRL a more effective method for scheduling research in complex flexible manufacturing systems.

At present, DRL is widely used in workshop scheduling, such as for single machines, parallel machines, flow shop, and job shop. Generally, the scheduling rules used to solve the FJSP can be divided into two types: job selection rules and machine selection rules. For these two types of rules, scholars have defined FJSP as a Markov decision process (MDP) and used DRL for scheduling research. Luo [36] studied the dynamic FJSP under the condition of new job insertion with the objective of minimizing total tardiness. A real-time scheduling method based on the deep Q-network (DQN) was designed and used to select appropriate actions at scheduling decision points and complete the selection of jobs and machines. The research results show that the proposed method had better advantages and versatility compared to various combination rules, classical scheduling rules, and standard Q-learning. Han et al. [37] proposed an end-to-end DRL framework to solve the FJSP. In this framework, according to selected scheduling characteristics, pointer networks are used to encode scheduling operations, and a recursive neural network is used to model the decoding network. The experimental results showed that this method had better performance than classical heuristic rules.

The studies above all adopted the centralized model of a single agent and assumed that it was globally observable. This method lacks flexibility and autonomy. In order to overcome this shortcoming, Luo et al. [38] proposed a real-time scheduling method based on hierarchical multi-agent DRL. This method includes three agents: scheduling objective, job selection, and machine selection agents. This method effectively solves the dynamic multi-objective FJSP with new job insertion and machine failure. Liu et al. [39] proposed a layered and distributed framework to solve the dynamic flexible job shop scheduling problem. Based on the double-deep Q-network (DDQN), the machine selection agent and job sequencing agent are trained to make real-time scheduling decisions for the FJSP with the job deadline. Johnson et al. [40] proposed a DDQN-based multi-agent reinforcement learning method to solve the FJSP problem of robot assembly cells. Each agent in the assembly unit is trained in a centralized way and executes scheduling decisions independently according to local observations. The experimental results showed that this method had good performance in optimizing the maximum completion time.

However, in the above research, each agent only performed the decision of one task, which can only be adapted to small-scale scheduling problems. In a complex workshop environment, agents often need to be able to make decisions on multiple tasks to adapt to problems on a larger scale. Therefore, agents are required to have the ability to complete multiple task decisions. Lei et al. [41] noted that in the FJSP environment, an agent needs to control multiple actions at the same time, and they proposed a multi-pointer graph network architecture and multi-optimal policy optimization training algorithm to learn action policies of machine and job selection, in order to achieve the scheduling of allocating jobs to machines. The results showed that the agent could learn high-quality scheduling strategies, outperform heuristic scheduling rules in terms of the quality of solutions, outperform metaheuristic algorithms in terms of running time, and have good generalization performance on large-scale instances. Some scholars put forward the paradigm of multi-task learning based on shared representation. Jaing et al. [42] proposed a multi-task DRL method to solve the complex 3D boxing problem. The agent task includes three subtasks: sequence, direction, and position. This method can solve more large-scale instances and was shown to have good performance. Omidshafiei et al. [43] studied the locally observable multi-task multi-agent reinforcement learning problem, introduced a distributed single task learning method, which was robust to the cooperation between agents, and proposed a method to refine the single task policy into a unified policy, which performed well in multiple related tasks.

In this paper, for the dual-resource FJSP with robots, multiple agents are required to complete the decision to improve the scheduling performance, and each agent needs to have decision-making capability for multiple tasks. This poses a challenge to the existing multi-task and multi-agent RL method, because it is necessary to design an applicable framework according to the particularity of the problem. This framework not only requires coordination between agents to obtain good performance, but also ensures the universality of all policies to make more reasonable scheduling decisions using local observations.

To sum up, in order to solve the production scheduling problem of a typical com-plex flexible manufacturing workshop, the FJSP studied in this paper considers the dual-resource constraints of robots and machines (with each robot supervising multiple machines) and flexible process planning, which is the FJSP with dual resources and process plan flexibility (FJSP-DP). A DRL method is designed to solve the real-time scheduling problem. First, the FJSP-DP problem is described, and its mixed integer programming model is established to analyze and construct the scheduling environment. Second, combining the ideas of centralized training and decentralized execution, a real-time scheduling framework for multi-task multi-agent reinforcement learning (MTMARL) based on the DDQN algorithm is designed. The robot of each work cell acts as an agent to complete the scheduling decision tasks of the corresponding cell, including job sequencing, machine selection, and process planning. The centralized training method is adopted, and the value network of each agent evaluates and optimizes the policy network of its task execution action selection by sharing local observations. The policy network is composed of multiple neural networks for training and learning multiple task decisions. Then, the state, action, reward, and learning policies required by reinforcement learning training are designed to improve the learning efficiency and performance of the agent. Considering full cooperation between agents, the rewards include global and local rewards. Based on the scheduling decision tasks that each agent must complete, local rewards are decomposed into multiple sub-rewards for training the network parameters related to each task. Then, according to the designed reinforcement learning environment and the scheduling problem, the proposed framework training algorithm is developed. Finally, the scheduling simulation environment is built, and the algorithm training and performance analysis are carried out using the designed simulation examples to verify the effectiveness of the proposed method.

This paper makes the following contributions through developing and evaluating the proposed method:

- We establish the mixed integer programming model of FJSP-DP. In the model, each operation is scheduled by considering the flexibility of the process planning, the flexibility of the machine, which work cell to choose, and the loading and unloading activities.
- We develop the MTMARL approach for the real-time scheduling system of FJSP-DP. The approach has the functions of centralized training and decentralized execution of scheduling decisions. Each agent independently makes decision and communicates with other agents in real-time.
- We evaluate the feasibility and effectiveness of the proposed approach by developing a simulation environment of FJSP-DP and the MTMARL algorithm based on numerical experiments.

PROBLEM DESCRIPTION

The FJSP-DP is restricted by two kinds of resources: machines and robots. Where, the type of robot we assume is a robotic arm with a single gripper. Each of them has the same capacity regarding material handling (i.e., loading and unloading). The composition of the workshop is shown in Figure 1, with m machines and w robots (w < m). Robot k supervises the loading and unloading activities of each machine, and the machine set it supervises is $\{M_k^l\}_{l=1}^{N_k}$ $(M_k^l \in M)$. Robot k and the machines it supervises form a work cell (shown in Figure 1a). The buffer in the work cell is used to store jobs awaiting processing and completed jobs. There are n jobs, and the job set is $J = \{J_i\}_{i=1}^{n}$. Job i has a process plan set (as shown in Figure 1b), which is denoted as $P_i = \{O_{ip_i}\}_{p_i=1}^{\tau_i}$, and $j\ (j \in O_{ip_i})$ represents the j-th operation in the p_i-th process plan of job i. Each operation performs three sequential activities on the same machine: loading, processing, and unloading. After the robot completes the activity of one operation, it can perform the activity of other operations. Job i enter the corresponding work cell of each operation in turn according to its process plan until all operational activities are completed.

The relative assumptions are as follows:

(1) Each machine or robot can only process at most one job at a time.

(2) Each job can be processed by no more than one machine at one time.

(3) The transport time of the job between work cells is not considered.

(4) The buffer has unlimited capacity.

(5) Setup time is ignored.

(6) Rework and job loss are not considered.

(7) Preemption is prohibited, and the machine does not interrupt.

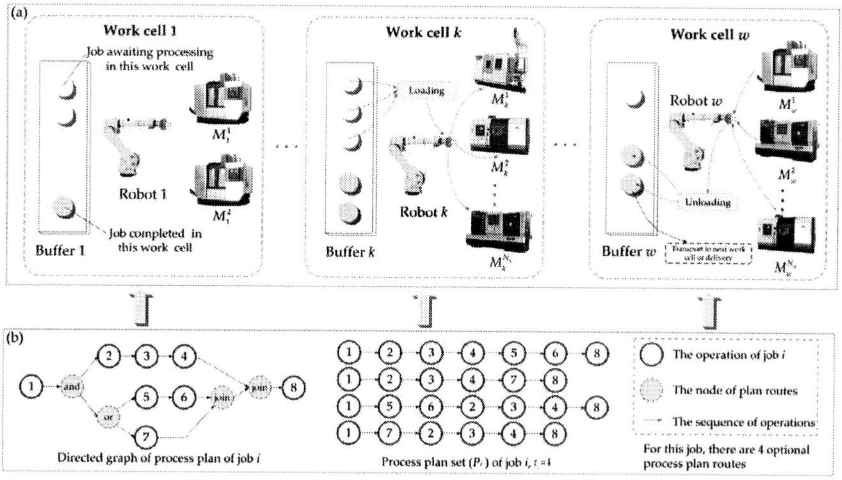

Figure 1. Composition of workshop: (a) schematic diagram of w work cells; (b) schematic diagram of process planning for a job.

Notation

According to the problem description, the mathematical symbols are as follows:

Parameters:

k Index of robots (or work cells); k ∈ W ∈

h Index of machines; h ∈ M ∈

i Index of jobs; I ∈ J ∈

j Index of operations; $j \in O_{ip_i}$

p_i Process plan for job i; $p_i \in P_i \in$

a (b, c) Loading or unloading activity; a (b, c) ∈ A

M Set of machines: M={1, 2, …, m}

M_j Set of machines available for processing operation j

W Set of robots: W={1, 2, …, w}

J Set of jobs: J={1, 2, …, n}

O_{ip_i} Set of operations belonging to the p_i-th process plan of job i

P_i Set of process plans belonging to job i

A Set of activities; A={1, 2} (1 loading, 2 unloading)

Input variables:

m Number of machines

w Number of robots

n Number of jobs

D_i Deadline for job i

T_{ip_ijh} Processing time of operation j, which belongs to the p_i-th process plan of job i on machine h

T_{ja} Execution time of activity a of operation j

L A large number

Decision variables:

$X_{khjah'j'b}$ Equals 1 if robot k completes activity a of operation j on machine h, before performing activity b of operation j′ on machine h′, and 0 otherwise

Y_{ip_ijh} Equals 1 if operation j, which belongs to the p_i-th process plan of job i, is processed by machine h, and 0 otherwise

Z_{ip_i} Equals 1 if job i select the p_i-th process plan, and 0 otherwise

$u_{jj'}$ Equals 1 if loading of operation j performed before unloading of operation j′ on the same machine, and 0 otherwise

S_{ja} Starting time of active a, which belongs to operation j

C_{ja} Completion time of active a, which belongs to operation j

C_{ip_ijh} Completion time of operation j, which belongs to the pi-th process plan of job i on machine h

C_i Completion time of job i

C_{max} Makespan

Formulation

The optimization objectives of FJSP-DP mainly consider delivery time and resource load. The scheduling of delivery time is conducted to obtain a scheme with a minimum tardiness penalty, whose objective is given by Formula (1).

$$\text{Minimize } \sum_{i=1}^{n} \max(C_i - D_i, 0) \tag{1}$$

The resource load considers machine and robot resources. For the machine, the optimization objective is expressed as minimizing the maximum machine utilization. Its objective is given by Formula (2).

$$\text{Minimize } \max\left(\sum_{i\in J} \sum_{p_i\in P_i} \sum_{j\in O_{ip_i}} \frac{Y_{ip_ijh} T_{ip_ijh}}{C_{max}}\right) \tag{2}$$

For robots, the load of each robot is measured by calculating its total working time (total loading and unloading time).

Suppose TW_k is the total working time of robot k and $\overline{TW}$ is the average total working time of all robots. Formula (3) is used to calculate the load deviation of all robots. The objective is to minimize the load deviation.

$$\text{Minimize } \sqrt{\sum_{k=1}^{w} \left(TW_k - \overline{TW}\right)^2} \tag{3}$$

s.t.,

$$\sum_{p_i\in P_i} Z_{ip_i} = 1 \; (\forall i \in J) \tag{4}$$

$$\sum_{h\in M_j} Y_{ip_ijh} = 1 \; (\forall i \in J, \forall p_i \in P_i, \forall j \in O_{ip_i}) \tag{5}$$

$$\sum_{k\in W} \sum_{h\in M_j} \sum_{j\in O_{ip_i}} \sum_{a\in A} \sum_{h'\in M_{j'}} X_{khjah'j'b} = 1 \; (\forall b \in A,\, j' \in O_{i'p_{i'}}) \tag{6}$$

$$\sum_{k\in W} \sum_{h\in M_j} \sum_{h'\in M_{j'}} \sum_{j'\in O_{i'p_{i'}}} \sum_{b\in A} X_{khjah'j'b} \le 1 \; (\forall a \in A,\, j \in O_{ip_i}) \tag{7}$$

$$\sum_{k\in W} \sum_{h\in M_j} \sum_{j\in O_{ip_i}} \sum_{a\in A} X_{khjah'j'b} - \sum_{k'\in W} \sum_{h''\in M_{j''}} \sum_{j''\in O_{i''p_{i''}}} \sum_{c\in A} X_{k'h''j''ch'j'b} = 0 \; (\forall h' \in M,\, j' \in O_{i'p_{i'}}) \tag{8}$$

$$\sum_{h\in M_j} \sum_{j\in O_{ip_i}} \sum_{a\in A} X_{khjah'j'b} \ge \sum_{h''\in M_{j''}} \sum_{j''\in O_{i''p_{i''}}} \sum_{c\in A} X_{kh'j'bh''j''c} \; (\forall k \in W,\, h' \in M,\, j' \in O_{i'p_{i'}}, b \in A) \tag{9}$$

$$\begin{cases} C_{j'1} - C_{j''2} \geq \sum_{k\in W}\sum_{h\in M}\sum_{j\in O_{ip_i}}\sum_{a\in A} T_{j'1}\cdot X_{khjah'j'1} - L\cdot(2-\sum_{k\in W}\sum_{h\in M}\sum_{j\in O_{ip_i}}\sum_{a\in A}(X_{khjah'j'1}+X_{khjah'j''1}) + U_{j''j'}) \\ C_{j''1} - C_{j'2} \geq \sum_{k\in W}\sum_{h\in M}\sum_{j\in O_{ip_i}}\sum_{a\in A} T_{j''1}\cdot X_{khjah'j'1} - L\cdot(2-\sum_{k\in W}\sum_{h\in M}\sum_{j\in O_{ip_i}}\sum_{a\in A}(X_{khjah'j'1}+X_{khjah'j''1}) + 1 - U_{j''j'}) \\ (\forall h'\in M;\ j'\in O_{i'p_{i'}};\ j''\in O_{i''p_{i''}}) \end{cases} \quad (10)$$

$$C_{ja} - S_{ja} \geq T_{ja}\ (\forall a\in A,\ j\in O_{ip_i}) \quad (11)$$

$$S_{j'b} - C_{ja} \geq -L\cdot(1-\sum_{k\in W}\sum_{h\in M_j}\sum_{h'\in M_{j'}} X_{khjah'j'b})\ (\forall a,\ b\in A;\ j\in O_{ip_i};\ j'\in O_{i'p_{i'}}) \quad (12)$$

$$C_{j2} - C_{ip_ijh} \geq T_{j2}\ (\forall i\in J,\ p_i\in P_i,\ j\in O_{ip_i},\ h\in M_j) \quad (13)$$

$$C_{ip_ijh} - C_{j1} = T_{ip_ijh}\ (\forall i\in J,\ p_i\in P_i,\ j\in O_{ip_i},\ h\in M_j) \quad (14)$$

$$S_{j1} \geq C_{(j-1)2}\ (\forall j\in O_{ip_i}) \quad (15)$$

$$C_{02} = 0 \quad (16)$$

$$C_i \geq C_{j2}\ (\forall i\in J;\ j\in O_{ip_i}) \quad (17)$$

$$C_{max} \geq C_i\ (\forall i\in J) \quad (18)$$

$$TW_k = \sum_{h\in M_j}\sum_{j\in O_{ip_i}}\sum_{a\in A}\sum_{h'\in M_{j'}}\sum_{j'\in O_{i'p_{i'}}}\sum_{b\in A} X_{khjah'j'b}\cdot T_{j'b}\ (\forall k\in W) \quad (19)$$

$$\begin{cases} X_{khjah'j'b}\in\{0,1\}\ (\forall k\in W;\ h,h'\in M;\ j\in O_{ip_i};\ j'\in O_{i'p_{i'}};a,b\in A) \\ Y_{ip_ijh}\in\{0,1\}\ (\forall i\in J;\ p_i\in P_i;\ j\in O_{ip_i};\ h\in M) \\ Z_{ip_i}\in\{0,1\}\ (\forall i\in J;\ p_i\in P_i) \\ U_{jj'}\in\{0,1\}\ (\forall j\in O_{ip_i};\ j'\in O_{i'p_{i'}}) \end{cases} \quad (20)$$

Constraint (4) indicates that only one process plan can be selected for each part.

Constraint (5) imposes that each operation can only be scheduled once.

Constraint (6) specifies that any activity of any operation is only assigned to one robot and one machine, and the activity of operation j′ is performed after the activity of operation j is completed.

Constraint (7) imposes that the robot can only perform one activity at a time.

Constraint (8) indicates that loading and unloading activities of one operation are completed on the same machine.

Constraint (9) ensures the sequence feasibility of activities: if activity b of operation j′ is prior to activity c of operation j″, there must be activity a of its previous operation j.

Constraint (10) ensures the sequence feasibility on each machine: if loading of operation j′ and unloading of operation j″ are processed on the same machine, unloading of operation j″ must be completed before loading of operation j′ starts, and vice versa.

Constraint (11) indicates that the activity completion time of operation j.

Constraint (12) imposes that a robot executes two adjacent activities, starting time of the activity is greater than completion time of the previous activity.

Constraint (13) indicates that after completing an operation, unloading activity can be performed.

Constraint (14) specifies that each machine starts processing operation immediately after completing loading activity.

Constraint (15) ensures that loading activity of the current operation of the same job is carried out after unloading activity of the previous operation is completed.

Constraint (16) defines the virtual operation 0 of each job, whose unloading completion time is 0, and ensures that start processing time of each job is greater than 0.

Constraint (17) defines that completion time of the job is after unloading of its last operation.

Constraint (18) defines the makespan.

Constraint (19) is used to calculate the total working time of each robot.

Constraint (20) specifies that the decision variables, including $X_{khjah'j'b'}$, Y_{ip_ijh}, Z_{ip_l}, and $U_{jj'}$ are binary.

METHODOLOGY AND FRAMEWORK

Real-Time Scheduling Decision Tasks

Breakdown of Tasks

Real-time scheduling needs to consider the decisions of scheduling tasks, the scheduling rule corresponding to each decision, and the definitions of scheduling decision points. The scheduling task of FJSP-DP can be divided into two tasks:

(1) Scheduling of the work cell: Complete the scheduling decision of allocating work pieces to the machine in the cell, which includes job sequencing and machine selection. According to the decision of job sequencing, a job will be selected in the temporary storage area queue, which determines the processing order of the job in the work cell. The machine selection decision is used to determine which machine will process the selected job. According to the priority rule of machine selection, a suitable machine is determined in the machining cell.

(2) Scheduling between work cells: The work cells corresponding to the next operation of the completed job will be determined in the current work cell, which is determined by the priority rules of process planning. Different from the traditional process planning, which determines in advance, the next operation should be selected from the flexible process planning set according to the real-time production status under the demand of real-time scheduling.

Therefore, this paper adopts the process planning method based on the operation tree [44] to build a directed graph model of dynamic process planning. Figure 1b was transformed into the directed graph model of the operation tree shown in Figure 2. Here, the operation tree is defined as follows:

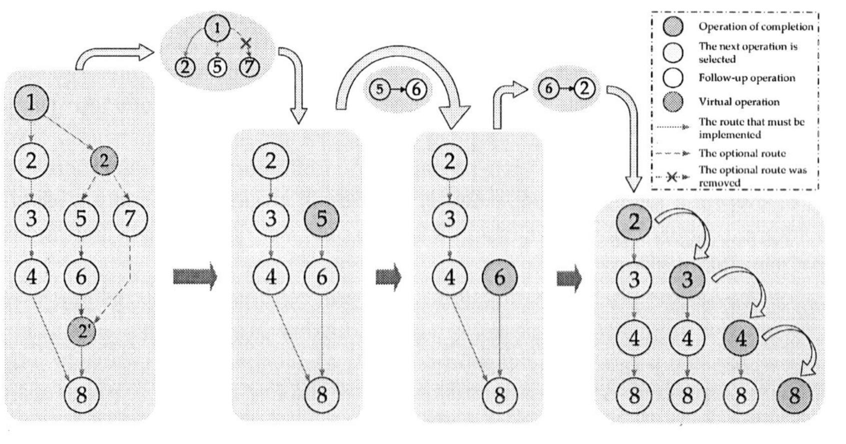

Figure 2. Dynamic updating diagram of process planning based on process tree.

(a) There are three operation types in the operation tree: leaf operation, node operation, and root operation. Root node operation is the last operation of the job. When the root node operation is completed, the job processing is completed.

(b) The current executable operations in the operation tree can only be leaf operations (node and root operations can only be executed if they become leaf operations). After the leaf operation is completed, it will fall off and update the operation tree.

(c) When all leaf operations corresponding to node operations are completed and fall off from the number of operations, the node operation is converted to leaf operation and can be executed.

(d) Redundant routes in the flexible process planning are represented by dotted lines in the operation tree. When the process planning is selected, only one redundant path can be selected for execution. The solid line in the process tree is the route that must be executed.

(e) In order to consider the constraints between process path branches, virtual operation pairs are introduced (2, 2'), as shown in Figure 2. Operation pairs contain multiple redundant paths that can be selected.

Virtual operation 2 indicates that the operation before operation 2 must be completed before operation 5 or 7 can be processed. Virtual operation 2 indicates the end of redundant routing, and the next path can be executed.

In real-time scheduling, it is necessary to obtain the information of the next executable operation according to the operation tree. The precondition for obtaining this information is to judge the node type of the operation. Therefore, in the directed graph model of dynamic process planning, the node type is determined by the degree of output and input of nodes. If the degree of penetration is 0, it indicates a leaf node; if the degree of output or input is greater than 1, it indicates node operation; and if the output is 0, it indicates root node operation. In the directed graph, the constraint relationship between process nodes is represented by an adjacency matrix. Therefore, in real-time scheduling, the dynamic changes of the operation tree can be effectively expressed by the degree of nodes and the adjacency matrix.

In real-time scheduling, it is necessary to obtain the information of the next executable operation according to the operation tree. The precondition for obtaining the information is to judge the node type of the operation. Therefore, in the directed graph model of the dynamic process planning, the node type is determined by the degree of output and degree of input of nodes. If the degree of penetration is 0, it indicates the leaf node; If the degree of output or input is greater than 1, it indicates a node operation; If the output is 0, it indicates the root node operation. In the directed graph, the constraint relationship between process nodes is represented by the adjacency matrix. Therefore, in the real-time scheduling, the dynamic changes of the operation tree can be effectively expressed by the degree of nodes and the adjacency matrix.

This paper considers both process planning flexibility and machine operation flexibility, which ultimately determines the next operation and the corresponding work cell. Therefore, in the dynamic flexible planning process, the next operation and the required processing unit are determined as follows:

Step 1: Calculate the output of the current operation node. If the output is equal to 0, jump to step 5; if it is equal to 1, jump to step 3; and if it is greater than 1, go to step 2.

Step 2: Select the next operation to be executed from the next operation set according to the process data information and the priority rule of process planning.

Step 3: Retrieve the set of machines required for the selected next operation and divide the set of selectable processing units for that operation.

Step 4: According to the real-time status information of the processing unit, select a processing unit through the priority rule, then transfer the job to the processing unit.

Step 5: After the job is processed in the work cell, calculate the node output. If it is 0, it means the job is processed and the next work cell does not need to be selected; otherwise, go back to step 1.

Decision Point and Decision Flow

There are two decision points corresponding to the scheduling task of FJSP-DP. Due to the constraints of dual resources, scheduling in cells should take into account the occupations of robots and machines. Therefore, the designed scheduling decision point in the cell meets the following conditions: there are idle machines in a work cell, there are jobs waiting to be processed in the buffer zone, and the robot is not occupied. Scheduling between cells mainly considers the next operation of the job and its corresponding work cells. The condition of its scheduling decision point is that there are finished jobs in the staging area and the jobs have remaining operations. When the job is in the 0-th operation, a priority rule is randomly selected to complete the determination of the unit for the first operation and directly enter the unit. When the jobs in the staging area have completed all operations, they are delivered directly. No decision needs to be made for the entry and exit of the above artifacts. The priority is higher for robot unloading than loading. When multiple unload requests occur at the same time, unload in the order of first request and first unload. The execution process of the FJSP-DP scheduling decision is shown in Figure 3.

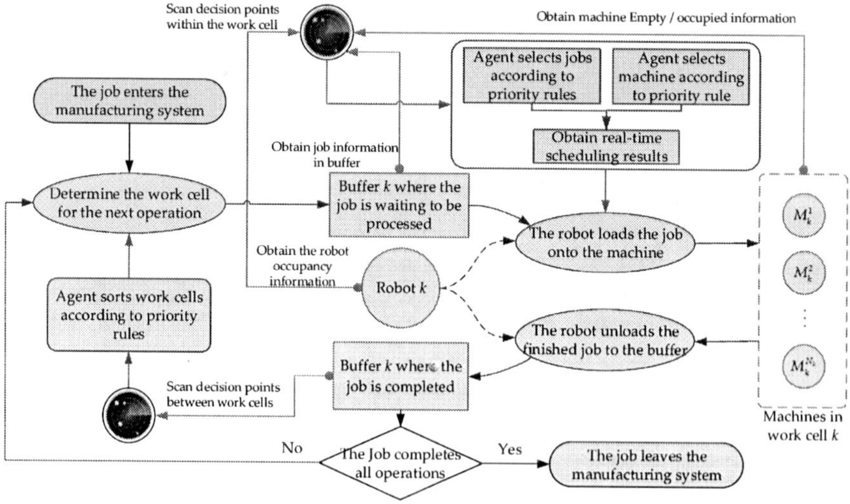

Figure 3. Execution process of scheduling decision.

Scheduling Decision via DDQN

DQN is an effective method to solve discrete system decision problems. It combines reinforcement Q learning with the nonlinear value function, trains the neural network through reinforcement learning, and uses the neural network to approximate the Q value function, which is the policy of action selection [45,46]. DQN includes an online network (Q-Net) and a target network ($\hat{Q}$-Net), and the output of these two networks is the Q value of the action. The experience tuple (s_t, a_t, r_t, s_{t+1}) generated at each time step are stored in the replay memory during the training process of the agent's interaction with the environment. Tuple data are randomly sampled through small batch updating, and the gradient descent policy is used to modify online network parameter θ_t to maximize the Q value function. The parameter update formula of online network is

$$\theta_{t+1} = \theta_t + \eta(y_t - Q(s_t, a_t; \theta_t)) \cdot \nabla_\theta Q(s_t, a_t; \theta_t) \tag{21}$$

where η is the learning rate used by the gradient descent algorithm, $\nabla\theta$ is the gradient descent policy, and y_t is the estimated target value. The iteration formula for each time step is

$$y_t^{DQN} = r_{t+1} + \gamma Q(s_{t+1}, \underset{a}{\mathrm{argmax}}(s_{t+1}, a; \hat{\theta}_t); \hat{\theta}_t) \tag{22}$$

where γ is the discount factor in the Q-learning algorithm and $\hat{\theta}_t$ is the parameter of the target network. Obviously, when DQN estimates the target value, it always selects the maximum output value of target network Q(s_{t+1}, a), which will lead to overestimation problems, could greatly reduce the learning quality of the agent, and is not conducive to the stability of learning. In order to reduce overestimation of Q value, Hassell et al. proposed DDQN based on DQN [47]. Unlike DQN, DDQN inputs the status st+1 to both the online and target network. First, DDQN finds the action with the maximum output value from the online network, and then the output value of the target network corresponding to the action. The Q value of the online network provides the behavior policy to select actions, and the target network output is used to evaluate the Q value of the action. Therefore, the formula for calculating the target value of DDQN estimation is

$$y_t^{DDQN} = r_{t+1} + \gamma Q(s_{t+1}, \underset{a}{\mathrm{argmax}}(s_{t+1}, a; \theta_t); \hat{\theta}_t) \tag{23}$$

The process of agent learning and training in the scheduling environment using deep reinforcement learning based on DDQN is shown in Figure 4. The agent obtains real-time production data of the flexible job shop environment and processes the data to form a state s_t. The online network obtains the Q(s_t, a; θ) of each action according to s_t, and uses the ε-greedy policy to select action a_t. Action a_t is converted into the corresponding scheduling rules, and then job sequencing is executed, with machine selection or process planning to make the environmental transition to the next state s_{t+1}, to obtain reward r_t related to the scheduling objective.

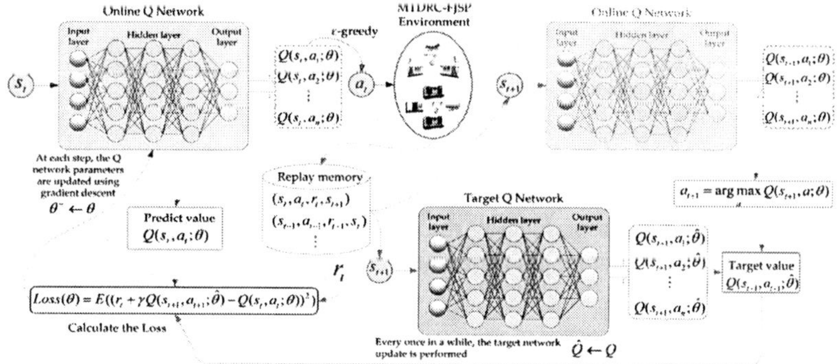

Figure 4. Principle of DDQN for solving scheduling.

At the same time, the learning experience (s_t, a_t, r_t, s_{t+1}) is stored in the memory buffer. With the real-time interaction between the agent and the scheduling environment, the memory buffer is constantly updated. At each time step, a batch of scheduling decision experience data is obtained from the memory buffer, and each s_{t+1} is input into the online and target networks.

The online network outputs the a_{t+1} corresponding to the maximum Q value, and the target network obtains the value Q(s_{t+1}, at+1; θ) corresponding to a_{t+1}, which is combined with reward r_t as the target estimate y_t.

Using Q(s_t, a; θ) as the prediction value, DDQN calculates the loss function Loss(θ), and then updates the online network parameter θ according to the gradient descent policy. Therefore, once the agent interacts with the scheduling environment, the online network parameter θ will be updated once. During the continuous interaction between the agent and the scheduling environment, the target network parameter $\hat{\theta}$ is occasionally updated with online network parameter θ. This interactive iteratively updating learning process makes the scheduling decision performance continuously improve.

Framework of Centralized Training and Decentralized Execution

As described in the previous section, when DDQN is used to solve the scheduling problem, it is a scenario where the agent interacts with the environment and completes the scheduling decision. In the MTMARL, the multi-agent is the subject of scheduling decisions—it can be a software system. Manufacturing resources (including robots) or computers can be the carrier of the agent. The control system of the robot can be installed with a multi-agent decision module so that the robot has scheduling decision ability. In this FJSP-DP, each robot acts as an agent and executes the agent's decision results. Multiple agents complete their decision-making tasks by sharing local observations. The decision objectives of each agent are consistent in order to optimize the scheduling objectives and obtain the same return. Therefore, multiple agents have a full cooperative relationship. Based on the analysis of scheduling tasks, each agent should have decision ability for job sequencing, machine selection, and process planning at the same time.

Considering the complete cooperation among multiple agents, a centralized training and decentralized execution reinforcement learning framework is adopted to solve the FJSP-DP in this paper. The framework is based on the DDQN, as shown in Figure 5. Each agent interacts with the environment by executing actions and receives feedback from the environment in the form of states and rewards. In the centralized training phase, the value of network critical k in the central controller is used to evaluate the decision actions made by agent k, which is used to train and optimize policy network actor k. In the decentralized execution phase, agent k acquires local observations o^k, inputs them into its policy network actor k, and makes scheduling decisions. This decision process does not require communication between agents. This kind of decentralized decision is fast and can achieve real-time results.

There are w value networks in the central controller to evaluate the learning policies of each agent. The value network is a group of neural networks with the same structure, and the parameter w^k of each neural network k may be different. These neural networks are used to fit the Q function (i.e., $q^k(O, a; w^k)$) in reinforcement learning, where $O=\{o^1,o^2, \cdots, o^w\}$ is a global observation consisting of each local observation. In the process of centralized training, each agent conducts the training of the policy network ($a^k \sim \pi(\cdot \mid o^k; \theta^k)$ by sharing their own observations. Agent k interacts with the environment, and critical k scores according to the actions given by actor k. This centralized training process realizes cooperation among multiple agents.

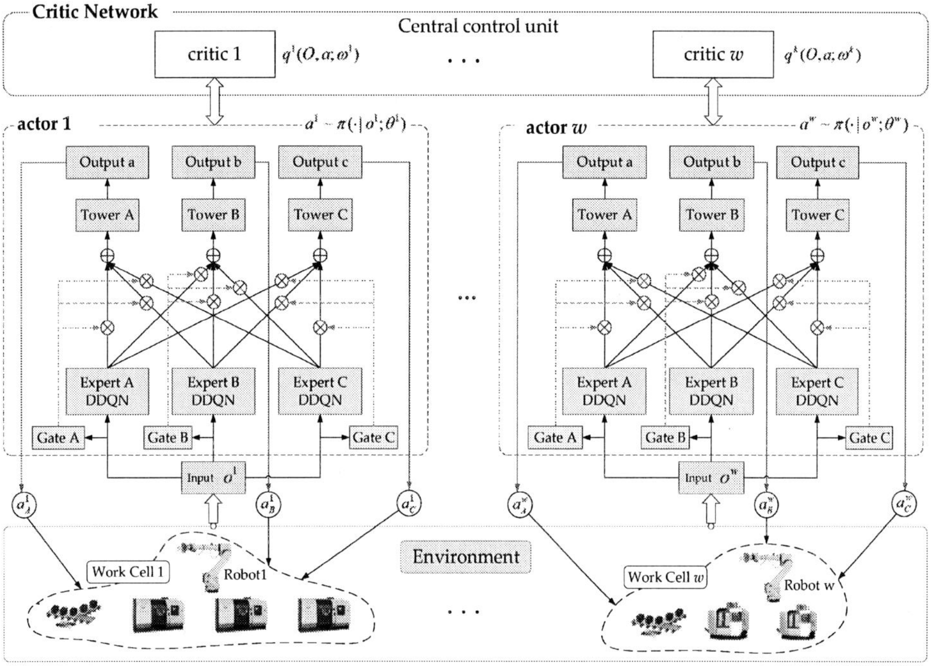

Figure 5. Scheduling decision framework.

The policy network of each agent in Figure 5 is built based on the network structure of the multi-gate mixture-of-experts. It functions in the training and decision stages. In this structure, there are three experts (A, B, and C), which correspond to three scheduling decision tasks: process planning, job sequencing, and machine selection. Each expert consists of a DDQN. The network of DDQN belongs to the sharing layer, and the downstream tower layer shares the output of the three experts. Each expert outputs a vector after forward propagation. In this model, three vectors are output. Each vector corresponds to the information of a decision task. The tower layer is used to select an action in the corresponding action space. The tower layer is composed of three neural networks. The input layer and hidden layer of the three neural networks have the same structure, and the number of nodes in the output layer is consistent with the size of the action space of the corresponding decision-making task. In order to consider the impact relationship between multiple tasks, each tower should receive information from the three experts. At the same time, in order to make each tower pay more attention to its own tasks, an attention mechanism is introduced, and a gate layer is added to each tower in this model. The gate is a shallow neural network. Finally, three scalars are output through the softmax layer, and each expert is assigned a weight parameter (the sum of all weight parameters is equal to 1). Each tower has a corresponding gate, which is used to train its relevant decision-making tasks. Through the attention mechanism of this structure, experts who are good at different tasks are selected to handle this task, thus realizing information interaction between multiple tasks.

ALGORITHM DESIGN

This section describes the multi-agent environment and its related observation, action, reward, policy, and training algorithm design for reinforcement learning modeling. Among them, the design of the reward function takes into account the multi-task situation. As agents, the robots interacts with their shared scheduling environment and takes actions according to their policy, aiming to solve the optimization problem of Formulas (1)–(3). At each scheduling decision time t, the robot obtains corresponding action according to the observed local observation. The environment switches to a new state by the action, and the agent gains reward.

Observation

In most reinforcement learning-based scheduling methods, state characteristics are defined as production data related to scheduling elements, such as jobs and resources. In order to solve FJSP-DP, it is necessary to design suitable state characteristics based on the production data. Since the decision-making abilities of the agents are the same, their observation characteristics are also the same. For the observation design, we needed some basic state data of scheduling elements. Therefore, $CT_h(t)$ was defined as the completion time of the last operation completed on machine h at time t. The utilization of machine h at time t is expressed as

$$U_h(t) = \frac{\sum_{i=1}^{n} \sum_{j=1}^{OP_i(t)} X_{ijh} T_{ijh}}{CT_h(t)} \quad (24)$$

where, X_{ijh} indicates that machine h has completed operation j of job i, and T_{ijh} indicates its processing time. $OP_i(t)$ is defined as the number of operations completed by job i at time t. Similarly, if CTk(t) is defined as the completion time of the last activity completed on robot k at time t, then the utilization of robot k at time t is expressed as

$$U_k^{\text{robot}}(t) = \frac{\sum_{i=1}^{n} \sum_{j=1}^{OP_i(t)} X_{ijk} \cdot (T_{j1}+T_{j2})}{CT_k(t)} \quad (25)$$

The completion rate of job i at time t generally represents the ratio of the current completed quantity to the total operation quantity. However, due to the dynamic selection in process planning, the total number of final execution operations cannot be obtained in advance, so the completion rate cannot be calculated in the manner described above. In order to calculate the completion rate of the job at time t, an estimation method is adopted. According to the dynamic directed graph model of process planning, there may be multiple process planning routes, and then the remaining operation quantity $\overline{n_i}(t)$ at time t is obtained by recursive calculation. Therefore, the completion rate of job i at time t is expressed as

$$CJ_i(t) = \frac{OP_i(t)}{OP_i(t)+\overline{n_i}(t)} \quad (26)$$

The estimated slack time of the j-th operation of the remaining job i at time t is

$$ST_i(t) = D_i - (T_{cur}+T_i) \quad (27)$$

where T_{cur} indicates the average completion time of the last operation on all machines at that time: $T_{cur} = \frac{\sum_{h=1}^{m} CT_h(t)}{m}$. T_I represents the remaining processing time of job i. $T_i = \sum_{j=OP_i(t)+1}^{\overline{n_i}} \overline{t}_{I,j}$. $\overline{t}_{I,j}$ represents the average processing time of the j-th operation of job i in the selected machine set.

Based on the above, the local observation of agent k at decision time t are defined in this paper as the utilization rate of work cell k, quantity of work in process (WIP) within work cell k, the utilization rate of robot k, the average completion rate, estimated tardiness rate and actual tardiness rate of all jobs within work cell k. The data tuples corresponding to the six observation characteristics are as follows:

$$o_t^k = \left\{U_k^{\text{cell}}(t),\ N_k^{\text{WIP}}(t),\ U_k^{\text{robot}}(t),\ CRJ_k(t),\ Tard_k^{\text{e}}(t),\ Tard_k^{\text{a}}(t)\right\} \tag{28}$$

According to Formula (24), the utilization rate of work cell k can be calculated as follows:

$$U_k^{\text{cell}}(t) = \frac{\sum_{h=1}^{m} X_{kh} U_h(t)}{N_k} \tag{29}$$

where X_{kh} indicates that machine h belongs to work cell k.

The average completion rate, estimated tardiness rate and actual tardiness rate of all jobs within work cell k are calculated by Formulas (30)–(32). The estimated tardiness rate is defined as the estimated number of tardy operations divided by the number of outstanding operations belonging to all remaining jobs. The actual tardiness rate is defined as the number of actual delayed operations divided by the number of outstanding operations belonging to all remaining jobs.

$$CRJ_k(t) = \frac{\sum_{i\in J_k} CJ_i(t)}{N_k^{\text{WIP}}(t)} \tag{30}$$

$$Tard_k^{\text{e}}(t) = \frac{\sum_{i\in J_k} \sum_{j=OP_i(t)+1}^{\overline{n_i}(t)} \max(0,\ \text{sgn}(\bar{t}_{i,j} - ST_i(t)))}{\sum_{i\in J_k} (\overline{n_i}(t))} \tag{31}$$

$$Tard_k^{\text{a}}(t) = \frac{\sum_{i\in J_k} \max(0,\ \text{sgn}(C_{iOP_i(t)} - D_i))}{\sum_{i\in J_k} (\overline{n_i}(t))} \tag{32}$$

where J_k indicates that all jobs within work cell k. $N_k^{\text{WIP}}(t)$ can be obtained through statistics in the scheduling environment.

Action

In dynamic scheduling, researchers often use a number of empirical methods and rules extracted from production practice for real-time scheduling [48]. In this field, no rule can perform well in all scheduling environments and meet all performance objectives, so different scheduling rules should be used to correspond to different production states. These scheduling rules correspond to the action space in reinforcement learning. In this paper, according to the three scheduling decision tasks of process planning, job sequencing, and machine selection, the scheduling rules required by the action space are designed.

Process Planning

When the buffer of work cell k contains jobs that have been processed in this work cell, it is necessary to determine the next work cell to enter for this job. According to the analysis of dynamic process planning, based on the flexibility of process planning and machine, when the job completes the current operation, there may be multiple candidates for the next operation. The process planning rules need to determine the next operation and its corresponding work cell, so the related rules are composite scheduling rules. In process planning, the action selection should not only consider the remaining time for process planning, but also the state of the work cell corresponding to the candidate operation. Therefore, the process planning rules designed are as follows:

(1) Composite dispatching rule 1: Composite scheduling rule 1 selects the process planning of the shortest remaining processing time, corresponding to the next operation in the operation candidate set. Then, we obtain the work cell set that can handle the selected operation, and we determine the next work cell according to the principle of the lowest workload first.

(2) Composite dispatching rule 2: Composite scheduling rule 2 selects the next operation in the same way as rule 1. The difference is that when the next work cell is selected, it is executed according to the principle of the lowest quantity of WIP in the work cell.

Job Sequencing

When the buffer of work cell k contains jobs, it is necessary to sort them according to the priority rules, so as to realize the selection of jobs before scheduling is executed. In the design of job sequencing rules, many factors should be considered, including man hours, remaining man hours, delivery date, operation quantity, and so on. In this paper, we designed the following job sequencing rules based on the particularities of the proposed FJSP-DP problem:

(1) Dispatching rule 3: The jobs are sorted according to the maximum estimated tardiness time or the minimum average operation slack time. In the set of jobs to be selected, if there are jobs with estimated tardiness, the one with the maximum estimated tardiness will be selected. Otherwise, we calculate the slack time of each job at the current time and the number of remaining operations, then calculate the average slack time of the operation of the job through divide slack time by remaining operations. Finally, we select the job of the minimum average slack time.

(2) Dispatching rule 4: The jobs are sorted according to the maximum estimated tardiness time or the minimum slack rate. In the job set to be selected, if there are jobs with estimated tardiness, the one with the maximum estimated tardiness will be selected. Otherwise, we calculate the slack time of each job and its remaining processing time, then calculate the slack rate of the job through divide slack time by remaining processing time. Finally, we select the job with the lowest slack rate.

(3) Dispatching rule 5: According to the estimated tardiness time, completion rate, and slack time, the jobs are sorted. In the job set to be selected, if there are jobs with estimated tardiness, the one with the maximum value that divide estimated tardiness time by completion rate will be selected. Otherwise, the job with the maximum value that estimated tardiness time times completion rate will be selected.

Machine Selection

At the decision time t, when work cell k contains empty machines, it is necessary to sort the machine according to the priority rules, so as to realize machine selection before scheduling execution. The set of empty machines in work cell k is represented as M_k^{empty}. Machine selection should consider the machine load, the processing time of the job on the machine, the waiting time of the machine, and other information. The machine selection rule and the calculation method designed in this paper are shown in Table 1.

Table 1. Rules for machine selection

Rule	Description	Formula
Dispatching rule 6	Select machine with the lowest workload	$\text{argmin}_{h \in M_k^{\text{empty}}} \sum_{i=1}^{n} \sum_{j=1}^{OP_i(t)} X_{ijh} T_{ijh} 1$
Dispatching rule 7	Select machine with the longest waiting time	$\text{argmax}_{h \in M_k^{\text{empty}}} (t - CT_h(t))$
Dispatching rule 8	Select machine that takes the least time to process the selected job	$\text{argmin}_{h \in M_k^{\text{empty}}} X_{ijh} T_{ijh}$

Reward

Global Reward

One objective of the proposed scheduling optimization is to minimize total tardiness. Considering the full cooperation of multiple agents, a global real-time reward function is designed to optimize total tardiness. The objective of the reinforcement learning algorithm is to maximize the cumulative reward, and the increasing direction of the reward function value should be consistent with the decreasing direction of the optimization objective value. Therefore, we designed relevant rewards based on the form of the sigmoid function. The calculation formula of the global reward function at time t is given in Equation (33):

$$r_t = -\max\left(\frac{1}{1+\exp(-\sum_{k \in W} Tard_k^e(t))}, 0.5\right) \times 10 + 5 \tag{33}$$

where $r_t \in (-5, 0)$ and $\sum_{k \in W} Tard_k^e(t)$ is the total tardiness of all jobs at time t. If there is no job tardiness, reward value r_t=0; otherwise, when the total tardiness value is infinite, $r_t \approx -5$.

Local Reward

For each agent k, it is necessary to consider the immediate reward after the action of executing each task. For task A of process planning, it is necessary to consider the load balance of all work cells that can process the next operation of job i. For task B of job sequencing, the job deadline needs to be considered. For task C selected by the machine, information such as machine utilization and waiting time should be considered. The local reward design for task A is

$$r_t^A = -1 \times \frac{1}{1+\exp(\text{abs}(U_i^k(t) - \overline{U}_{ave}^{\text{cell}}(t)))} \tag{34}$$

where $r_t^A \in (-1, -0.5)$, $U_i^k(t)$ is the utilization rate of work cell k that process job i at time t, and $\overline{U}_{ave}^{\text{cell}}(t)$ is the average utilization rate of all work cells at time t. $U_i^k(t)$ and $\overline{U}_{ave}^{\text{cell}}(t)$ can be calculated by Formula (29).

When designing the local reward for task B, the priority should be given to processing jobs with large tardiness. If the tardiness is greater, the penalty will be greater. If there is no tardiness, the reward will be 0. Therefore, the reward function designed for task B after selecting job i is

$$r_t^B = \left(1 + \exp\left(\min(ST_i - T_i, 0) + \frac{\min(ST_i - \overline{ST}, 0) + \frac{\min(T_i - \overline{T}, 0)}{\max_{i \in J_s}(T_i)}}{\max_{i \in J_s}(D_i)}\right)\right)^{-1} \tag{35}$$

where $r_t^B \in (-0.5, 0)$ represents a set of optional jobs when sorting jobs. The calculation method for ST_i and T_i is given in Formula (27). $\overline{ST}$ and $\overline{T}$ are their averages, respectively. Regarding the reward design of task C, considering the occupied time of the selected machine, the reward function is

$$r_t^C = 1 - U_h(t) \tag{36}$$

where $r_t^C \in (0, 1)$, $U_h(t)$ is the utilization rate of machine h at time t. Formula (24) gives the calculation method.

Exploration and Exploitation

In the DRL, exploration means that each action has the same random selection probability and involves action with the maximum Q value. Due to the limited learning time, exploration and exploitation are contradictory. In order to maximize the cumulative reward, a compromise must be made between exploration and exploitation. In the ε-greedy policy, ε decreases with the training process. However, the fixed linear reduction rate has poor adaptability to scheduling problems of different scales. In order to appropriately adjust the size of the exploration according to the solution space of FJSP-DP, we designed a ε descent policy to adapt to different scales. The gradual decrease of ε with the number of training steps during training is shown in Formula (37):

$$\varepsilon = \max(0.1, 1 - \frac{step}{N_{OP}}) \tag{37}$$

where stepstep is the stepstep-th scheduling decision and N_{OP} is the total number of operations in the scheduling problem. The larger the scale of the scheduling problem, the larger the total operands N_{OP}, which means that exploration rate ε decreases more slowly, thus increasing the exploration process.

Algorithm Architecture

FJSP-DP is transformed into an RL problem through the designed state, the action, and the reward. According to the described scheduling decision process and the proposed algorithm model architecture, the RL environment characteristics designed, the action set of three scheduling tasks, the reward definition based on scheduling optimization objectives, and the adopted behavior policy, the scheduling decision agent is trained to achieve real-time scheduling for the FJSP-DP. The general framework of the training method is given in Algorithm 1.

Algorithm 1 Procedure of training

Initialize $Q^{\omega^k}, \theta^k, \omega^k$
Initialize replay memory M
For i = 1: Episodes **do**
  Observe initial state s_0
  For t = 1: T (T is the terminal time) **do**
    Agent k performs the policy function $\pi(a_t|\theta_t^k)$, and selects an action a_t
    Execute action a_t, observe reward r_t and next state s_{t+1}
  End for

Calculate functions of agent *k*: UE $=\left\{o_{loc}^{k},\ a_{t}^{k},\ r_{t}\right\}_{t=1}^{T},\ \{\hat{Q}^{k}(s_{t},a_{t})\}_{t=1}^{T}$

Critic network performs evaluation with $\left\{C^{k}(s_{t}^{k},\ a_{t})\right\}_{t=1}^{T}$

Store the values $\left\{\left[a_{t}^{k}(\mathrm{loc}), a_{t}^{k}, \hat{Q}^{k}(s_{t},a_{t}), C^{k}(s_{t}^{k},a_{t})_{k=1}^{w}\right]\right\}_{t=1}^{T}$ of muti agents in *M*

For count = 1: COUNT **do**

Mix and rearrange the data in the *M* and divide data ([1, *T*]) into *P* groups

For *j* = 1: *T*/*P* **do**

$$M_{j}=\left\{\left[o_{loc}^{k}, a_{i}^{k}, \hat{Q}^{k}(s_{i},a_{i}), C^{k}(s_{i},a_{i})_{k=1}^{w}\right]\right\}_{i=1+P_{j}}^{P(j+1)}$$

For *k* = 1: *w* **do**

Calculate $\Delta\theta^{k}$, $\Delta\omega^{k}$

Perform gradient optimization on θ^{k} and ω^{k}

End for

End for

End for

Update the hyperparameters θ^{k} of policy function π and the neural network parameter ω^{k} for of each actor

End for

NUMERICAL EXPERIMENTS

In this section we verify the effectiveness of the proposed real-time scheduling decision method based on MTMARL. The scheduling environment was developed using digital factory simulation software. The reinforcement learning training framework was developed in Python 3.8 according to Algorithm 1. The Socket communication mode was used for the interaction between the agent and the simulation environment to achieve performance training of the agent, as shown in Figure 6. Here, the Python development environment served as the server, and the scheduling simulation environment served as the client. As the digital factory simulation software can directly handle the data collection and command control in the workshop, this integrated interaction method improves the applicability of solving practical problems. The scheduling decision performance was studied throughout the simulation process by changing the number of cells, machines, and jobs, and the process planning data of jobs.

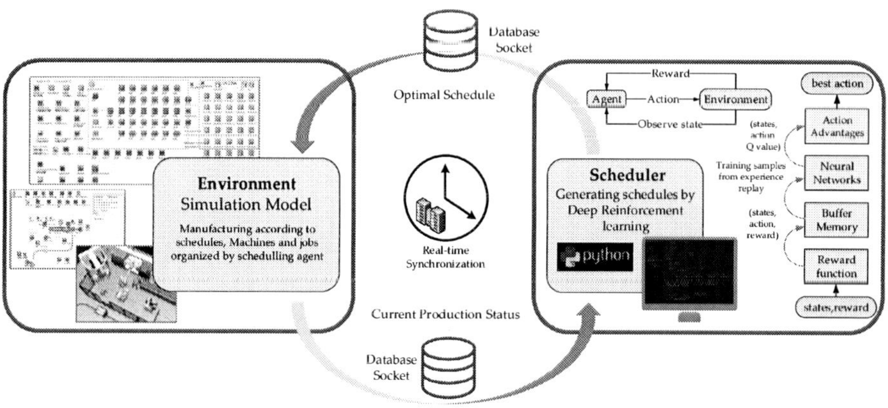

Figure 6. Real-time interaction of agent with scheduling environment.

Parameters Descriptions

Due to the particularity of the scheduling problem proposed in this paper, there were no standard examples to support the experimental analysis. Therefore, in order to obtain data related to the FJSP-DP, the required simulation examples were randomly generated based on the data of MK01–MK10 examples provided by Brandimarte, which are standard examples of FJSP. In the example, the due time of job i is set to $D_i = \alpha \sum_{j=1}^{n_i} \bar{t}_{ij}$, that is, the cumulative average processing time of all operations on the job. α is a random coefficient between 1 and 2. It indicates the tightness of delivery date. For examples on different scales, the number of robots is 2–5 and the number of machines supervised by each robot at the same time conforms to the uniform distribution U [2–4]. The time for the robot to perform loading and unloading activities is related to the relative angular displacement of the robot base and the machine. In combination with the directed graph model of the process planning in Figure 2, U [2–5] node operations and the corresponding virtual operations are randomly generated. The number of operations and the processing time of the job are consistent with operations in the standard example, thus initializing the adjacency matrix of flexible process planning for each job. The above parameters are shown in Table 2.

Table 2. Scheduling environment parameters

Parameter	Value
Number of robots	2–5
Number of machines supervised by each robot	U [2–4]
Number of node operations of the job	U [2–5]
Speed robot performs loading and unloading	30°/time unit
Number of jobs	See standard example
Number of machines	See standard example
Number of operations	See standard example

The number of jobs and resources and the environmental layout of each calculation example based on the parameters in Table 2 are shown in Figure 7. For example, MK05 (15,106,4,2) represents the scheduling environment generated by MK05, which contains 15 jobs, 106 operations, and 4 machines divided into 2 work cells and 2 robots.

The values of all hyperparameters of the algorithm were determined according to the size of the FJSP-DP example and the adjustment of the training process. The list of hyperparameters with their values is shown in Table 3.

Table 3. Neural network parameters and their values

Parameter	Value
Replay buffer size	50,000
Minibatch	64
Size of hidden layers in policy network	3/64, 64, 1
Size of hidden layers in critic network	3/64, 64, 12
Size of hidden layers in target policy network	3/64, 64, 1

Size of hidden layers in target critic network	3/64, 64, 12
Learning rate	0.01
Discount factor	0.95
Update rate of target network	0.01
Episode	200–500

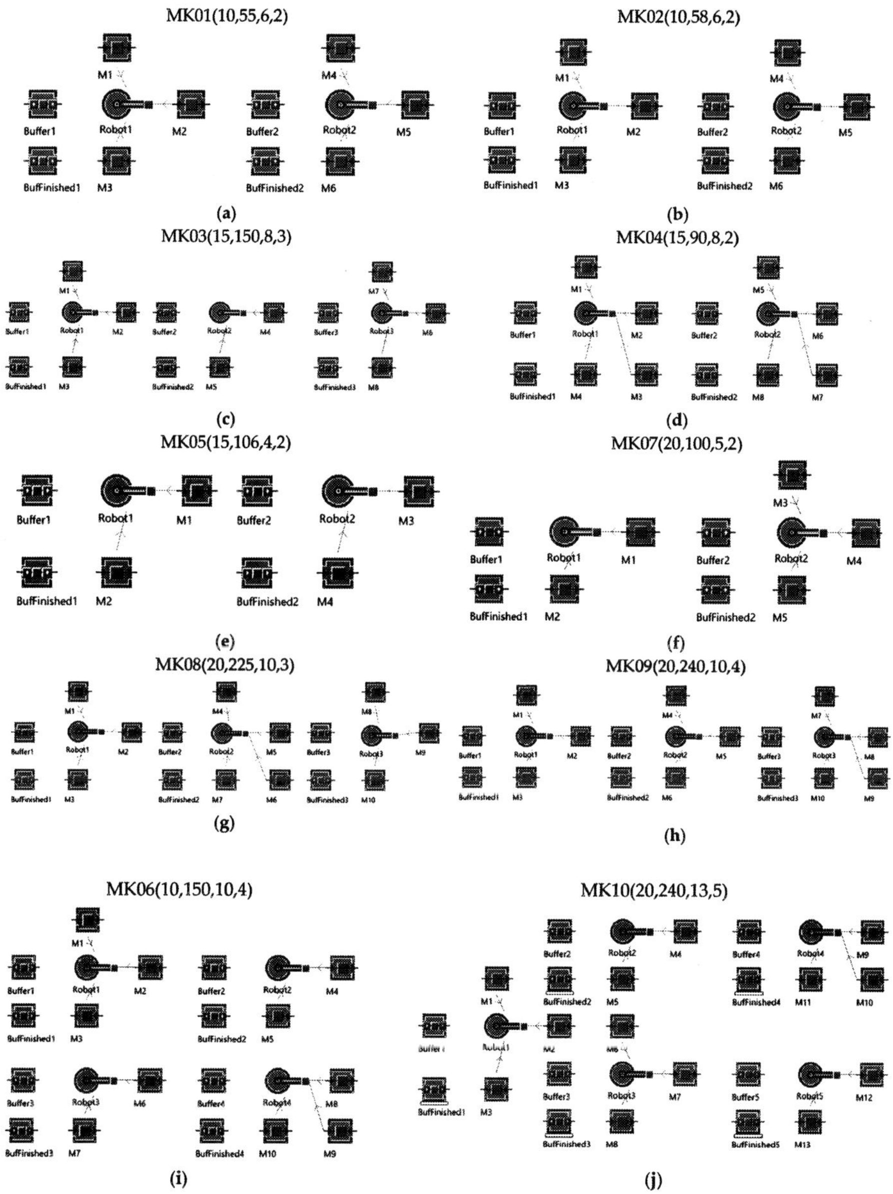

Figure 7. Example scheduling environment layout diagrams.

Analysis of Results

Scheduling Process Data

The designed reinforcement learning scheduling framework interacts with the scheduling environment in each example. Obtain global state information through local observations. The state data of production scheduling were collected in the interaction process, so as to objectively evaluate the correlations between state characteristics. In this paper, the results obtained from MK01 were used for correlation analysis. In this example environment (shown in Figure 7a), there are two robots; each robot is responsible for supervising 3 machines, the number of jobs is 10, and the number of operations is 55. Figure 8a shows the change trend of state characteristic values with the decision time steps. According to the curve of the change trend, the state characteristics related to resources, including the average utilization rate of machines, the standard deviation of work cell utilization rate, and the average utilization rate of robots and its standard deviation, can quickly reach a stable numerical range as the number of decision steps increases. It can also be seen from the figure that after the trend stabilizes, the utilization rate of machines and robots is relatively close, which is about 60%. First, the utilization rate of the machine indirectly reflects the utilization rate of the work cell, which can be verified by Formula (29). Second, the utilization rate of the robot is restricted by tasks and resources in the work cell. The utilization rate of the robot is related to the work cell, which can be verified by the standard deviation curve of the utilization rate in Figure 8a. Therefore, the average utilization ratio of machines and robots is close. At the same time, the standard deviation of work cell and robot utilization rates is maintained around 10%, indicating that the load of each robot, work cell, and processing task are relatively balanced, effectively reflecting the scheduling objective of Formula (3) to minimize the workload difference among all robots.

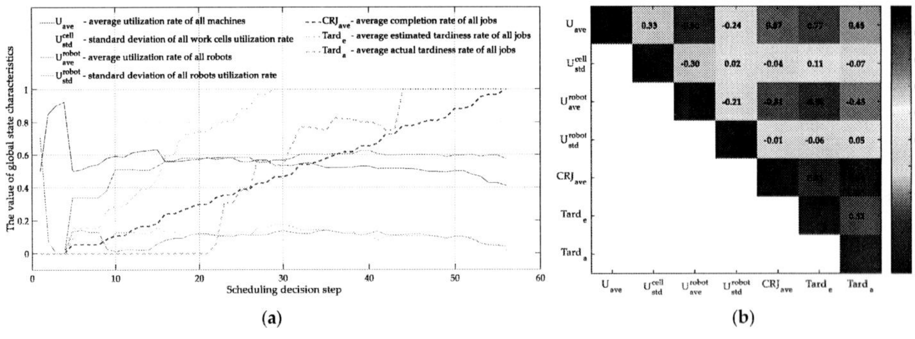

Figure 8. (a) Change curve and (b) correlation analysis of global state characteristics.

On the other hand, the states related to the job task basically show a gradual linear increasing trend until the value becomes 1. We found that the estimated rate of tardiness changed earlier than the actual rate, and the trends were highly correlated, which shows that the method of calculating the estimated tardiness rate can effectively predict tardiness in advance and provide more accurate state parameters for the effective selection of corresponding scheduling rules. The correlation between state characteristics is shown in Figure 8b. Among them, the average completion rate, estimated tardiness rate, and actual tardiness rate related to the job show high correlation of 0.81, 0.85, and 0.94, respectively, because the process of calculating them is related to the number of completed job operations. At the same time, the average utilization rate of the machine is also highly correlated with the estimated tardiness of the job, because these are the main influencing factors in the reward design. Therefore, when the agent makes scheduling decisions, it will obtain greater rewards if it chooses jobs with large tardiness and low utilization, which makes the agent pay more attention to this selection policy. This mechanism is ultimately reflected in the correlation of state characteristics. The correlation between other state features is low, which shows that having state features with low coupling is more conducive to the effective learning of agents.

In addition, a Gantt chart of scheduling at each time was continuously generated in the process of real-time interaction between the scheduling environment and the agent. This real-time scheduling chart for the MK01 example environment is shown in Figure 9. In this Gantt chart, there are two kinds of color blocks. (1) Wider and intermittent color blocks. One block represents one operation of a certain job. One color represents one job. The length of the color block indicates the time of processing, loading, or unloading. The sequence of each job on the machine or robot is displayed by the order of the corresponding color blocks on the time axis. (2) Narrow and continuous color blocks. There are three colors in total, namely gray, green, and yellow. Among them, gray indicates that the machine or robot is in an idle state, green indicates that the machine is processing or the robot is in motion, and yellow indicates that the job on the machine has been processed and is waiting to be unloaded. The length of the color blocks indicates the duration of each state. It can be found that the robot has loaded and unloaded each job, and the machine has completed the processing of the job, and various constraints have been met in the scheduling model. The Gantt chart shows that the designed scheduling environment and reinforcement learning real-time scheduling method are suitable for solving the scheduling problem proposed in this paper.

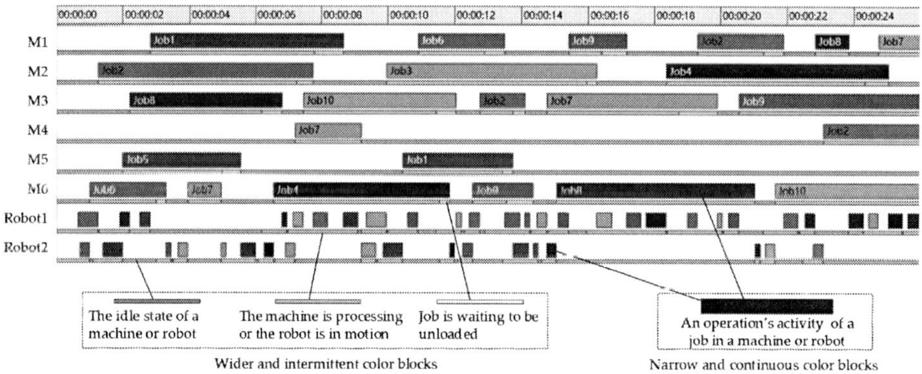

Figure 9. Gantt chart of real-time scheduling of FJSP-DP (MK01).

Global Reward Convergence

In order to further analyze the effectiveness of the proposed multi-task multi-agent reinforcement learning algorithm to solve the FJSP-DP problem, the convergence performance of the 10 groups of data derived from MK01–MK10 was analyzed. Different episodes were selected according to the size of the example. Figure 10 shows the global reward convergence of the proposed algorithm when solving scheduling problems of different scales. The red line in the figure is the convergence curve of the global reward function. It can be seen that with increased training rounds, the global reward function value gradually converges to a certain value.

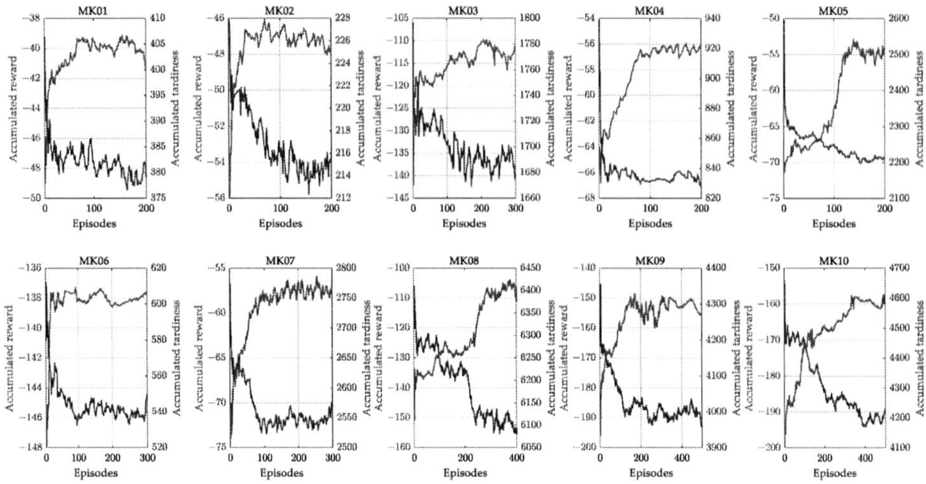

Figure 10. Convergence curve of global reward and tardiness.

The due time for the scheduling objective corresponding to the global reward is shown in the figure with a blue line. The delay time is inversely proportional to the overall reward, which is consistent with the trend reflected in the reward design. In the training process, it is obvious that the number of turns required to achieve convergence is related to the number of operations. However, it can be found in the figure that the number of rounds required is not too large, and the algorithm can converge to a relatively stable state, indicating that the convergence speed of the proposed algorithm is fast. In general, the scheduling agent learns appropriate scheduling rules according to changes in the production status, which improves the adaptability of FJSP-DP.

Local Reward Convergence

In order to analyze the performance of each agent when executing multi-task decisions, the convergence performance of local reward for each decision task was analyzed based on the FJSP-DP scheduling example using MK10, whose environment layout as shown in Figure 7a. Figure 11 shows the local reward convergence of each agent executing its own scheduling decision task in this example. For each decision task of each agent, its corresponding local reward function curve was drawn. There are two obvious trends in the figure. First, it can be seen that all agents were able to complete their associated tasks and maximize the specified reward function. Second, the proposed algorithm has a fast convergence rate. For most agents, the reward function for most tasks will converge when there are fewer than 100 episodes. Moreover, the stability of local reward convergence is better.

As the total number of operations is relatively large compared with the available processing resources, there is high competition between agents when selecting work cells to obtain the available processing resources. Therefore, the agents must share resources. This problem is crucial, because each agent selects the action corresponding to the task according to its own observation. It also implies that all agents in the scheduling decision system achieve balance in some way. The scheduling decision in the cell not only promotes each agent to select appropriate processing resources through global evaluation, but also stimulates the agent to complete the selection of jobs and machines in the cell through the local evaluation. Through training, the reward function converges, and the scheduling goal approaches the optimal value.

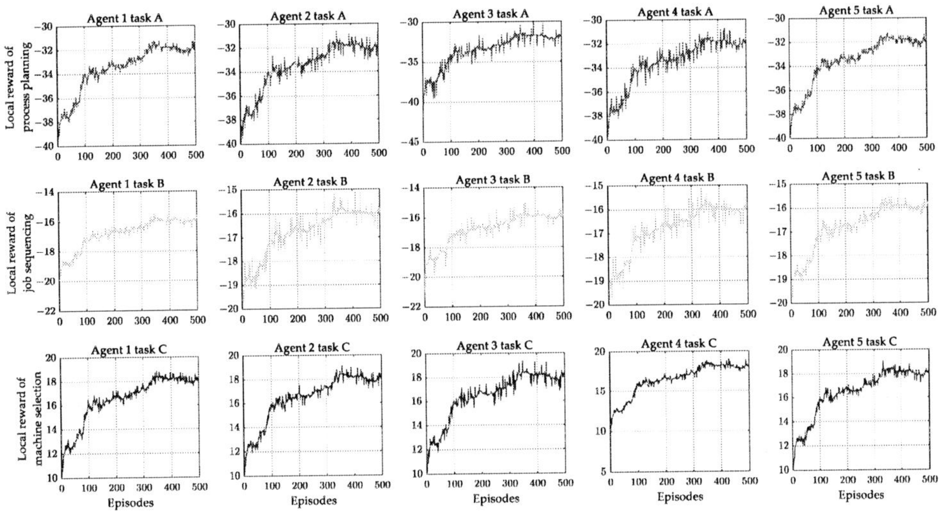

Figure 11. Convergence curve of local reward for each task of FJSP-DP (MK10).

CONCLUSIONS AND PROSPECTS

In this paper, a mixed integer programming scheduling model is established to solve the dual resource FJSP problem with robots as well as flexible process planning. The scheduling decision task and dynamic process planning process are defined from the perspective of real-time scheduling. The scheduling task is decomposed into three decision tasks: job sequencing, machine selection, and process planning. In order to realize real-time scheduling decisions, a MTMARL framework based on centralized training and decentralized execution is proposed. The robot acts as an agent and interacts with the scheduling environment. In the process of centralized training, the value network is used to train and optimize the policy network of each agent to achieve cooperation among multiple agents. The policy network is constructed of three neural network layers: the expert layer composed of DDQN, the tower layer composed of neural networks, and the gate layer for entering the attention mechanism. The gate control layer is used to solve the information sharing of decision tasks. In the process of decentralized implementation, each agent completes three scheduling decision tasks for the corresponding work cell through its local observation according to the trained policy network. The state, action, and reward functions for reinforcement learning training in the context of the scheduling problem were designed, and the training algorithm was developed. Finally, the scheduling simulation environment was derived from international standard examples, and an example experiment was carried out. The results were discussed from the four aspects of state feature correlation, scheduling results, and global and local reward convergence of the algorithm. The results show that the proposed method can effectively solve the FJSP-DP. Meanwhile, the proposed MTMARL framework is conducive to the realization of real-time scheduling decisions with self-organization, self-learning, and self-optimization.

At present, this study has some limitations. In the MTMARL framework, the feature of the gate layer neural network for multi-task coordination is designed subjectively. This may lead to insufficient discrimination of the specificity for multi-task. To make up for this shortcoming, an automatic feature extraction method can be added to the framework to improve the overall performance of the algorithm. In addition, this framework is based on the mode of centralized training and decentralized execution. Although it effectively solves the real-time scheduling of FJSP-DP, we think that it may not be a multi-tasking system in the strict sense. This shortcoming can be addressed by combining the latest multi-task reinforcement learning, such as IMPALA (Importance-Weighted Actor-Learner Architectures). In addition, future research should consider logistical factors between work cells, such as AGV, and expand the adaptability of scheduling models and methods.

AUTHOR CONTRIBUTIONS

Conceptualization, X.Z. and J.G.; data curation, X.Z.; investigation, X.Z. and J.X.; methodology, X.Z. and J.G.; project administration, J.X. and Y.W.; resources and software, J.X. and Z.X.; funding acquisition, Z.X.; writing—original draft, X.Z.; writing—review and editing, X.Z. and J.G. All authors have read and agreed to the published version of the manuscript.

ACKNOWLEDGMENTS

The authors are grateful to the editor and reviewers for their constructive comments and suggestions, which have improved this paper.

REFERENCES

1. Bouazza, W.; Sallez, Y.; Beldjilali, B. A distributed approach solving partially flexible job-shop scheduling problem with a Q-learning effect. IFAC Pap. 2017, 50, 15890–15895.
2. Chang, J.; Yu, D.; Hu, Y.; He, W.; Yu, H. Deep Reinforcement Learning for Dynamic Flexible Job Shop Scheduling with Random Job Arrival. Processes 2022, 10, 760.
3. Lu, Y.; Xu, X.; Wang, L. Smart manufacturing process and system automation–a critical review of the standards and envisioned scenarios. J. Manuf. Syst. 2020, 56, 312–325.
4. Wang, S.; Wan, J.; Li, D.; Zhang, C. Implementing smart factory of industrie 4.0: An outlook. Int. J. Distrib. Sens. N. 2016, 12, 3159805.
5. Arents, J.; Greitans, M. Smart Industrial Robot Control Trends, Challenges and Opportunities within Manufacturing. Appl. Sci. 2022, 12, 937.
6. ElMaraghy, H.; Patel, V.; Ben Abdallah, I. Scheduling of manufacturing systems under dual-resource constraints using genetic algorithms. J. Manuf. Syst. 2000, 19, 186–201.
7. Li, X.; Gao, L. Review for Flexible Job Shop Scheduling; Engineering Applications of Computational Methods; Springer: Berlin/Heidelberg, Germany, 2020; pp. 17–45.
8. Brucker, P.; Schlie, R. Job-shop scheduling with multi-purpose machines. Computing 1990, 45, 369–375.

9. Chaudhry, I.A.; Khan, A.A. A research survey: Review of flexible job shop scheduling techniques. Int. Trans. Oper. Res. 2016, 23, 551–591.

10. Xie, J.; Gao, L.; Peng, K.; Li, X.; Li, H. Review on flexible job shop scheduling. IET Collab. Intell. Manuf. 2019, 1, 67–77.

11. Gao, K.; Cao, Z.; Zhang, L.; Chen, Z.; Han, Y.; Pan, Q. A review on swarm intelligence and evolutionary algorithms for solving flexible job shop scheduling problems. IEEE/CAA J. Autom. Sin. 2019, 6, 904–916.

12. Zhang, X.; Liao, Z.X.; Ma, L.C.; Yao, J. Hierarchical multistrategy genetic algorithm for integrated process planning and scheduling. J. Intell. Manuf. 2020, 33, 223–246.

13. Lin, C.S.; Li, P.Y.; Wei, J.M.; Wu, M.C. Integration of process planning and scheduling for distributed flexible job shops. Comput. Oper. Res. 2020, 124, 105053.

14. Özgüven, C.; Özbakır, L.; Yavuz, Y. Mathematical models for job-shop scheduling problems with routing and process plan flexibility. Appl. Math. Model. 2010, 34, 1539–1548.

15. Phanden, R.K.; Jain, A.; Verma, R. Integration of process planning and scheduling: A state-of-the-art review. Int. J. Comput. Integr. Manuf. 2011, 24, 517–534.

16. Brucker, P.; Burke, E.K.; Groenemeyer, S. A branch and bound algorithm for the cyclic job-shop problem with transportation. Comput. Oper. Res. 2012, 39, 3200–3214.

17. Fatemi-Anaraki, S.; Tavakkoli-Moghaddam, R.; Foumani, M.; Vahedi-Nouri, B. Scheduling of Multi-Robot Job Shop Systems in Dynamic Environments: Mixed-Integer Linear Programming and Constraint Programming Approaches. Omega 2023, 115, 102770.

18. Ham, A. Transfer-robot task scheduling in flexible job shop. J. Intell. Manuf. 2020, 31, 1783–1793.

19. Vital-Soto, A.; Azab, A.; Baki, M.F. Mathematical modeling and a hybridized bacterial foraging optimization algorithm for the flexible job-shop scheduling problem with sequencing flexibility. J. Manuf. Syst. 2020, 54, 74–93.

20. Wu, X.; Peng, J.; Xiao, X.; Wu, S. An effective approach for the dual-resource flexible job shop scheduling problem considering loading and unloading. J. Intell. Manuf. 2020, 32, 707–728.

21. He, Z.; Tang, B.; Luan, F. An Improved African Vulture Optimization Algorithm for Dual-Resource Constrained Multi-Objective Flexible Job Shop Scheduling Problems. Sensors 2023, 23, 90.

22. Jiang, T.; Zhu, H.; Gu, J.; Liu, L.; Song, H. A discrete animal migration algorithm for dual-resource constrained energy-saving flexible job shop scheduling problem. J. Intell. Fuzzy Syst. 2022, 42, 3431–3444.

23. Hongyu, L.; Xiuli, W. A survival duration-guided NSGA-III for sustainable flexible job shop scheduling problem considering dual resources. IET Collab. Intell. Manuf. 2021, 3, 119–130.

24. Akbar, M.; Irohara, T. Scheduling for sustainable manufacturing: A review. J. Clean Prod. 2018, 205, 866–883.

25. Costa, A.; Cappadonna, F.A.; Fichera, S. A hybrid genetic algorithm for job sequencing and worker allocation in parallel unrelated machines with sequence-dependent setup times. Int. J. Adv. Manuf. Technol. 2013, 69, 2799–2817.

26. Akbar, M.; Irohara, T. Dual Resource Constrained Scheduling Considering Operator Working Modes and Moving in Identical Parallel Machines Using a Permutation-Based Genetic Algorithm. In Proceedings of the IFIP WG 5.7 International Conference on Advances in Production Management Systems (APMS), Seoul, Republic of Korea, 26–30 August 2018; pp. 464–472.

27. Akbar, M.; Irohara, T. A social-conscious scheduling model of dual resources constrained identical parallel machine to minimize makespan and operator workload balance. In Proceedings of the Asia Pacific Industrial Engineering & Management System Conference, Auckland, New Zealand, 2–5 December 2018.

28. Akbar, M.; Irohara, T. Metaheuristics for the multi-task simultaneous supervision dual resource-constrained scheduling problem. Eng. Appl. Artif. Intell. 2020, 96, 104004.
29. Qin, Z.; Lu, Y. Self-organizing manufacturing network: A paradigm towards smart manufacturing in mass personalization. J. Manuf. Syst. 2021, 60, 35–47.
30. Unterberger, E.; Hofmann, U.; Min, S.; Glasschröder, J.; Reinhart, G. Modeling of an energy-flexible production control with SysML. Procedia CIRP 2018, 72, 432–437.
31. Yue, H.; Xing, K.; Hu, H.; Wu, W.; Su, H. Supervisory control of deadlock-prone production systems with routing flexibility and unreliable resources. IEEE Trans. Syst. Man Cybern. Syst. 2019, 50, 3528–3540.
32. Assid, M.; Gharbi, A.; Hajji, A. Production control of failure-prone manufacturing-remanufacturing systems using mixed dedicated and shared facilities. Int. J. Prod. Econ. 2020, 224, 107549.
33. Ma, Y.-M.; Qiao, F.; Chen, X.; Tian, K.; Wu, X.-H. Dynamic scheduling approach based on SVM for semiconductor production line. Comput. Integr. Manuf. Syst. 2015, 21, 733–739.
34. Azab, E.; Nafea, M.; Shihata, L.A.; Mashaly, M. A Machine-Learning-Assisted Simulation Approach for Incorporating Predictive Maintenance in Dynamic Flow-Shop Scheduling. Appl. Sci. Basel 2021, 11, 11725.
35. Xiong, W.; Fu, D. A new immune multi-Agent system for the flexible job shop scheduling problem. J. Intell. Manuf. 2018, 29, 857–873.
36. Luo, S. Dynamic scheduling for flexible job shop with new job insertions by deep reinforcement learning. Appl. Soft. Comput. 2020, 91, 106208.
37. Han, B.; Yang, J. A deep reinforcement learning based solution for flexible job shop scheduling problem. Int. J. Simul. Model. 2021, 20, 375–386.
38. Luo, S.; Zhang, L.; Fan, Y. Real-Time Scheduling for Dynamic Partial-No-Wait Multiobjective Flexible Job Shop by Deep Reinforcement Learning. IEEE Trans. Autom. Sci. Eng. 2021, 19, 3020–3038.
39. Liu, R.; Piplani, R.; Toro, C. Deep reinforcement learning for dynamic scheduling of a flexible job shop. Int. J. Prod. Res. 2022, 60, 4049–4069.
40. Johnson, D.; Chen, G.; Lu, Y. Multi-Agent Reinforcement Learning for Real-Time Dynamic Production Scheduling in a Robot Assembly Cell. IEEE Robot Autom. Let. 2022, 7, 7684–7691.
41. Lei, K.; Guo, P.; Zhao, W.C.; Wang, Y.; Qian, L.M.; Meng, X.Y.; Tang, L.S. A multi-action deep reinforcement learning framework for flexible Job-shop scheduling problem. Expert Syst. Appl. 2022, 205, 117796.
42. Jiang, Y.; Cao, Z.; Zhang, J. Learning to Solve 3-D Bin Packing Problem via Deep Reinforcement Learning and Constraint Programming. IEEE T. Cybern. 2021, 1–12.
43. Omidshafiei, S.; Pazis, J.; Amato, C.; How, J.P.; Vian, J. Deep Decentralized Multi-task Multi-Agent Reinforcement Learning under Partial Observability. In Proceedings of the 34th International Conference on Machine Learning, Sydney, Australia, 6–11 August 2017.
44. Liu, X.; Zhang, G. A flexible job shop online scheduling approach based on process-tree. J. Theor. Appl. Inf. Technol. 2012, 44, 259–264.
45. Mnih, V.; Kavukcuoglu, K.; Silver, D.; Graves, A.; Antonoglou, I.; Wierstra, D.; Riedmiller, M. Playing atari with deep reinforcement learning. arXiv 2013, arXiv:1312.5602.
46. Mnih, V.; Kavukcuoglu, K.; Silver, D.; Rusu, A.A.; Veness, J.; Bellemare, M.G.; Graves, A.; Riedmiller, M.; Fidjeland, A.K.; Ostrovski, G. Human-level control through deep reinforcement learning. Nature 2015, 518, 529–533.
47. Van Hasselt, H.; Guez, A.; Silver, D. Deep reinforcement learning with double q-learning. In AAAI Conference on Artificial Intelligence; AAAI: Palo Alto, CA, USA, 2016; pp. 2094–2100.
48. Panwalkar, S.S.; Iskander, W. A Survey of Scheduling Rules. Oper. Res. 1977, 25, 45–61.

2

Graphic Model for Shop Floor Simulation and Control in the Context of Industry 5.0

Nuno Fernandes[1], João-Paulo Barros[1,2] and Rogerio Campos-Rebelo[1,2]

[1]Polytechnic Institute of Beja, School of Technology and Management, 7800-295 Beja, Portugal

[2]UNINOVA, Centre of Technology and Systems, 2829-516 Monte de Caparica, Portugal

ABSTRACT

Industry 5.0 changes the paradigm of the current production model, with repercussions throughout the value chain, and opens up opportunities for new approaches that include reducing waste to optimize the use of the planet's resources. This paper proposes a functional and executable model that implements a Holonic Manufacturing System (HMS) architecture inspired by the I5.0 guidelines. This architecture presents the factory floor as a service provider for the product to be built, intending to make the manufacturing process adaptable to changes. The model uses Reference nets as the modeling language, a high-level class of Petri nets, Java programming language as the annotation language, and free tool support. The model can be used to perform software-level simulations and can also be interconnected to existing physical devices using Internet of things technologies, enabling interactions between Cyber–Physical Systems (CPSs). It thus allows for the control of the shop floor and the reuse of the current machine park to make its adoption more sustainable. The model was used to generate several simulation results, which are presented and analyzed, thus demonstrating the model's usefulness.

Keywords: *i5.0; Model, Petri nets, Renew, CPS, IoT, PRESIB*

INTRODUCTION

Industrial development has had an enormous impact on European society [1]. Since the first industrial revolution, industry has been the engine of European prosperity.

The concept Industry 4.0 (i4.0), coined in Germany in 2011 [2], describes how the industry will use technology to better cope with a changing world and economy. The special requirements for a "green production" and carbon-neutral and energy-efficient industry are part of the i4.0 concept.

China has identified how to apply the concept in its context. The government initiative "Made in China 2025" is directly inspired by i4.0, focusing on revitalizing China's manufacturing industry in the process of soft change.

A survey presented by Deutsche Bank in 2014 [3] suggested the adoption of i4.0 as the "factory manufacturer of the world". Professor Klaus Schwab describes in [4,5] how i4.0 fundamentally differs from previous industrial concepts, characterized primarily by technological advances.

The European Commission presented the Industry 5.0 (i5.0) [6] concept in which the ability of the industry to achieve social goals beyond employment and growth is recognized as a resilient source of prosperity. Production respects our planet's limits, and the workers' well-being is now at the heart of the production process. It complements the existing i4.0 paradigm, where research and innovation will drive the transition to a sustainable, human-centered model and a resilient European industry. There is a shift from an exclusive focus on shareholder value to stakeholder value.

As highlighted in the [6] document, adopting i5.0 requires new technologies. However, the replacement of equipment has repercussions in the volume of investment and, consequently, in the consumption of natural resources.

The use of Business Process Model and Notation (BPMN)-based [7] models (e.g., [8,9,10]) or Petri-nets-based ones (e.g., [11,12,13,14]) has been proposed for performing simulations and for integration with the physical equipment in the industry.

This paper contributes an architecture and a presentation of a functional model that implements a *Holonic Manufacturing System* (HMS) architecture. The I5.0 guidelines inspire the architecture. The model is intended to be used to perform simulations or connect with existing equipment and enable, enabling Cyber–Physical System (CPS) interactions. It thus allows for the reuse of the current machine park to make the adoption more sustainable. Simulations were performed and their results are presented to demonstrate the model's usefulness.

RELATED WORK

Holonic Manufacturing Systems (HMSs) are proposed in *IMT Test Case 5* [15]. These systems are an adaptation of the social concepts proposed by [16], which describe the concept of *holons*. The *holon* is based on the observation, in nature, that something that is simultaneously a whole and a part, e.g., atom, are a whole but also part of cells.

In the same year, 1994, Valckenaers presented the results of a test [17], concluding that adopting the HMS architecture has advantages for manufacturing processes. The same article highlighted the high adoption costs due to the lack of suitable technologies.

Van Brussel, in 1997, proposed the *Product-Resource-Order-Staff Architecture* (PROSA) [18], which introduced significant innovations, naming the decoupling of the system structure from the control algorithm and disassociation of logistical aspects from technical ones. In the same document, we identify three basic types of *holons*, represented in Figure 1 as the building blocks for an HMS architecture. The relationships between *holons* identifies the type of knowledge exchanged between them.

PROSA introduces the *staff holon* as an optional element that can assist basic *holons* in the performance of tasks and allow for the incorporation of centralized solutions. Thus, *staff holons* are useful for problems that do not use a distributed solution, allowing for an easy migration of current hierarchical systems to *holonical* solutions. Finally, *staff holons* do not introduce hierarchical rigidity into the system since they only advise basic *holons*.

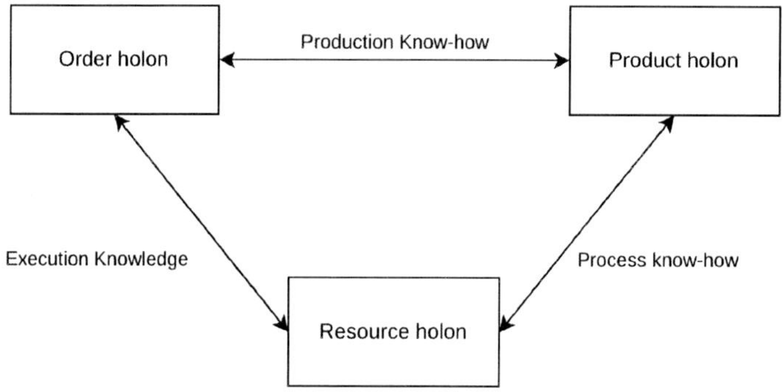

Figure 1. Relations between basic holons.

Subsequently, Ounnar presented the *Product, Resource, Order and Simulation Isoarchic System* (PROSIS) [19]. This architecture introduces significant differences in PROSA, namely (1) a new interpretation of the three basic concepts of holons, (2) the disappearance of the *staff holon* concept, unnecessary in the context of an isocratic system where all holons have equal access to the command, and (3) the addition of the concept of holon simulation in order to anticipate any failure.

It proposes a fully decentralized control system that optimizes resources and allows for real-time production system management. This is achieved by reducing failures and participating in increasing productivity. The PROSIS approach aims to obtain the "best" solution based on the actual state of all *holons*. The proposed self-organized and isocratic control system is based on the autonomous real-time control capability associated with each *holon*. Control decision making in PROSIS requires the participation of all entities (products, resources, and orders).

In recent years, more holonic architectures have been proposed, e.g., QHAR [20], ADACOR [21], ADACOR2 [22], and HCBA [23].

Reference Nets

Since Carl Adam Petri introduced Petri nets in 1962, they have been an object of study in works related to CPS modeling (e.g., [12,24,25]).

Reference nets are a colored Petri nets class that uses the Java programming language as the annotation language [26].

In addition, Reference nets also support the concept of nets within nets, where a *token* can be a reference to a net, and not just a value of some kind [27]. This concept means that nets can dynamically create, destroy, and encapsulate other nets. Each Reference net can be seen as a class used to create objects, also called net instances. These net instances fire their transitions when they run, creating or destroying other net instances, values, and variables.

As in other Petri nets, Reference nets contain places, transitions, and various types of arcs. In addition to the typical arc found in most Petri net classes, the model presented in this work used test arcs (no arrows), *clear arcs* (with a white double arrow), and inhibitory arcs (with a small black circle at each end). All information about arc types can be found in the Renew tool user manual, which provides a complete presentation of the Reference nets and the Renew tool [28].

The Renew tool can be extended with the *plugins* feature [28]. Hence, although it was developed primarily for Petri nets modeling, *plugins* provide support for different modeling techniques, i.e., Unified Modeling Language (UML) [29] or BPMN diagrams.

Next, we present the proposed PRESIB architecture.

PROPOSED ARCHITECTURE

The PRESIB architecture, initially presented in [14], is inspired by the PROSIS architecture. PRESIB is also a distributed architecture but suppresses the *order holon.* Consequently, the features are distributed among the *product holon* (Ph), which becomes the holder of the production plan, and the *resource holon* (Rh) responsible for the task execution quality since it provides the service.

A holonic architecture has different planes of interaction. In PRESIB, each plane is called a *Playground*, which defines the interaction between *holons*, from which the system's behavior emerges.

In Figure 2, different *Playgrounds* are represented at different levels. Reading Figure 2 top to bottom, we can see that we have the product distributed by sectors. Each sector distributes the corresponding part of the product through the factories. In turn, each factory distributes part of the products by its machines. At each of the different levels, the interaction takes place in a context, represented by the *Playground.* Each actor is an Rh, just as the product is a Ph. This is how the model's applicability is carried out at different levels, highlighting the *holonic* characteristic of the architecture.

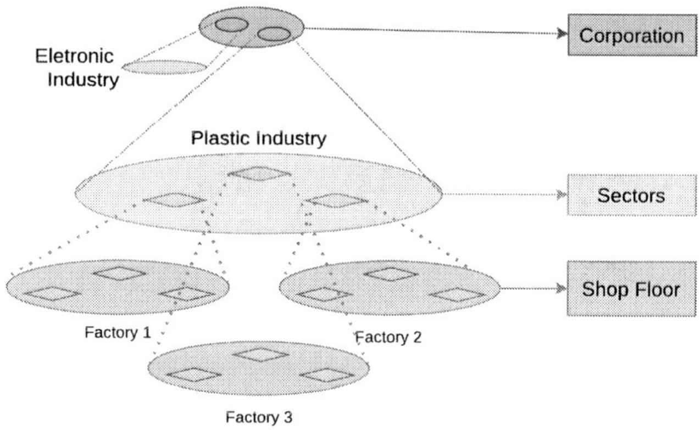

Figure 2. Holonic representation of PRESIB architecture.

The *Playground* acts as the service provider for Ph, since it is the common element between the Ph *holon* and Rh *holon.* The Ph seeks the services the Rh provides in the *Playground.*

Thus, at different levels, the services provided by Rh are also different. Consequently, the *Playground* offers different services at different levels.

A *holon* is composed of two components, one logic and the other physical; this topic is covered in greater detail in this chapter dedicated to the PRESIB model. It is from the integration of these two components that the Cyber–Physical Systems (CPSs) emerge as autonomous units that interact with each other to achieve a result.

MODEL

The model was inspired by the need to process different products on a hypothetical shop floor. This concept is shown in Figure 3. This shop floor (in this scenario, named Playground) is composed of machines *A, B, C, D* (Rh) with similar features and services. Transporters *A, B, C* are also machines whose services are limited to the transport of the product (Ph) to be produced between machines or to the warehouse after its completion.

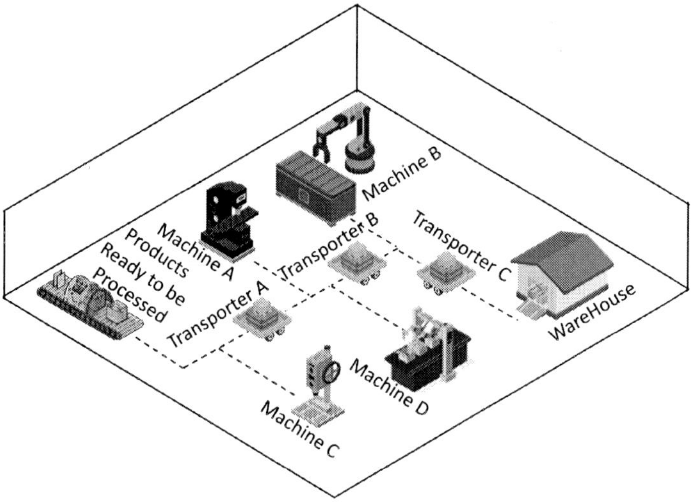

Figure 3. Example of a shop floor to be modeled.

Following the PRESIB architecture, the *Playground* is a service provider for the Ph. Simultaneously, the Ph is the holder of the production list composed of a sequence of services necessary for its execution.

Thus, the Ph informs the Playground that it needs to perform a particular service, and, in response, the Playground informs which available Rh will perform the requested service. Next, the Ph requests a transportation service from the Playground, which, in turn, provides the information of the Rh that will provide the transport service. The Ph then waits to be collected and transported to the Rh that will perform the service initially requested from the production list.

After running all of these services, the Ph again requests an available Rh to execute the next service according to the next step in the production list.

The Ph will perform this sequence as often as necessary until it is transported to the warehouse, which is the last step in the production list.

Based on the use case description, Figure 4 represents the sequence of actions between the main actors. In the sequence diagram, the Ph represents multiple instances of the Ph net, the Playground is the single instance of the Playground net, and the Rh transporter and Rh machine represent multiple instances of the Rh net. In the beginning, steps 1, 2, and 3 occur without a predefined order, as this will depend on each net instantiation process. As soon as step 3 receives a response, the sequence will be the one shown in the diagram. From the Ph's point of view, the execution of the set of steps will be repeated as often as services are required to execute the products' production plan.

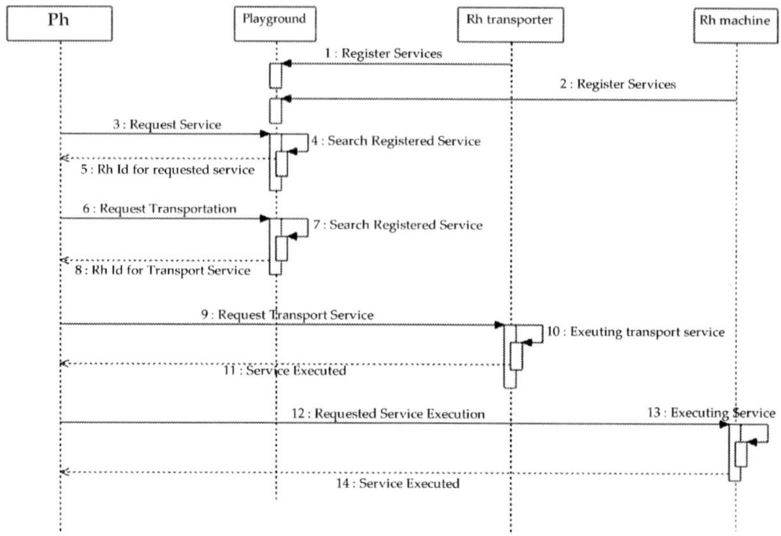

Figure 4. Sequence of actions between Playground, Rn net machine, Rh net transporter, and Ph net.

It is possible to identify three actions, as seen in the UML Use Case diagram shown in Figure 5, to be performed by the main nets of the model, represented as actors in the same figure.

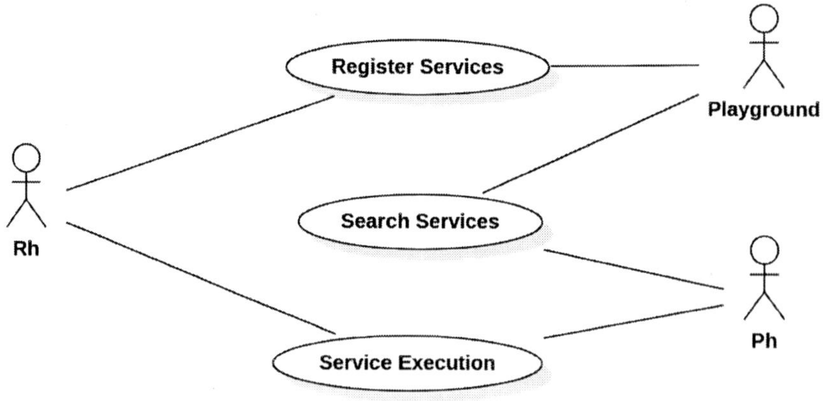

Figure 5. Interaction between Ph, Rh, and Playground.

The *Register Services* action is the act of the Rh registering the services that can run on the Playground. This action is performed in the Rh net startup process and whenever the service runs.

The *Search Services* action is performed by the Ph to run the production list. In this case, it was modeled on the Rh net where, whenever it gets the Rh to run the production service, it has to request a transport service. However, this can be changed by adapting the net modeling to the needs of the implementation.

Finally, the *Service Execution* action represents the execution of a service by an Rh in a given Ph.

For the implementation of this model, a series of components were used to perform the intended case study simulations. Figure 6 presents the various components used and the technologies to communicate between them. Next, the represented components are described:

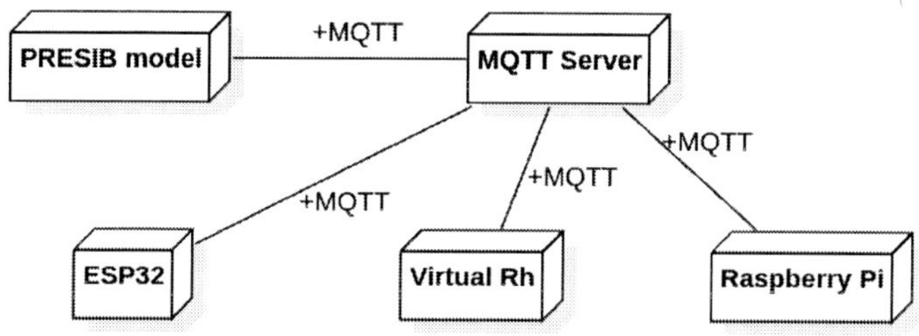

Figure 6. Deployment diagram.

- PRESIB Model – composed of *Helios* and *Hermes* packages.
- Transporter Micro Controller – Device (ESP32 Dev Kit) simulates a carrier.
- Machine Micro Controller – Device (Arduino Uno with *hat* ethernet) that simulates a machine.
- MQTT public server – Public server for asynchronous communication through MQTT protocol
- Virtual Microcontroller App–App developed to simulate responses from microcontrollers as a replacement for non-available physical equipment.

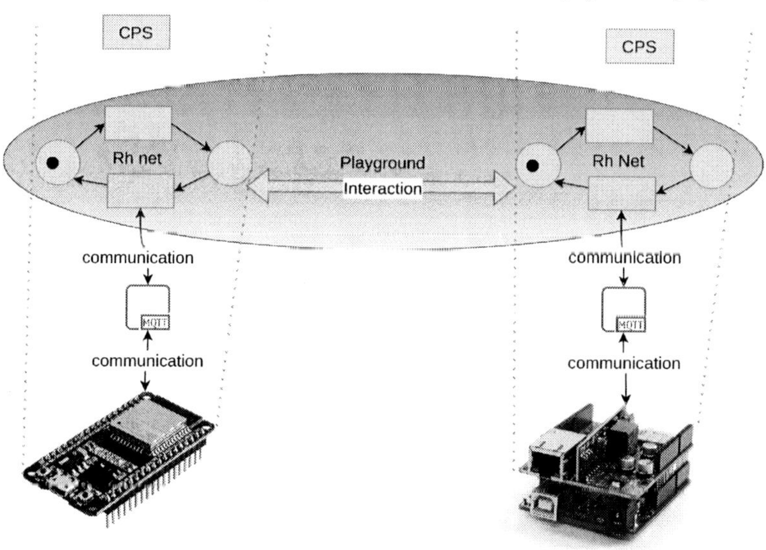

Figure 7. CPS concept on PRESIB model.

Except for the *machine microcontroller* and due to the limited availability of connectivity equipment, the system primarily communicates using WiFi technology.

The *Message Queuing Telemetry Transport* MQTT protocol was selected over other possibilities (e.g., the *Open Platform Communications—Unified Architecture* (OPC-UA) protocol) due to its popularity and consequent availability of public servers for test use scenarios.

Thus, the MQTT protocol enables asynchronous bidirectional communication between microcontrollers (physical or simulated in the application) and their Rh net instances, as represented in Figure 7. By creating this two-way communication between the digital element (the net) and its physical element (the microcontroller), we face a CPS. This approach allows for the extension of existing equipment in the digital plane, provides new features or services, and reuses the current equipment.

MODEL DETAIL

The PRESIB architecture model is a functional executable model. It can be used to perform simulations and supports the creation of CPS. It was built using a high-level Petri nets class named Reference nets. This class of nets is supported by a freely available tool that uses a general-purpose programming language, allowing for more compact graphical models and multiple model extensions, including communication with other models and physical devices [26,28].

As represented in Figure 8, the model consists of two main packages, which have been given names of entities from Greek mythology, *Helios* and *Hermes*.

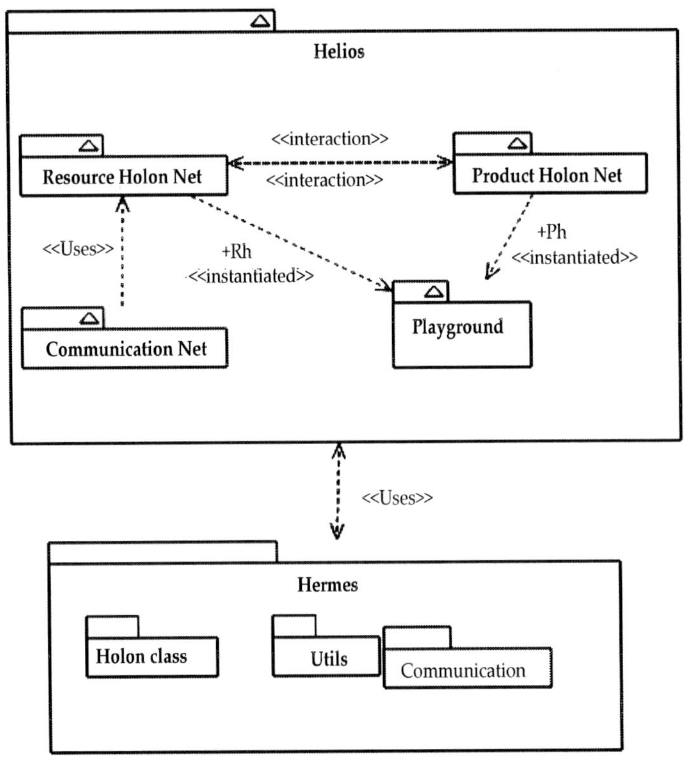

Figure 8. Representation of the structure of the PRESIB model.

Helios represents the Reference nets that make up the model, and *Hermes* represents the Java classes developed to extend the functionality of the *Helios* nets. Both packages complement each other in order to create the PRESIB model.

The next subsections provide details about the *Helios* and *Hermes* packages.

Helios

Reflecting the PRESIB architecture, the Rh and Ph are represented in the model by the nets *Resource Holon Net* (Rh net) and *Product Holon Net* (Ph net), respectively. As presented in Figure 2, the interaction between the Ph and Rh takes place in a given context that is represented in the model by the Playground net. The objectives of the PRESIB architecture is to enable the creation of CPS. For this purpose, the nets that correspond to *holons* use the package *Hermes* to create communication channels with the desired equipment.

The *Helios* package template is composed of the following nets:

- Resource Holon net—Net corresponding to *resource holons.*
- Product Holon net—Net corresponding to *product holons.*
- Communication net—Auxiliary net used for communication between Rh nets and their physical components.
- Auxiliary Net—For registering services in the Playground.
- Playground—Instantiates the Rh nets and the Ph nets; it is the catalog of available services.

All nets are available for consultation through the PRESIB website [30].

Hermes

The Renew tool is developed in Java and allows for the execution of Java classes; in essence, Renew nets are Java classes [28]. In the PRESIB model, the functionalities of the nets are extended by a Java package. This extension of the features is achieved not only by instantiating and using Java classes from within the nets but also by using nets from within Java classes. *Hermes* provides utility classes that are used in any model net and offers classes specific to certain nets, such as nets for *holons.*

EXECUTION

Initially, the execution of the nets representing the holons is described, followed by an explanation of the execution of the *Playground* net. Although the nets interact with instances of Java classes and vice versa, this paper addresses the net model execution as a whole.

Resource Holon *Net*

The *resource holon net* (Rh net) is represented in Figure 9. At the time of instantiation, it is assigned a unique identifier that relates it to its physical counterpart.

After instantiation, the net performs a series of checks. It retrieves and publishes the list of services on the *Playground* net using the *service_register*; see Figure 10.

The end of this boot process is indicated by a *token* at the *waiting for job* place. When the execution of a service is assigned to the net, the transitions following the *waiting for job* place are performed. These transitions are composed of a series of commands that are sent to the physical part to indicate what operation to perform.

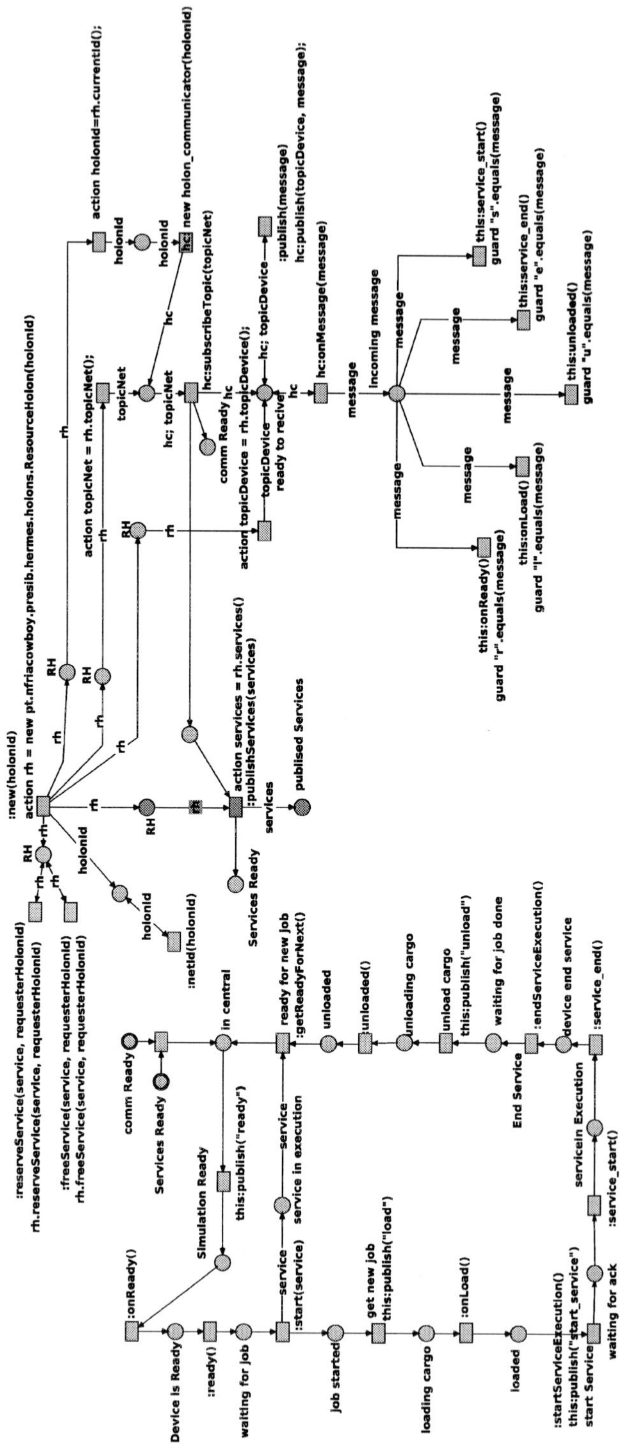

Figure 9. Resource holon net.

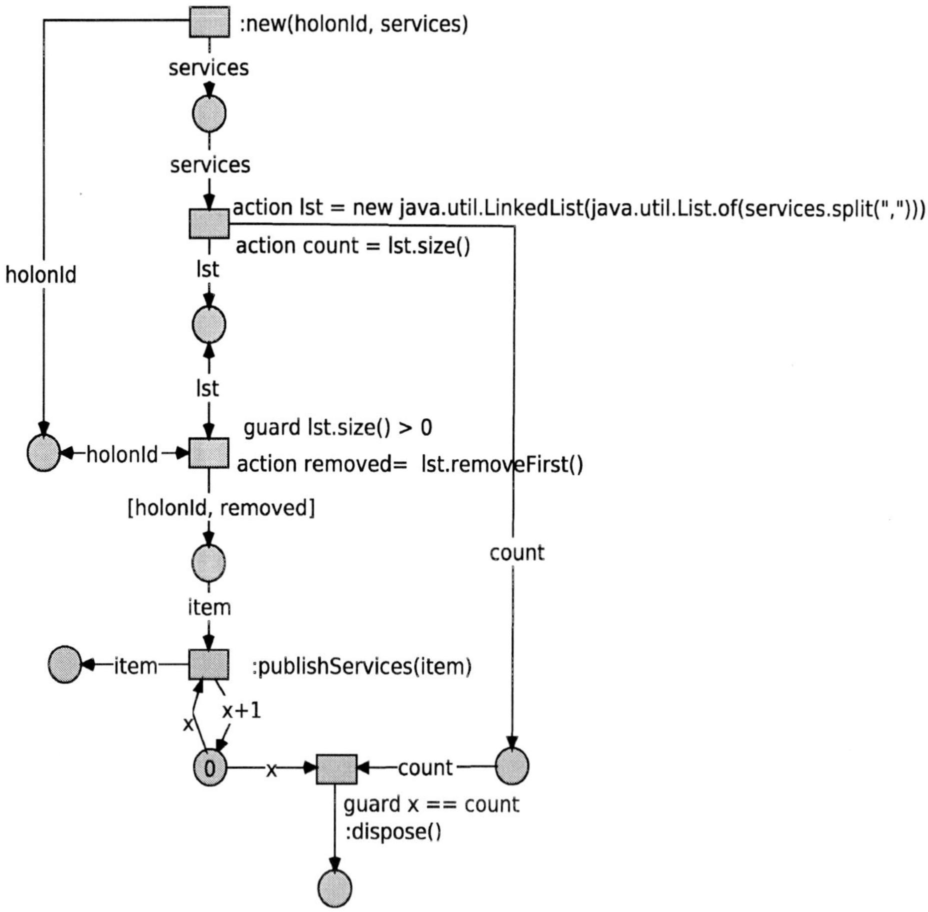

Figure 10. Service logging auxiliary net.

After executing the command, the net waits for the physical component response to proceed to the next step. By doing so, it completes the execution cycle, which is indicated by the *token*, again, in the place *waiting for job*.

In this implementation, all equipment that provides services, such as machines or transport, use this net.

Product Holon **Net**

At its instantiation, the *product holon net* (Ph net), presented in Figure 11, also receives a unique identifier that relates to the material to be processed. In its initial transition, the Java ProductHolon class is instantiated in the Ph variable that is used in various transitions throughout the model. It also provides the execution plan as a list of services to be executed. After its instantiation, the net requests the necessary service to the Playground net. By convention, it has been modeled that, after obtaining the reference of the instance of the Rh net that will provide the requested service, the Ph net will always request a transport service.

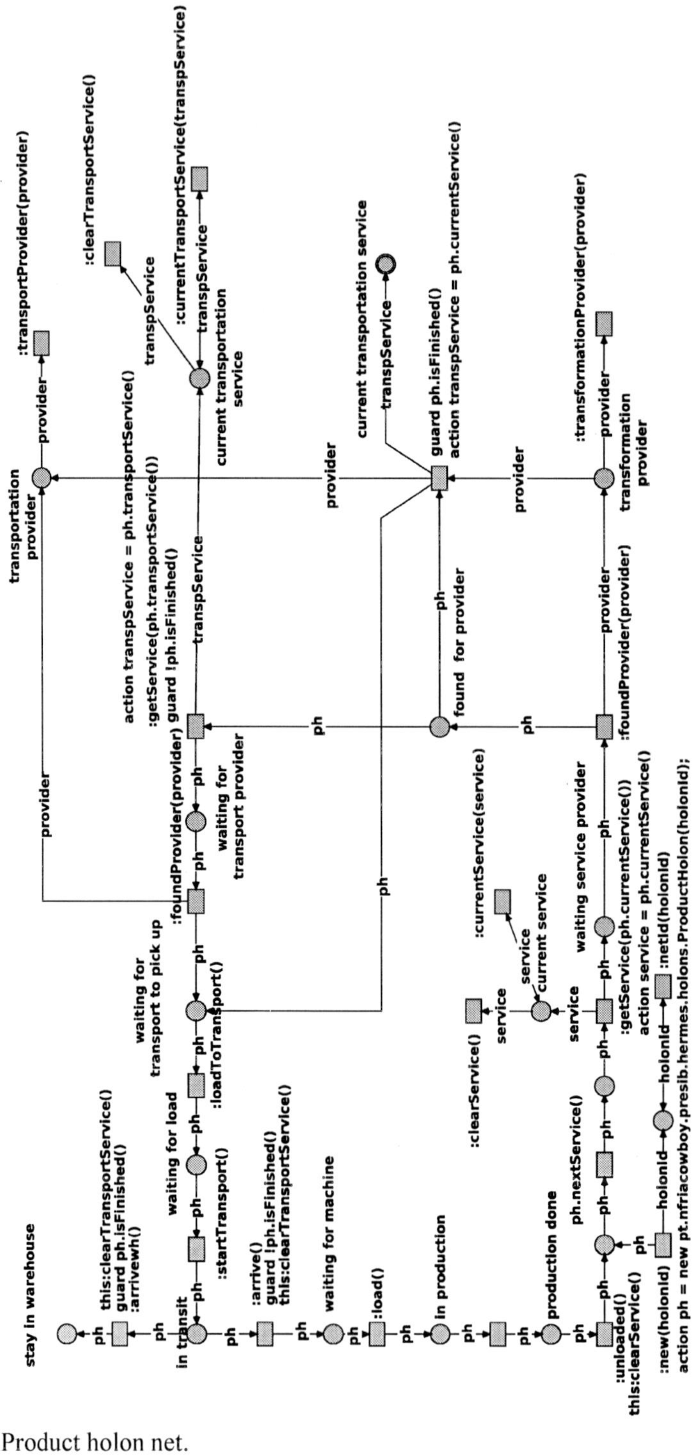

Figure 11. Product holon net.

Communication Net

Figure 12 shows the holon_comunicator net. It handles the communication between the net model and the physical device and uses a Java class and the *mqtt_message_receiver* net, presented in Figure 13, to implement the observer partner, enabling the model to send and receive the MQTT messages between the holon net and its physical component.

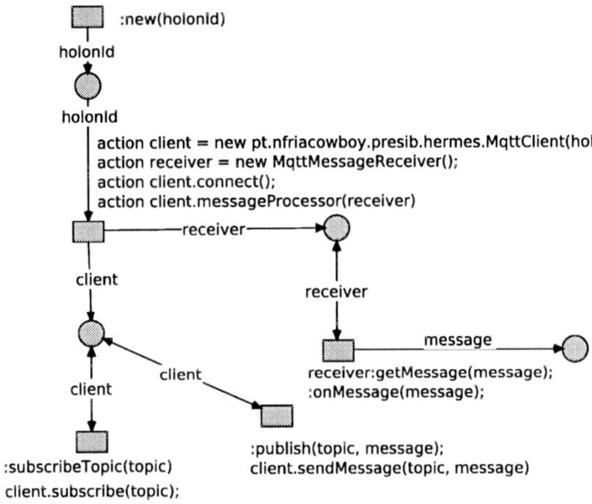

Figure 12. Communication client net.

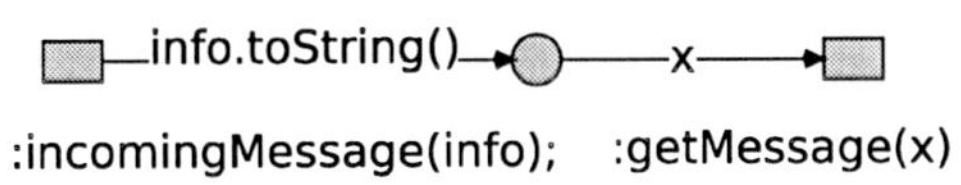

Figure 13. Usage of the *observer* in a net.

Playground Net

The Playground net is responsible for instantiating all Rh nets and Ph nets that will be used during the execution of the model (see Figure 14). In this implementation, counters were implemented to control the instantiation of nets according to the desired number (identifier). The instances of Ph nets are referenced in the net by the variable Ph. Rh nets are used for transport, and machines are instantiated in different sites and referenced by different variables. In the model, the rht variable references the Rh nets for transport, and the rhm variable references the Rh nets for machines.

After being instantiated in the Playground, the Rh nets register their services and are placed in the *service catalog* place in the form of *tuples*. In those tuples, the service name is associated with the holonID of the instance that registers it.

After their instantiation, the Ph nets request the first desired service to the Playground. If the service is available in the *service catalog* place, then the Ph is informed of which rhm holonID will provide the service. The *tuple [holonId, service]* is removed from the *service catalog* place to prevent the service from that rhm being available to other Ph.

After a Ph orders the execution service (the ones provided by the machines), it returns to the *request service* place to order a transport service.

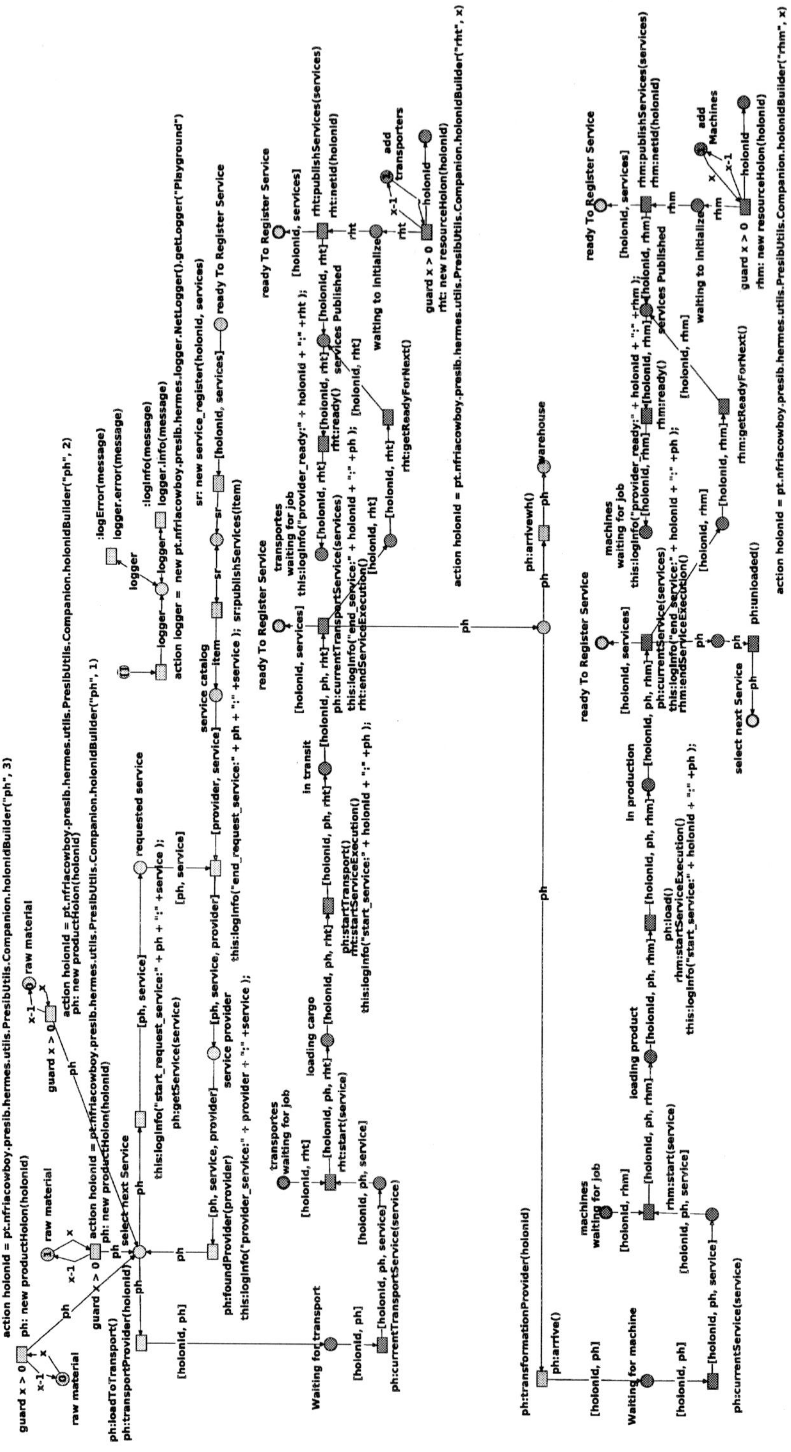

Figure 14. Playground net.

After a transport is assigned, the Ph is placed in the *waiting for transport* place to wait for the transport to perform its service. At the end of the transport service execution, the Ph is put in the *waiting for machine* place, waiting for the machine to start its service execution process. After execution, the service returns to the *request service* place to continue to the production plan.

The Ph will be in this cycle until transported to the warehouse, represented by the *warehouse* place, which indicates its completion.

The model provides a central *log* functionality. By adding an action in a transition, it is possible to write a log from any transition on the model, as represented in the Listing 1.

Listing 1. Command to produce a log in the transition.

```
this : loginfo( "Star_service" + holonId + ":" + ph) ;
```

The logs capability is important because it allows for adding custom logs that can be parsed after the execution of the simulation to perform an analysis on the results.

SIMULATIONS

The case study described in this chapter inspired the model's elaboration and simulations. The model was executed while connected to physical devices. The following analyses were carried out from the results of the simulations:

- Size of the infrastructure required to support communication between the physical and logical components of the CPSs;
- Analyze the actions of each simulation;
- Obtain execution and wait times by service and by simulation;
- Check the randomness of the execution of a given scenario.

Twenty-five simulations were performed, divided into two groups. One group represents simulations with a single service type and the same amount of services. The files generated by the simulations are presented in Table 1 and divided into two subgroups. The table's column with the tile "Fixed number of Rh" shows the filenames of the logs with the same amount of Rh but a variable amount of Ph. The column with the tile "Fixed number of Ph" represents the simulations performed with a variable amount of Rh.

Table 1. Simulations in which Ph have single service type and the same amount

Fixed Number of Rh	Fixed Number of Ph
1ph_10xserv1_1ph_10xserv2_1ph_10xserv3__10rht_10rhm	100ph_10xserv1_5rht_10rhm
10ph_10xserv1_10ph_10xserv2_10ph_10xserv3__10rht_10rhm	100ph_10xserv1_10rht_10rhm
100ph_10xserv1_100ph_10xserv2_100ph_10xserv3__10rht_10rhm	100ph_10xserv1_10rht_20rhm
	100ph_10xserv2_5rht_10rhm
	100ph_10xserv2_10rht_10rhm
	100ph_10xserv2_10rht_20rhm
	100ph_10xserv3_5rht_10rhm
	100ph_10xserv3_10rht_10rhm
	100ph_10xserv3_10rht_20rhm

The other group is composed of simulations where the service type and the amount of services per Ph are variable. The logs generated by those simulations are represented in Table 2. Also in this table, the logs are divided into two columns: one with the tile "Fixed number of Rh", which shows the logs of the simulations with the same amount of Rh but different numbers of Ph between them, and another column with the title "Same simulation 10 times", which shows the logs files of the same simulation executed 10 times.

Table 2. Simulations in which Ph have multiple service types and different amounts

Fixed Number of Rh	Same Simulation 10 Times
3diff_ph_10rht_10rhm	300diff_ph_10rht_10rhm_1
30diff_ph_10rht_10rhm	300diff_ph_10rht_10rhm_2
300diff_ph_10rht_10rhm	300diff_ph_10rht_10rhm_3
	300diff_ph_10rht_10rhm_4
	300diff_ph_10rht_10rhm_5
	300diff_ph_10rht_10rhm_6
	300diff_ph_10rht_10rhm_7
	300diff_ph_10rht_10rhm_8
	300diff_ph_10rht_10rhm_9
	300diff_ph_10rht_10rhm_10

The names of the simulations also describe the configuration used. In Table 1, the names follow the following convention:

amount of Ph_amount of services_rh carrier quantity_amount of Rh machine

In Table 2 the names follow the convention:

amount of Ph_rh carrier quantity_rh machine quantity

In the *Same simulation column 10 times*, the name of each file is preceded by *_n*, which represents the simulation number.

The full results list, with the corresponding links to the files, is available in [31].

Through a tool developed for this purpose, described in [32], the following files were generated for each simulation:

- procustion_steps_simulation_name.csv—The times of each action described in the stock sequence are displayed per line. Which instance of Rh machine and transport Rh performed the service is also displayed in each line.
- times_per_Service_simulation_name.csv—The name of the service, the sum of the runtime, and the sum of the request time are displayed per line.
- times_per_Service_simulation_name.svg—Representation on a bar chart of the values of the csv file with the same name.
- total_times_simulation_name.csv—Displays total simulation times
- total_times_simulation_name.svg—Representation on a bar chart of the values from the comma-separated values (CSVs) file with the same name.

RESULTS AND DISCUSSION

The following analyses were carried out based on the results obtained from the simulations.

Scale the Infrastructure Needed to Support Communication between the Physical and Logical Components of the CPS

The total amount of messages sent during the simulation was analyzed to scale the infrastructure needed to support communications between the physical and logical components of the CPS; that is, between the Rh net and its microcontroller. Several simulations were performed in which only one change was made between each to identify how many messages correspond to this change.

A simulation was initially performed consisting of a Ph, an Rh transport, and an Rh machine. The Ph production list consisted of a service named *"serv1"* and transport to the warehouse. Rh transport offers two services: the shuttle service and the warehouse transport service. The Rh machine only made available the service with the name *"serv1"*. The total number of messages was 31.

Then, a series of simulations were performed, changing a single parameter in the reference simulation. For example, increasing the number of services in the Ph's production list by one or adding another Ph or Rh.

The analysis of the results allowed us to identify that the set of 31 messages of the initial simulation is composed as follows:

- Eighteen messages per service in ph list;
- Two messages per Rh;
- Nine constant messages regardless of any change.

With this information, it is possible to estimate the infrastructure to accommodate the volume of messages generated during the execution of the model. For example, in a setup of 20 Rh with both machines and transporters, with the goal of producing 1000 Ph, and assuming that each Ph will need four services to be executed, it is possible to calculate the total messages using the following formula:

$$TotalPh \times AmountOfServices \times MessagesPerService + TotalRh \times MessagesPerRh + 9$$

where:
TotalPh = 1000;
Amount Of Services= 3;
MessagesPerService= 18;
TotalRh = 20;
MessagesPerRh = 2.
Replacing the variables is the formula, the result is the following:
$1000 \times 3 \times 18 + 20 \times 2 + 9 = 54{,}049$

The average load of each service message depends on the amount of information needed in the communication between the physical machine and the logical counter part. However, if assumed that the average load is 300 Bytes, it is possible to calculate the total load using this formula:

TotalPh × Amount of Services × Messages Per Service × 300 B
Replacing the variables, the result is
1000 × 3 × 18 × 300 B − 16,200,000 B (16,200 KB)

Analyze the Actions of Each Simulation

Files with the prefix *procustion_steps_* display the steps performed for each service. Table 3 displays a portion of the contents of one of those files with the CSV format. The sample file is available online [33].

Table 3. Example of file content with simulation execution steps

ph	Step	startServiceRequest	startTransportRequest	Service	transportService	isForWarehouse	endServiceRequest	endTransportRequest	rhtId	startTransport	endTransport	rhmId	startService	endService
productHolon[12]	2	2022-06-17 08:27:50,615	2022-06-17 08:27:51,794	serv1	transport	false	2022-06-17 08:27:51,729	2022-06-17 08:27:52,875	rht-005	2022-06-17 08:27:53,282	2022-06-17 08:27:53,516	rhm-008	2022-06-17 08:27:53,737	2022-06-17 08:27:53,908
productHolon[4]	3	2022-06-17 08:27:50,732	2022-06-17 08:27:52,789	serv3	transport	false	2022-06-17 08:27:52,461	2022-06-17 08:27:52,875	rht-010	2022-06-17 08:27:53,425	2022-06-17 08:27:53,811	rhm-009	2022-06-17 08:27:53,942	2022-06-17 08:27:54,315
productHolon[7]	1	2022-06-17 08:27:50,520	2022-06-17 08:27:52,914	serv2	transport	false	2022-06-17 08:27:52,797	2022-06-17 08:27:52,924	rht-004	2022-06-17 08:27:53,578	2022-06-17 08:27:53,812	rhm-009	2022-06-17 08:27:54,633	2022-06-17 08:27:54,822
productHolon[4]	5	2022-06-17 08:27:54,462	2022-06-17 08:27:54,483	serv3	transport	false	2022-06-17 08:27:54,464	2022-06-17 08:27:54,515	rht-006	2022-06-17 08:27:54,560	2022-06-17 08:27:54,713	rhm-004	2022-06-17 08:27:55,144	2022-06-17 08:27:55,286
productHolon[12]	4	2022-06-17 08:27:54,070	2022-06-17 08:27:54,149	serv1	transport	false	2022-06-17 08:27:54,086	2022-06-17 08:27:54,160	rht-007	2022-06-17 08:27:54,561	2022-06-17 08:27:54,632	rhm-006	2022-06-17 08:27:55,030	2022-06-17 08:27:55,287
productHolon[7]	6	2022-06-17 08:27:54,893	2022-06-17 08:27:55,011	serv2	transport	false	2022-06-17 08:27:54,895	2022-06-17 08:27:55,012	rht-009	2022-06-17 08:27:55,184	2022-06-17 08:27:55,555	rhm-010	2022-06-17 08:27:55,923	2022-06-17 08:27:55,951
productHolon[4]	8	2022-06-17 08:27:55,559	2022-06-17 08:27:55,644	serv3	transport	false	2022-06-17 08:27:55,576	2022-06-17 08:27:55,648	rht-004	2022-06-17 08:27:55,764	2022-06-17 08:27:55,883	rhm-006	2022-06-17 08:27:56,007	2022-06-17 08:27:56,360
productHolon[12]	7	2022-06-17 08:27:55,488	2022-06-17 08:27:55,620	serv1	transport	false	2022-06-17 08:27:55,494	2022-06-17 08:27:55,623	rht-005	2022-06-17 08:27:55,758	2022-06-17 08:27:55,916	rhm-008	2022-06-17 08:27:56,168	2022-06-17 08:27:56,459
productHolon[7]	9	2022-06-17 08:27:56,133	2022-06-17 08:27:56,240	serv2	transport	false	2022-06-17 08:27:56,137	2022-06-17 08:27:56,243	rht-005	2022-06-17 08:27:56,526	2022-06-17 08:27:56,722	rhm-006	2022-06-17 08:27:56,953	2022-06-17 08:27:57,203
productHolon[4]	10	2022-06-17 08:27:56,524	2022-06-17 08:27:56,554	serv3	transport	false	2022-06-17 08:27:56,550	2022-06-17 08:27:56,559	rht-010	2022-06-17 08:27:56,693	2022-06-17 08:27:56,721	rhm-002	2022-06-17 08:27:57,169	2022-06-17 08:27:57,203
productHolon[12]	11	2022-06-17 08:27:56,609	2022-06-17 08:27:56,744	serv1	transport	false	2022-06-17 08:27:56,643	2022-06-17 08:27:56,751	rht-006	2022-06-17 08:27:56,936	2022-06-17 08:27:57,205	rhm-003	2022-06-17 08:27:57,286	2022-06-17 08:27:57,640
productHolon[12]	14	2022-06-17 08:27:57,693	2022-06-17 08:27:57,698	serv1	transport	false	2022-06-17 08:27:57,695	2022-06-17 08:27:57,708	rht-003	2022-06-17 08:27:57,739	2022-06-17 08:27:57,798	rhm-003	2022-06-17 08:27:58,098	2022-06-17 08:27:58,127
productHolon[4]	13	2022-06-17 08:27:57,489	2022-06-17 08:27:57,496	serv3	transport	false	2022-06-17 08:27:57,493	2022-06-17 08:27:57,502	rht-001	2022-06-17 08:27:57,631	2022-06-17 08:27:57,798	rhm-001	2022-06-17 08:27:58,385	2022-06-17 08:27:58,522
productHolon[7]	12	2022-06-17 08:27:57,426	2022-06-17 08:27:57,538	serv2	transport	false	2022-06-17 08:27:57,491	2022-06-17 08:27:57,540	rht-010	2022-06-17 08:27:57,632	2022-06-17 08:27:57,869	rhm-003	2022-06-17 08:27:58,385	2022-06-17 08:27:58,522
productHolon[12]	15	2022-06-17 08:27:58,253	2022-06-17 08:27:58,259	serv1	transport	false	2022-06-17 08:27:58,256	2022-06-17 08:27:58,263	rht-004	2022-06-17 08:27:58,269	2022-06-17 08:27:58,473	rhm-006	2022-06-17 08:27:58,608	2022-06-17 08:27:58,794
productHolon[7]	16	2022-06-17 08:27:58,704	2022-06-17 08:27:58,723	serv2	transport	false	2022-06-17 08:27:58,709	2022-06-17 08:27:58,725	rht-010	2022-06-17 08:27:58,836	2022-06-17 08:27:59,077	rhm-003	2022-06-17 08:27:59,347	2022-06-17 08:27:59,378
productHolon[4]	17	2022-06-17 08:27:58,834	2022-06-17 08:27:58,948	serv3	transport	false	2022-06-17 08:27:58,879	2022-06-17 08:27:58,949	rht-001	2022-06-17 08:27:58,998	2022-06-17 08:27:59,310	rhm-005	2022-06-17 08:27:59,633	2022-06-17 08:27:59,809
productHolon[7]	19	2022-06-17 08:27:59,544	2022-06-17 08:27:59,614	serv2	transport	false	2022-06-17 08:27:59,547	2022-06-17 08:27:59,630	rht-003	2022-06-17 08:27:59,687	2022-06-17 08:27:59,801	rhm-004	2022-06-17 08:27:59,910	2022-06-17 08:28:00,046
productHolon[12]	18	2022-06-17 08:27:59,038	2022-06-17 08:27:59,080	serv1	transport	false	2022-06-17 08:27:59,075	2022-06-17 08:27:59,081	rht-008	2022-06-17 08:27:59,157	2022-06-17 08:27:59,311	rhm-003	2022-06-17 08:27:59,800	2022-06-17 08:28:00,047
productHolon[4]	20	2022-06-17 08:27:59,878	2022-06-17 08:27:59,914	serv3	transport	false	2022-06-17 08:27:59,881	2022-06-17 08:27:59,945	rht-003	2022-06-17 08:28:00,094	2022-06-17 08:28:00,246	rhm-004	2022-06-17 08:28:00,552	2022-06-17 08:28:00,575
productHolon[12]	21	2022-06-17 08:28:00,193	2022-06-17 08:28:00,282	serv1	transport	false	2022-06-17 08:28:00,232	2022-06-17 08:28:00,283	rht-007	2022-06-17 08:28:00,430	2022-06-17 08:28:00,581	rhm-001	2022-06-17 08:28:01,030	2022-06-17 08:28:01,208
productHolon[7]	22	2022-06-17 08:28:00,229	2022-06-17 08:28:00,281	serv2	transport	false	2022-06-17 08:28:00,243	2022-06-17 08:28:00,290	rht-001	2022-06-17 08:28:00,430	2022-06-17 08:28:00,697	rhm-005	2022-06-17 08:28:01,121	2022-06-17 08:28:01,209
productHolon[4]	23	2022-06-17 08:28:00,815	2022-06-17 08:28:00,821	serv3	transport	false	2022-06-17 08:28:00,817	2022-06-17 08:28:00,824	rht-005	2022-06-17 08:28:00,862	2022-06-17 08:28:01,152	rhm-002	2022-06-17 08:28:01,361	2022-06-17 08:28:01,477
productHolon[7]	24	2022-06-17 08:28:01,450	2022-06-17 08:28:01,520	serv2	transport	false	2022-06-17 08:28:01,486	2022-06-17 08:28:01,524	rht-007	2022-06-17 08:28:01,672	2022-06-17 08:28:01,865	rhm-010	2022-06-17 08:28:02,158	2022-06-17 08:28:02,336
productHolon[4]	26	2022-06-17 08:28:01,613	2022-06-17 08:28:01,668	serv3	in transport	false	2022-06-17 08:28:01,654	2022-06-17 08:28:01,669	rht-009	2022-06-17 08:28:01,817	2022-06-17 08:28:01,947	rhm-008	2022-06-17 08:28:02,369	2022-06-17 08:28:02,607
productHolon[12]	25	2022-06-17 08:28:01,525	2022-06-17 08:28:01,561	serv1	transport	false	2022-06-17 08:28:01,558	2022-06-17 08:28:01,566	rht-006	2022-06-17 08:28:01,671	2022-06-17 08:28:01,866	rhm-010	2022-06-17 08:28:02,564	2022-06-17 08:28:02,814
productHolon[7]	27	2022-06-17 08:28:02,370	2022-06-17 08:28:02,557	serv2	transport	false	2022-06-17 08:28:02,372	2022-06-17 08:28:02,566	rht-008	2022-06-17 08:28:02,727	2022-06-17 08:28:02,894	rhm-007	2022-06-17 08:28:02,941	2022-06-17 08:28:03,210
productHolon[4]	28	2022-06-17 08:28:02,643	2022-06-17 08:28:02,665	serv3	transport	false	2022-06-17 08:28:02,653	2022-06-17 08:28:02,667	rht-005	2022-06-17 08:28:02,727	2022-06-17 08:28:02,894	rhm-005	2022-06-17 08:28:03,098	2022-06-17 08:28:03,210
productHolon[12]	29	2022-06-17 08:28:02,858	2022-06-17 08:28:02,903	serv1	transport	false	2022-06-17 08:28:02,891	2022-06-17 08:28:02,909	rht-007	2022-06-17 08:28:03,137	2022-06-17 08:28:03,375	rhm-004	2022-06-17 08:28:03,554	2022-06-17 08:28:03,578
productHolon[4]	31	2022-06-17 08:28:03,386		tr.warehouse		true	2022-06-17 08:28:03,413		rht-007	2022-06-17 08:28:03,586	2022-06-17 08:28:03,767			
productHolon[12]	32	2022-06-17 08:28:03,692	2022-06-17 08:28:03,764	tr.warehouse	transport	true	2022-06-17 08:28:03,717		rht-003	2022-06-17 08:28:03,797	2022-06-17 08:28:03,885			
productHolon[7]	30	2022-06-17 08:28:03,344	2022-06-17 08:28:03,449	serv2	transport	false	2022-06-17 08:28:03,377	2022-06-17 08:28:03,489	rht-006	2022-06-17 08:28:03,652	2022-06-17 08:28:03,767	rhm-008	2022-06-17 08:28:04,020	2022-06-17 08:28:04,263
productHolon[7]	33	2022-06-17 08:28:04,368	2022-06-17 08:28:04,375	tr.warehouse	transport	true	2022-06-17 08:28:04,371		rht-008	2022-06-17 08:28:04,486	2022-06-17 08:28:04,656			

Next, we present a description of each column:

- ph—Identification of the Ph net instance that requests to run a service;
- step—Execution order in model;
- startServiceRequest—Time information of when the service request was made;
- startTransportRequest—Time information of when the transport request was made;
- service—Production list service ordered;
- transportService—Name of the requested transport service;
- isForWarehouse—Identifies whether it is a shipping order for the warehouse;
- endServiceRequest—Time information of when the service request was answered;
- endTransportRequest—Time information of when the transport request was answered;
- rhtId—Rh net instance identifier that runs the requested transport service;
- startTransport—Time information on when the transport service starts;
- endTransport—Time information on when the transport service was completed;
- rhmId—Identifier of the Rh net instance that runs the requested service;
- startService—Time information on when production service execution starts;
- endService—Time information from when production service execution was completed.

The rows are sorted by the *endService* column in ascending order to provide the perspective of completing the execution of a given service.

By analyzing the sequence of the values of the *step* and *endService* columns, it is found that the order of completion is not identical to the order in which the service request happened. This characteristic can be checked in other files with this prefix and indicates no sequence or prioritization in the execution of services. It is also possible to verify that the execution of the services by the Rh does not follow any pattern. Although there is a sequence of actions for completing the execution of a service, the executing actors (the involved Rh) and the order of the start and end are both random. Hence, the system's behavior is to perform the necessary actions in *"the possible way"*. The information in each file is used to generate the remaining files and tables shown below.

Obtain Execution and Wait Times by Service and Simulation

These data are obtained from files with the prefix *times_per_Service_1*. Table 4 displays the contents of one of these files, available through [33], whose columns are:

Table 4. Example of file content with run times per service

serviceRequest	**serviceExecution**	**Service**
0.02195	0.0331166666666667	serv1
0.0232666666666667	0.0962	transport
0.0313166666666667	0.0284	serv3
0.0406833333333333	0.0258166666666667	serv2
0.000916666666666667	0.00731666666666667	tr.warehouse

- serviceRequest—Sum of all service request times;
- serviceExecution—Sum of all service execution times;

- service—Service name.

The data in Table 4 are displayed as a graph in Figure 15.

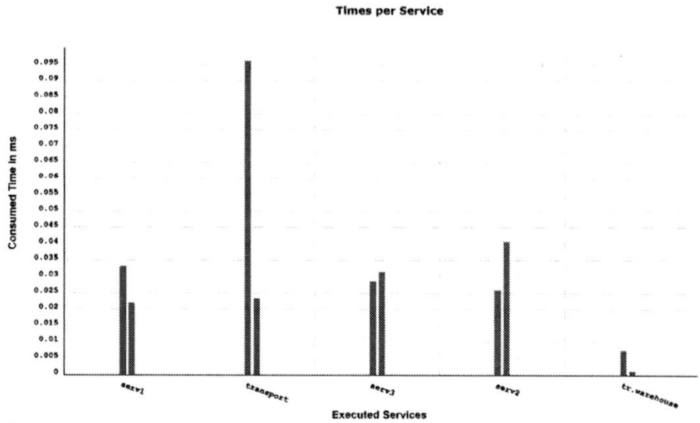

Figure 15. Sample graph based on file content with run times per service.

The time values are displayed in minutes in both the table and chart.

In the chart in Figure 15, the red bar corresponds to the values of the *serviceExecution* column in Table 4. The orange bar matches the *serviceRequest* column of the same table.

Reading this data allows us to understand where most time is being consumed, in what service, and in what action.

In this case, most of the runtime refers to the execution of the transport service. According to the sequence of actions represented in Figure 4, it is verified that a transport service is executed for each production service. In this simulation, three production services were run ten times, so the transport service runs thirty times. Roughly speaking, the total execution time of each production service is one-third of the total execution of the transport service. This shows that the execution times between the various services are distributed in a homogeneous way.

Check the Randomness of Running a Given Scenario

To check the system's randomness, the same simulation was performed ten times. Table 5 is an extract from the comparison of the columns:

Table 5. Comparison of steps between simulations

Simulation 1				
ph	step	service	rhtId	rhmId
productHolon[248]	9	serv1	rht-008	rhm-010
productHolon[60]	2	serv1	rht-003	rhm-009
productHolon[901]	18	serv1	rht-008	rhm-008
productHolon[54]	6	serv1	rht-002	rhm-007
productHolon[790]	15	serv1	rht-005	rhm-006

productHolon[1392]	43	serv1	rht-003	rhm-004
productHolon[949]	25	serv1	rht-004	rhm-001
productHolon[1771]	109	serv1	rht-007	rhm-004
productHolon[463]	32	serv1	rht-002	rhm-002
productHolon[318]	19	serv1	rht-009	rhm-007
productHolon[1732]	90	serv1	rht-008	rhm-001
productHolon[1331]	58	serv1	rht-005	rhm-009
productHolon[790]	136	serv2	rht-007	rhm-009
productHolon[1464]	40	serv1	rht-005	rhm-003
productHolon[228]	21	serv1	rht-001	rhm-010
productHolon[939]	66	serv1	rht-005	rhm-009
productHolon[1015]	38	serv1	rht-004	rhm-007
productHolon[2089]	149	serv1	rht-009	rhm-002

Simulation 2				
ph	step	service	rhtId	rhmId
productHolon[55]	2	serv1	rht-010	rhm-009
productHolon[876]	20	serv1	rht-001	rhm-005
productHolon[400]	46	serv1	rht-002	rhm-001
productHolon[48]	30	serv1	rht-008	rhm-002
productHolon[1003]	48	serv1	rht-006	rhm-008
productHolon[219]	11	serv1	rht-001	rhm-005
productHolon[604]	17	serv1	rht-002	rhm-004
productHolon[1158]	34	serv1	rht-007	rhm-003
productHolon[228]	16	serv1	rht-005	rhm-002
productHolon[1347]	118	serv1	rht-004	rhm-008
productHolon[616]	19	serv1	rht-006	rhm-001
productHolon[140]	5	serv1	rht-005	rhm-006
productHolon[1532]	143	serv1	rht-008	rhm-004
productHolon[876]	130	serv2	rht-004	rhm-009
productHolon[829]	101	serv1	rht-002	rhm-001
productHolon[219]	231	serv2	rht-005	rhm-004
productHolon[1532]	259	serv2	rht-006	rhm-003
productHolon[1158]	250	serv2	rht-001	rhm-005

Simulation 3				
ph	step	service	rhtId	rhmId

productHolon[935]	26	serv1	rht-008	rhm-002
productHolon[6]	8	serv1	rht-009	rhm-005
productHolon[115]	2	serv1	rht-005	rhm-009
productHolon[56]	17	serv1	rht-003	rhm-007
productHolon[647]	29	serv1	rht-006	rhm-008
productHolon[387]	25	serv1	rht-005	rhm-007
productHolon[104]	6	serv1	rht-007	rhm-009
productHolon[647]	191	serv2	rht-002	rhm-005
productHolon[14]	27	serv1	rht-004	rhm-004
productHolon[2025]	76	serv1	rht-001	rhm-007
productHolon[471]	38	serv1	rht-009	rhm-005
productHolon[229]	28	serv1	rht-010	rhm-002
productHolon[43]	32	serv1	rht-007	rhm-003
productHolon[6]	262	serv2	rht-006	rhm-006
productHolon[1318]	46	serv1	rht-002	rhm-001
productHolon[387]	268	serv2	rht-005	rhm-008
productHolon[104]	279	serv2	rht-003	rhm-004
productHolon[874]	39	serv1	rht-008	rhm-006

Simulation 4				
ph	step	service	rhtId	rhmId
productHolon[70]	3	serv1	rht-009	rhm-008
productHolon[766]	17	serv1	rht-008	rhm-005
productHolon[155]	19	serv1	rht-001	rhm-001
productHolon[213]	10	serv1	rht-006	rhm-006
productHolon[206]	7	serv1	rht-005	rhm-001
productHolon[69]	6	serv1	rht-006	rhm-003
productHolon[999]	40	serv1	rht-001	rhm-005
productHolon[1407]	33	serv1	rht-007	rhm-007
productHolon[1232]	42	serv1	rht-004	rhm-006
productHolon[284]	14	serv1	rht-010	rhm-010
productHolon[1514]	178	serv1	rht-009	rhm-003
productHolon[244]	27	serv1	rht-005	rhm-002
productHolon[174]	20	serv1	rht-006	rhm-008
productHolon[2235]	100	serv1	rht-007	rhm-005
productHolon[105]	37	serv1	rht-009	rhm-002
productHolon[791]	21	serv1	rht-010	rhm-001

productHolon[2697]	221	serv1	rht-007	rhm-010
productHolon[213]	287	serv2	rht-010	rhm-007

Simulation 5				
ph	step	service	rhtId	rhmId
productHolon[54]	5	serv1	rht-005	rhm-009
productHolon[299]	11	serv1	rht-009	rhm-008
productHolon[366]	13	serv1	rht-003	rhm-010
productHolon[148]	2	serv1	rht-003	rhm-004
productHolon[1967]	63	serv1	rht-008	rhm-010
productHolon[136]	3	serv1	rht-009	rhm-006
productHolon[1316]	41	serv1	rht-004	rhm-008
productHolon[114]	1	serv1	rht-010	rhm-005
productHolon[2601]	120	serv1	rht-002	rhm-006
productHolon[2556]	230	serv1	rht-003	rhm-008
productHolon[103]	19	serv1	rht-009	rhm-003
productHolon[2429]	87	serv1	rht-001	rhm-004
productHolon[2663]	146	serv1	rht-004	rhm-010
productHolon[93]	21	serv1	rht-010	rhm-009
productHolon[136]	253	serv2	rht-007	rhm-004
productHolon[789]	27	serv1	rht-009	rhm-007
productHolon[366]	188	serv2	rht-006	rhm-010
productHolon[2064]	122	serv1	rht-002	rhm-005

Simulation 6				
ph	step	service	rhtId	rhmId
productHolon[35]	8	serv1	rht-008	rhm-006
productHolon[230]	10	serv1	rht-003	rhm-008
productHolon[85]	2	serv1	rht-005	rhm-002
productHolon[788]	19	serv1	rht-007	rhm-004
productHolon[722]	60	serv1	rht-004	rhm-006
productHolon[56]	1	serv1	rht-006	rhm-007
productHolon[175]	37	serv1	rht-009	rhm-005
productHolon[489]	22	serv1	rht-001	rhm-003
productHolon[85]	105	serv2	rht-007	rhm-004
productHolon[371]	18	serv1	rht-002	rhm-008
productHolon[788]	141	serv2	rht-006	rhm-008

productHolon[151]	7	serv1	rht-007	rhm-010
productHolon[2246]	98	serv1	rht-008	rhm-007
productHolon[2670]	132	serv1	rht-003	rhm-003
productHolon[308]	16	serv1	rht-003	rhm-009
productHolon[522]	48	serv1	rht-007	rhm-005
productHolon[2586]	95	serv1	rht-010	rhm-002
productHolon[2198]	215	serv1	rht-008	rhm-003

Simulation 7				
ph	step	service	rhtId	rhmId
productHolon[148]	33	serv1	rht-005	rhm-005
productHolon[53]	1	serv1	rht-003	rhm-003
productHolon[228]	23	serv1	rht-005	rhm-001
productHolon[160]	14	serv1	rht-006	rhm-006
productHolon[148]	112	serv2	rht-008	rhm-007
productHolon[964]	25	serv1	rht-001	rhm-008
productHolon[956]	41	serv1	rht-003	rhm-003
productHolon[68]	4	serv1	rht-010	rhm-009
productHolon[360]	13	serv1	rht-008	rhm-004
productHolon[581]	9	serv1	rht-006	rhm-007
productHolon[53]	132	serv2	rht-005	rhm-001
productHolon[402]	52	serv1	rht-010	rhm-005
productHolon[2121]	155	serv1	rht-002	rhm-008
productHolon[228]	269	serv2	rht-004	rhm-006
productHolon[355]	12	serv1	rht-008	rhm-010
productHolon[1178]	36	serv1	rht-010	rhm-002
productHolon[1454]	197	serv1	rht-006	rhm-006
productHolon[2046]	124	serv1	rht-007	rhm-003

Simulation 8				
ph	step	service	rhtId	rhmId
productHolon[95]	3	serv1	rht-006	rhm-010
productHolon[281]	10	serv1	rht-010	rhm-003
productHolon[285]	30	serv1	rht-009	rhm-006
productHolon[163]	5	serv1	rht-010	rhm-004
productHolon[644]	32	serv1	rht-006	rhm-005
productHolon[954]	13	serv1	rht-009	rhm-001

productHolon[709]	21	serv1	rht-006	rhm-008
productHolon[499]	24	serv1	rht-009	rhm-003
productHolon[163]	202	serv2	rht-009	rhm-009
productHolon[1817]	148	serv1	rht-005	rhm-004
productHolon[1851]	75	serv1	rht-002	rhm-006
productHolon[1016]	16	serv1	rht-001	rhm-001
productHolon[139]	4	serv1	rht-008	rhm-002
productHolon[1045]	39	serv1	rht-005	rhm-005
productHolon[2275]	166	serv1	rht-002	rhm-003
productHolon[285]	185	serv2	rht-007	rhm-008
productHolon[1006]	20	serv1	rht-001	rhm-010
productHolon[1559]	146	serv1	rht-003	rhm-004

Simulation 9				
ph	step	service	rhtId	rhmId
productHolon[627]	31	serv1	rht-007	rhm-007
productHolon[696]	26	serv1	rht-003	rhm-003
productHolon[192]	23	serv1	rht-009	rhm-007
productHolon[686]	19	serv1	rht-001	rhm-006
productHolon[531]	17	serv1	rht-004	rhm-010
productHolon[86]	4	serv1	rht-005	rhm-004
productHolon[122]	3	serv1	rht-006	rhm-001
productHolon[1017]	25	serv1	rht-008	rhm-009
productHolon[854]	28	serv1	rht-009	rhm-005
productHolon[1182]	48	serv1	rht-005	rhm-008
productHolon[141]	8	serv1	rht-001	rhm-002
productHolon[2206]	171	serv1	rht-009	rhm-004
productHolon[2337]	107	serv1	rht-008	rhm-010
productHolon[294]	20	serv1	rht-010	rhm-009
productHolon[331]	10	serv1	rht-007	rhm-008
productHolon[1284]	34	serv1	rht-004	rhm-006
productHolon[854]	236	serv2	rht-003	rhm-008
productHolon[2243]	121	serv1	rht-005	rhm-002

Simulation 10				
ph	step	service	rhtId	rhmId
productHolon[214]	5	serv1	rht-010	rhm-009

productHolon[356]	12	serv1	rht-009	rhm-010
productHolon[908]	30	serv1	rht-002	rhm-002
productHolon[6]	11	serv1	rht-008	rhm-005
productHolon[273]	28	serv1	rht-009	rhm-005
productHolon[1371]	44	serv1	rht-008	rhm-009
productHolon[142]	128	serv1	rht-006	rhm-005
productHolon[528]	9	serv1	rht-005	rhm-002
productHolon[356]	130	serv2	rht-004	rhm-004
productHolon[13]	1	serv1	rht-010	rhm-006
productHolon[1351]	43	serv1	rht-006	rhm-001
productHolon[1436]	79	serv1	rht-003	rhm-005
productHolon[902]	17	serv1	rht-008	rhm-007
productHolon[150]	10	serv1	rht-010	rhm-003
productHolon[490]	78	serv1	rht-004	rhm-002
productHolon[715]	20	serv1	rht-002	rhm-004
productHolon[1917]	111	serv1	rht-007	rhm-001
productHolon[2493]	189	serv1	rht-001	rhm-009

ph—Product holon instance;

- step—Step of the simulation;
- service—Requested service;
- rhtId—Resource holon providing the transport service;
- rhmId—Resource holon providing the requested service.

It shows the first twenty lines of the logs of each simulation.

As can be observed, the sequence between simulations is always different. If the rows with a yellow background, from Table 5, are compared, it becomes evident that all simulations present different values for the columns ph, rhtId, and rhmId, and, in some simulations, until the service presented is the service 2.

This shows that although the model is deterministic in its execution, it is non-deterministic relative to who runs the services or the services to be executed.

This characteristic is the one that enables the model to find a way to perform the proposed task. For as long as an Rh provides the necessary service, the model will adapt to the use of this Rh.

Considering the case study, if there is a need to put one of the Rh under maintenance, the model continues running as long as another Rh or others guarantee the needed services. The model carries this out automatically and dynamically, without previous intervention or the need to stop production to reorganize the production chain.

The execution of the model in the form of simulations allows for validating the concept of using this class of Petri nets connected to physical devices leveraging the creation of CPSs. The interaction between the CPSs can be defined in the nets. The digital counterpart also enables the possibility of extending the current physical device.

In this work, the Playground net is presented as the factory's shop floor, where services are provided to the product holons. As the product holons are the ones that know the production plan, requesting them to the shop floor enables the adaptability of the execution to the available resources. Because the model allows for defining the information to log during the execution, it is possible to use the provided data of the logs to convert them into information to be analyzed for different purposes, as presented in the previous section. Finally, the PRESIB architecture characteristics match with the Industry 5.0 pillars as follows:

- Centered on the human being—Although the architecture is not centered on the human being, it allows for a way to interact with the shop floor through the model. The model can be adjusted to users and can be considered for different levels of digital literacy, the purpose of the model, and the level of automation or desired interaction;
- Sustainability—As presented in [34], mass customization allows for a better management of existing resources. PRESIB architecture fits this kind of production paradigm due to its adaptability to changes. However, sustainability also involves reusing the current equipment park to prevent them from becoming obsolete. PRESIB architecture enables the creation of CPSs by integrating physical systems with the networks of the model, and, in this way, the reuse of the current machinery park;
- Resilience—The adaptability to the change in PERSIB architecture allows for a reduction in the impact on the suppression of established supply chains as a consequence of the COVID-19 pandemic.

CONCLUSIONS

An architecture was presented and materialized in a model that dynamically adapts to production needs or to eventual changes, whether internal or external, without the need for human intervention or supervision.

In the proposed approach, the shop floor becomes a service provider for the products being built. In addition to contributing to the system's dynamic, this also creates new opportunities, such as *mass customization*.

The presented simulations demonstrate how the results obtained can be interpreted in several ways, attributing value to the model.

The ability to use the same model to perform simulations and to integrate with physical systems has the benefit of reducing the implementation error, either by programming errors or by a misinterpretation of requirements. It is also beneficial because it allows for the reuse of existing equipment. This characteristic of the model, integrated with physical equipment, also allows users to interact with the shop floor through the model, providing another alternative form of interaction between humans and machines. Finally, the suggested architecture follows the values of Industry 5.0.

REFERENCES

1. Eurostat. National Accounts and GDP. 2022. Available online: https://ec.europa.eu/eurostat/statistics-explained/index.php?title=National_accounts_and_GDP#Gross_value_added_in_the_EU_by_economic_activity (accessed on 23 November 2022).
2. Ingenieur.de. Industrie 4.0: Mit dem Internet der Dinge auf dem Weg zur 4. Industriellen Revolution—Ingenieur.de. 2011. Available online: https://www.ingenieur.de/technik/fachbereiche/produktion/industrie-40-mit-internet-dinge-weg-4-industriellen-revolution/ (accessed on 23 November 2022).

3. Li, J. Analyzing "Made in China 2025" Under the Background of "Industry 4.0". In Proceedings of the 23rd 508 International Conference on Industrial Engineering and Engineering Management 2016; Qi, E., Shen, J., Dou, R., Eds.; Atlantis 509 Press: Paris, France, 2017; pp. 169–171.
4. Schwab, K. The Fourth Industrial Revolution; World Economic Forum: Geneva, Switzerland, 2016.
5. Schwab, K.; Davis, N. Shaping the Future of the Fourth Industrial Revolution: A Guide to Building a Better World; Penguin Books Limited: London, UK, 2018.
6. Breque, M.; Nul, L.D.; Petridis, A. Industry 5.0—Towards a Sustainable, Human-Centric and Resilient European Industry. 2021. Available online: https://research-and-innovation.ec.europa.eu/knowledge-publications-tools-and-data/publications/all-publications/industry-50-towards-sustainable-human-centric-and-resilient-european-industry_en (accessed on 23 November 2022).
7. OMG Standards Development Organization. Business Process Model and Notation, Version 2.0.2. 2014. Available online: https://www.omg.org/spec/BPMN/ (accessed on 23 November 2022).
8. Valderas, P.; Torres, V.; Serral, E. Modelling and executing IoT-enhanced business processes through BPMN and microservices. J. Syst. Softw. 2022, 184, 111139.
9. Abouzid, I.; Bekali, Y.K.; Saidi, R. Modelling IoT Behaviour in Supply Chain Business Processes with BPMN: A Systematic Literature Review. J. ICT Stand. 2022, 10, 439–467.
10. Bocciarelli, P.; D'Ambrogio, A.; Giglio, A.; Paglia, E. A BPMN extension for modeling Cyber-Physical-Production-Systems in the context of Industry 4.0. In Proceedings of the 2017 IEEE 14th International Conference on Networking, Sensing and Control (ICNSC), Calabria, Italy, 16–18 May 2017; pp. 599–604.
11. Zurawski, R.; Zhou, M. Petri nets and industrial applications: A tutorial. IEEE Trans. Ind. Electron. 1994, 41, 567–583.
12. Pasandideh, S.; Gomes, L.; Maló, P. Modelling Cyber Physical Social Systems Using Dynamic Time Petri Nets. In Technological Innovation for Resilient Systems; Camarinha-Matos, L.M., Adu-Kankam, K.O., Julashokri, M., Eds.; Springer International Publishing: Cham, Switzerland, 2018; pp. 81–89.
13. Sood, V.; Nema, M.K.; Kumar, R.; Nene, M.J. Conceptual Verification of Distributed Cyber Physical Systems using Reference Nets. In Procedia Computer Science; Elsevier B.V.: Amsterdam, The Netherlands, 2020; Volume 171, pp. 81–90.
14. Fernandes, N.; Barros, J.P.; Campos-Rebelo, R. A Graphical and Executable Model for Production Simulation in the Context of Industry 5.0. IEEE Int. Symp. Ind. Electron. 2022, 2022, 233–238.
15. Valckenaers, P.; Van Brussel, H.; Bonneville, F.; Bongaerts, L.; Wyns, J. IMS Test Case 5: Holonic Manufacturing Systems. IFAC Proc. Vol. 1994, 27, 31–36.
16. Koestler, A. The Ghost in the Machine, 1990 ed.; Penguin (Non-Classics): London, UK, 1990.
17. Valckenaers, P.; Bonneville, F.; Van Brussel, H.; Bongaerts, L.; Wyns, J. Results of the holonic control system benchmark at KU Leuven. In Proceedings of the 4th International Conference on Computer Integrated Manufacturing and Automation Technology, CIMAT 1994, Troy, NY, USA, 10–12 October 1994; pp. 128–133.
18. Van Brussel, H.; Wyns, J.; Valckenaers, P.; Bongaerts, L.; Peeters, P. Reference architecture for holonic manufacturing systems: PROSA. Comput. Ind. 1998, 37, 255–274.
19. Ounnar, F.; Pujo, P. Pull control for job shop: Holonic manufacturing system approach using multicriteria decision-making. J. Intell. Manuf. 2012, 23, 141–153.
20. Macherki, D.; Diallo, T.M.L.; Choley, J.Y.; Guizani, A.; Barkallah, M.; Haddar, M. QHAR: Q-Holonic-Based ARchitecture for Self-Configuration of Cyber–Physical Production Systems. Appl. Sci. 2021, 11, 9013.

21. Leitão, P.; Restivo, F. ADACOR: A Holonic Architecture for Agile and Adaptive Manufacturing Control. Comput. Ind. 2006, 57, 121–130.
22. Barbosa, J.; Leitão, P.; Adam, E.; Trentesaux, D. Improving the ADACOR2 supervisor holon scheduling mechanism with genetic algorithms. AIP Conf. Proc. 2015, 1648, 140008.
23. Chirn, J.L.; McFarlane, D.C. A holonic component-based approach to reconfigurable manufacturing control architecture. In Proceedings of the 11th International Workshop on Database and Expert Systems Application, London, UK, 4–8 September 2000; pp. 219–223.
24. Wisniewski, R.; Grobelna, I.; Karatkevich, A. Determinism in Cyber-Physical Systems Specified by Interpreted Petri Nets. Sensors 2020, 20, 5565.
25. Pereira, F.; Gomes, L. Combining data-flows and petri nets for cyber-physical systems specification. In IFIP Advances in Information and Communication Technology; Springer: New York, NY, USA, 2016; Volume 470, pp. 65–76.
26. Kummer, O. Introduction to Petri Nets and Reference Nets. Sozionik. Aktuell 2001, 1, 1–9.
27. Desel, J.; Reisig, W.; Rozenberg, G. (Eds.) Lectures on Concurrency and Petri Nets; Lecture Notes in Computer Science; Springer: Berlin/Heidelberg, Germany, 2004; Volume 3098.
28. Kummer, O.; Wienberg, F.; Duvigneau, M.; Cabac, L.; Haustermann, M.; Mosteller, D.; Arbeitsbereich, D.M. Renew User Guide; Technical Report; University of Hamburg, Department for Informatics, Theoretical Foundations Group. 2022. Available online: https://www2.informatik.uni-hamburg.de/TGI/renew/4.0/renew4.0.pdf (accessed on 23 November 2022).
29. OMG Standards Development Organization. Unified Modeling Language. 2017. Available online: https://www.omg.org/spec/UML/ (accessed on 23 November 2022).
30. Fernandes, N. PRESIB—Official Site. Available online: https://presib.github.io/presib/ (accessed on 8 December 2022).
31. Fernandes, N. PRESIB MDI 2022 Paper Support. Available online: https://presib.github.io/presib/presib-mdpi-2022-paper-support.html#simulations-resources (accessed on 8 December 2022).
32. Fernandes, N. Ponos—The Log Parser Tool for PRESIB. Available online: https://presib.github.io/presib/ponos-the-log-parser-tool-for-presib.html (accessed on 8 December 2022).
33. Fernandes, N. PRESIB Documentation—Models and Simulation Results. Available online: https://github. com/ PRESIB/ documentation/blob/simulation_ june_ 2022/ simulation -results/ results/procustion_steps_1ph_10xserv1_1ph_ 10xserv2_1ph_10xserv3__ 10rht_10rhm.log_1658253879513.json_1658253895688.csv (accessed on 8 December 2022).
34. Alptekinoğlu, A.; Örsdemir, A. Is Adopting Mass Customization a Path to Environmentally Sustainable Fashion? Manuf. Serv. Oper. Manag. 2022, 24, 2982–3000.

3

Analysis of a Collaborative Scheduling Model Applied in a Job Shop Manufacturing Environment

Leonilde R. Varela[1], Cátia F. V. Alves[1], André S. Santos[2], Gaspar G. Vieira[1], Nuno Lopes[3] and Goran D. Putnik[1]

[1]Department of Production and Systems, School of Engineering, ALGORITMI Research Centre/LASI, University of Minho, 4804-533 Guimarães, Portugal

[2]Institute of Engineering, Polytechnic Institute of Porto-ISEP/IPP, Interdisciplinary Studies Research Center (ISRC), 4200-072 Porto, Portugal

[3]Polytechnic Institute of Cávado e Ave—IPCA, 4750-810 Barcelos, Portugal

ABSTRACT

Collaborative Manufacturing Scheduling (CMS) is not yet a properly explored decision making practice, although its potential for being currently explored, in the digital era, by combining efforts among a set of entities, either persons or machines, to jointly cooperate for solving some more or less complex scheduling problem, namely occurring in job shop manufacturing environments. In this paper, an interoperable scheduling system integrating a proposed scheduling model, along with varying kinds of solving algorithms, are put forward and analyzed through an industrial case study. The case study was decomposed in three application scenarios, for enabling the evaluation of the proposed scheduling model when envisioning the prioritization of internal–makespan-or external–number of tardy jobs-performance measures, along with a third scenario assigning a same importance or weight to both kinds of performance measures. The results obtained enabled us to realize that the weighted application scenario permitted reaching more balanced, thus a potentially more attractive global solution for the scheduling problem considered through the combination of different kinds of scheduling algorithms for the resolution of each underlying sub problem according to the proposed scheduling model. Besides, the decomposition of a global more complex scheduling problem into simpler sub-problems turns them easier to be solved through the different solving algorithms available, while further enabling to obtain a wider range of alternative schedules to be explored and evaluated. Thus, contributing to enriching the scheduling problem-solving process. A future exploration of the application in other types of manufacturing environments, namely occurring in the context of extended, networked, distributed or virtual production systems, integrating an increased and variable set of collaborating entities or factories, is also suggested.

Keywords: *Collaborative manufacturing scheduling model, Job shop, Interoperable scheduling system*

INTRODUCTION

Collaborative decision-making (CDM) implies an interaction and shared learning process among at least two entities, independent of both sharing the same objective or not [1,2] Although, usually, when the entities fall into a same context or business, they may also have a common goal, which can either occur in the context of traditional or in extended manufacturing environments (EMS) or in agile or virtual enterprises (A/VE), along with cyber physical systems [1,2,3,4,5,6,7,8]. The CDM processes are of the utmost importance nowadays, in the Industry 4.0, once enabling and promoting the interconnection and interoperation among integrated entities, either persons and/or communication and processing devices, along with diver kind of machines, horizontally and/or vertically integrated through the [I]oT ([Industrial] Internet of Things), and supported by appropriate middleware, tools, systems, and platforms [9,10,11,12,13].

In this paper a model is proposed for collaboratively solving a manufacturing scheduling model, which consists of an extension of the well-known Jackson's model that enables to define the production sequence of a set of jobs to be processed in a classical job shop environment, integrating just two machines or work centers [14]. The proposed scheduling model, besides being applicable to solve classical job shop scheduling problems, with two or more machines, can further be applied for solving scheduling problems occurring in EME or A/VE, integrating two or more factories, for the execution of the jobs, through a distributed manufacturing environment [15].

The proposed scheduling model consists of a novel contribution, as, as far as our knowledge, existing contributions are usually more specific, regarding either its application domain (kind of manufacturing environment) or the approach used for solving the scheduling problem, usually based on some specific or reduced combination of solving algorithms. Instead, through our proposed scheduling model, different approaches or methods/algorithms can be applied or combined to solve a set of underlying sub scheduling problems. Thus, being able to vary from the application of pure mathematical or optimization algorithms, up to the use of varying kind of meta-heuristics or be based on machine learning or agent-based approaches, among others [5,16,17,18].

In order to properly present the contribution put forward in this paper, it is organized as follows. A summarized overview of manufacturing scheduling approaches is presented. The proposed interoperable manufacturing scheduling system is briefly described. The proposed collaborative manufacturing scheduling model is put forward, for being further explored, through an illustrative example of application. A further analysis and discussion of the main results obtained through the application of the proposed scheduling model is also included, by using three different application scenarios. Finally, the main conclusions, along with future work suggestions, are provided.

MANUFACTURING SCHEDULING EVOLUTION

Scheduling Problems and Solving Approaches

Manufacturing Scheduling (MS) refers to the execution of a set of tasks or operations, usually also referred as jobs, at defined times on specific production resources or machines, also frequently mentioned as processors, workstations or work centers, and which can be locally available at a given shop floor or geographically distributed among factories or companies [19,20,21,22]. The tasks can be sequential and/or occur in parallel, among the production resources [23,24,25,26,27,28,29].

Other definitions of Manufacturing Scheduling are presented in [25,26], who describes, Manufacturing Scheduling as the part of the MPC (Manufacturing Planning and Control) that is responsible for the distribution of the operations by available resources, in order to optimize one or more performance measures. Pinedo & Chao, in 1999 [25] diddefine Manufacturing Scheduling as the process that distributes limited resources across activities, in order to optimize the company's productive capacity, or any other performance measure. In the meantime, Baker & Trietsche, in 2009 [24], described Manufacturing Scheduling as the decision process that seeks to answer the questions: "What is the best way to distribute resources across operations, to optimize a given performance measure? Besides, "What is the manufacturing sequence and/or production schedule that optimizes a given performance measure?".

Scheduling problems belong to a much broader class of combinatorial optimization ones that are difficult to solve, being called NP-hard problems. These problems are characterized by having a vast set of possible solutions, which have to be explored in the space of possible solutions for the problems under consideration.

Additionally, to being combinatorial optimization problems, MS problems are also usually dynamic, due to the dynamisms that arises from the real time arrival of new tasks to be scheduled and further to the availability of the production resources, which does also dynamically change over time. These two aspects combined turn industrial scheduling problems quite difficult to solve, which are thus usually solved by using different kind of heuristic methods, for instance, based on constraint programming or a widened set of diverse types of other heuristics or meta-heuristics, such as, Genetic Algorithms, Simulated Annealing or Tabu Search, among other meta-heuristics or approaches, for instance, based on Neural Networks, or Fuzzy Logic, among others [30,31].

Job shops are production systems' configurations which are arranged in such a way that permits them to take a superior advantage of more or less diversified production and in varied quantities, generally, and currently, in relatively small quantities. These manufacturing systems are usually further arranged according to a functional logic, e.g., grouped according to the functions or processes they perform, enabling different workflows, which provides this kind of production system a popularity or relative advantage when compared to other types of configurations or production systems, more limited or oriented to some kind of products of product families, such as the flow shops.

Although, similar to what happens in other kinds of manufacturing systems, in these kinds of job shop manufacturing environments, things rarely go as expected. This can occur due to several reasons, for instance, due to cancelled scheduled jobs and/or to the arrival of new jobs, namely with a higher priority. Moreover, this usually happens because given resources become unavailable and/or that new resources are considered. Besides, some other disturbances may occur on the shop floor, namely some scheduled tasks that take more or less time than planned, or tasks that arrive earlier or late. Further, other turbulences that may happen can be related, for instance, to machine failures, to operators' absence or to the unavailability of production tools and/or materials.

Besides, also some given production schedule might become unfeasible because of some unforeseen real time situation occurring on the shop floor. When this happens, a new schedule has to be generated to restore the manufacturing system performance by executing rescheduling, dynamic scheduling or also so-called a real-time scheduling [32,33].

The manufacturing scheduling problems are continuous and dynamic by nature, and a solution will quickly become obsolete. For example, a number of jobs are scheduled, and before all the jobs are processed, new jobs are released on the shop floor, making the solution obsolete before even being executed. Considering that classical, static, scheduling become non-optimal as soon as new manufacturing orders are launched into the shop floor [34,35], it is necessary to find ways to adapt scheduling solutions to the dynamic nature of the problem. Dynamic scheduling can be classified as Reactive, Predictive-Reactive and Proactive Scheduling, depending on how the initial solution is conceived and how it is adapted to changes in the characteristics of the problem [36]. Whenever it is necessary to adapt the solution to the changes in the problem, it is important to determine if an obsolete solution can be adapted to accommodate the changes in the problem, or if it is necessary to devise a completely new solution. Finally, it is necessary to determine when a solution is considered obsolete, that is, if the rescheduling is event-oriented, for example, whenever there is a change in the characteristics of the problem, or if the rescheduling happens periodically. There are different kinds of approaches that can be used for establishing production schedules, varying from enumerative algorithms to the application of simple priority rules. Moreover, these approaches can be based on pure mathematical programming models or use simulation technique among other approaches [5], for instance, based on multi-agents, among others [18,24,37,38,39].

The Jackson's Scheduling Model

Jackson, in 1956 [14] proposed a model for scheduling a set of jobs in a job shop integrating two machines (A and B), by sequencing the jobs according to the following order, on each one:

- Machine A: {A,B} -> {A} -> {B,A}
- Machine B: {B,A} -> {B} -> {A,B}

In which {A} represents the set of jobs that integrate just one operation, and which has to be processed on machine A, {B} represents the set of jobs that integrate also just one operation, and which has to be processed on machine B, {A,B} represents the set of jobs with two operations, in sequence, as in a flow shop, being the first one to be processed on machine A, and the second one on machine B, and {B,A} representing also a set of jobs in a reverse order of processing, e.g., being the first operation to be processed on machine B, and the second one on machine A. These flow shop scheduling sub problems, with two machines, are solved by the traditional Johnson's rule, and the single machine ones by applying simple sequencing rules, e.g., the Shorted Processing Time (SPT) [14].

Scheduling Process Complexity

Scheduling processes are complex in nature, particularly the ones occurring in job shop environments [16], as is the case of the classical job shop scheduling problem, where the scheduling problem complexity grows exponentially, with the increase in the number of sets of machines to order, according to the number of machines or work centers available in a job shop. The complexity of a job shop scheduling process can thus be analyzed by using the equation 1, resulting in the number of arrangements of machines to be considered for the jobs to be processed, being *m* the set size, i.e., the total number of machines in the sample, and *p* the subset size, i.e., the number of machines to be selected from the sample.

$$A(m,p) = \frac{m!}{(m-p)!} \tag{1}$$

For example, in the simplest case of a job shop with just m = 2 machines (A, and B), about the application of the Jackson's sequencing process of a set of m machines, it will be necessary to sequence or order four sets of machines, as follows: {A}, {B}, {A,B}, and {B,A}, which is calculated through equation 1 by A(2,2) + A(2,1) = 2 + 2 = 4 sets of machines. This job shop scheduling process complexity grows exponentially, and Figure 1 and Table 1 show this very fast increase in this complexity of the scheduling process, when increasing the number of machines up to 10, reaching 9,864,100 sets of machines to be sequenced. Therefore, it turns out to be of utmost importance to further explore alternative scenarios for carrying out the scheduling process, among a set of collaborating entities or even factories, for instance, in the context of EME or VE that jointly perform a scheduling process.

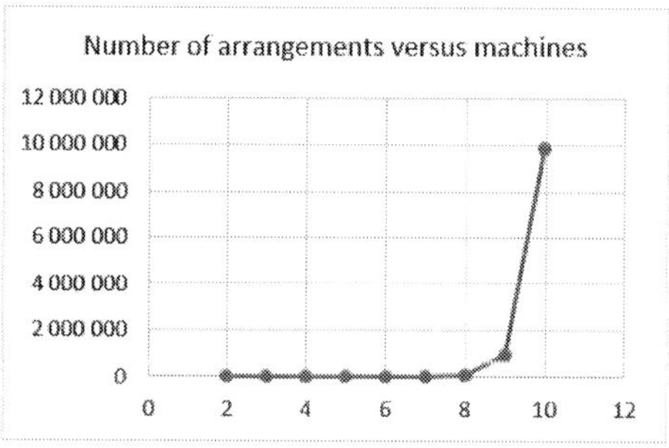

Figure 1. Relation between the number of machines and the number of sets of arrangements of machines to order.

Table 1. Problem complexity

Nº Machines	Complexity
2	4
3	15
4	64
5	325
6	1932
7	8659
8	109,600
9	986,400
10	9,864,100

INTEROPERABLE MANUFACTURING SCHEDULING SYSTEM

Scheduling System Architecture

In this work, a developed interoperable manufacturing scheduling system (IMSS) was used for solving problems occurring in different kind of more or less complex manufacturing environments, namely in a job shop, by enabling to decompose them into simpler ones through a proposed scheduling model that is an extension of the Jackson's model for enabling to solve general job shop scheduling problems with three or more work centers, by concatenating the partial solutions or schedules to form a complete solution for the whole original problem carried out by using a central or core scheduling system (CSS). In Figure 2, the architecture of the IMSS is shown, for an application example, occurring in an industrial company, which integrates three work centers (WC1, WC2, and WC3). This IMSS architecture includes thus the CSS, and which is interconnected with the work centers, enabling data sharing with the shop floor's operational level, and by enabling to automatically acquire data through RFID and store it in a local database, along with further processing through the use of smart objects and additional devices and technology [5,40,41]. Moreover, the CSS is linked to a pre-processing module, which permits the insertion of information arising from the clients' orders that is also inserted in the corresponding supporting database, and the whole set of information (joint factory and clients data) is subject to a pre-processing function of the IMSS, for data analysis, filtering and other pre-processing procedures, namely for dealing with incomplete data, with the support of historical data sets processed, along with methods for uncertainty treatment, based on dynamic, and fuzzy based approaches [42,43,44] (Figure 3 and Figure 4).

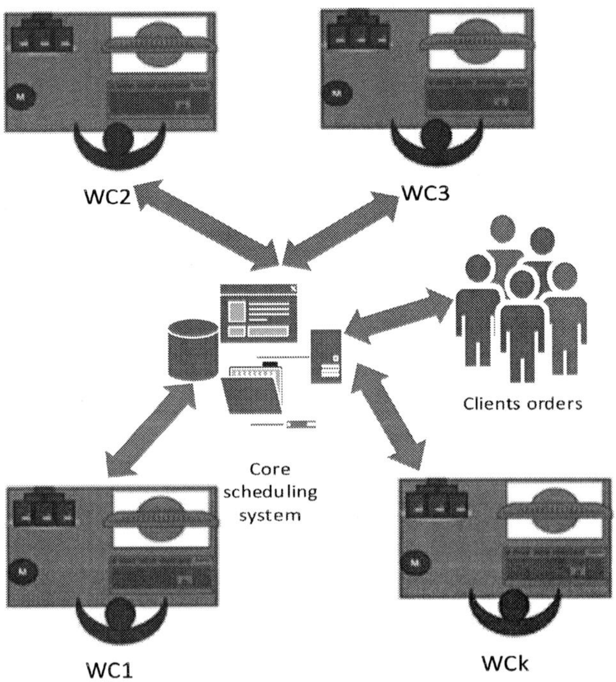

Figure 2. Interoperable manufacturing scheduling system architecture.

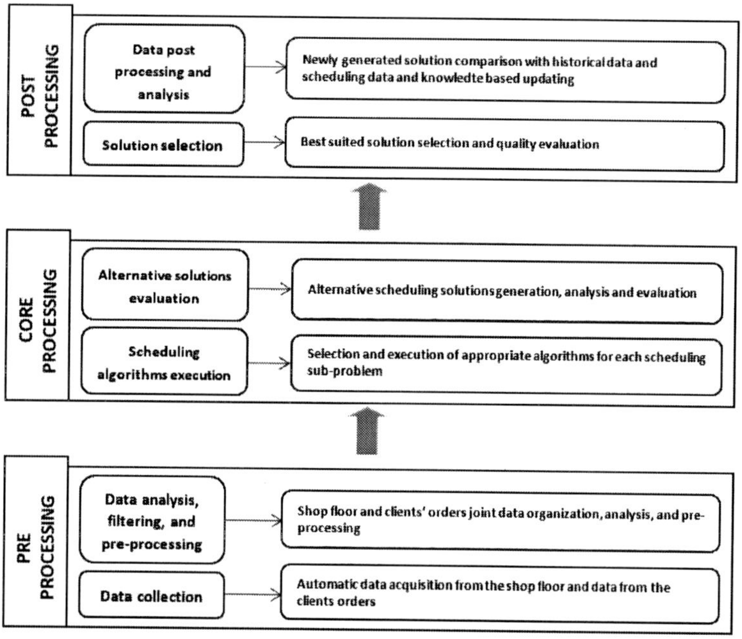

Figure 3. Scheduling framework.

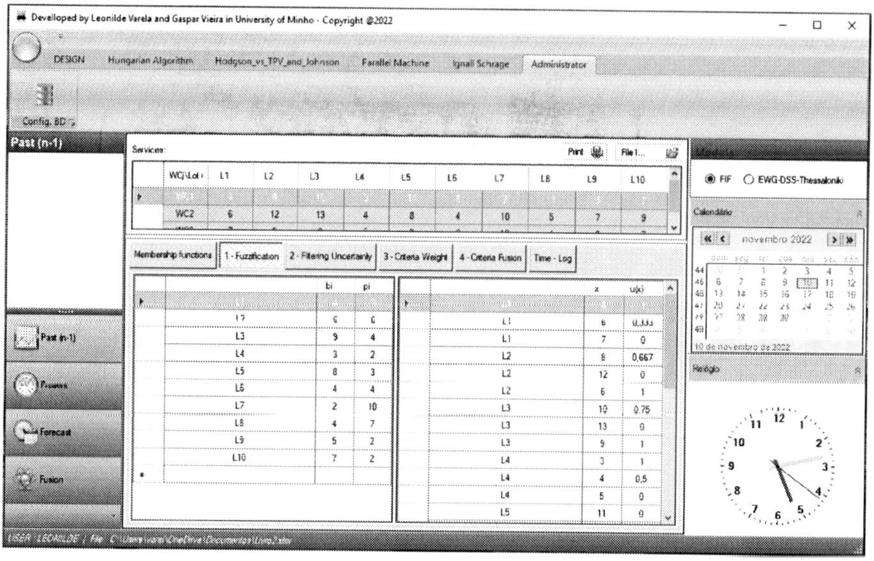

Figure 4. Scheduling system interface illustration.

The CSS includes a set of scheduling problems solving algorithms, varying from simple heuristics and dispatching rules up to more complex ones, namely based on a diverse kind of heuristics, and meta-heuristics [32,45], along with other AI-based approaches, for instance, based on machine learning [46], and others, namely based on cluster analysis

[18]. The IMSS does further include a post-processing module, which permits the selection of a considered best suited solution for a given scheduling problem, based on a comparative analysis of existing alternative solutions, through their quality evaluation, according to the specific companies' needs and preferences, namely regarding the higher or lower importance or priority assigned to different kind of performance measures, varying between internal and external ones, corresponding to the relative importance that is given, at a given time period, to factories objectives, namely based on production times and/or on client's oriented objectives, for instance, related to orders due dates, correspondingly. Besides, this post-processing module does further enables us to compare the generated scheduling solutions with historical information, and to dynamically update this repository.

Ilustrative Scheduling System Interface

The CSS has different kind of processes, through three levels, as expressed in the Figure 3, and by using appropriate interfaces, as illustrated in the Figure 4, which is about a module of the IMSS that enables to access past scheduling data, namely for being compared with some current or new data, and perform specific processes accordingly, namely for dealing with current incomplete or uncertain data about the processing times of some jobs to be scheduled, by applying appropriate data processing models and methods [5,44].

At the first level, the CSS permits automatic data collection and storage arising from the shop floor, along with its integration with information from the clients orders, and its further joint processing, namely for dealing with uncertain or incomplete data, and its further treatment to reach proper data sets for solving a given scheduling problem.

The second level is about the access, selection and execution of diverse kinds of scheduling algorithms put available through the CSS of the IMSS, through the resolution of each sub problem underlying a given scheduling problem, based the proposed scheduling model, which is going to be further described next.

Finally, at the third level the CSS enables further data post processing and analysis, namely for composing a global or complete solution for the scheduling problems considered, also based on the proposed model, and by further enabling other deeper solutions analysis, for instance, based on multivariate data series analysis methods [5,47].

COLLABORATIVE SCHEDULING

In this section is briefly described a proposed collaborative manufacturing scheduling (CMS) approach, based on a scheduling model that results from an extension of the Jachson's job shop scheduling model, in order to permit the resolution of more complex problems, for instance, occurring in varying kind of job shop manufacturing environments.

Proposed Scheduling Model

The proposed scheduling model for enabling CMS, based on the original approach proposed by Jackson, in 1956 [14], enables to establish the sequencing order of a set of jobs in a classical job shop environment, composed by two or more machines or work centers. Therefore, in this paper, this Jackson's scheduling approach is extended, in order to schedule jobs in a wider set of machines or work centers or any other kind of production units or factories, which may further be geographically dispersed.

In order to enable to carry out manufacturing scheduling of a set of n jobs in a general job shop manufacturing environment, integrating more than two machines, either in the context of a conventional or classical job shops or occurring in the context of some distributed manufacturing environment, were jobs have to be scheduled to be processed through a set of production units or factories or locally, by a set of machines or work centers, an extension of the Jackson's model is put forward. This model is represented next, for sequencing jobs in a set of three machines or work centers, defined as A, B, and C, by exploring four possible alternative sequences for processing the jobs in those work centers.

Work Center A

- Sequence 1:
- {A,B,C}->{A,C,B}->{B,A,C}->{A,B}->{A,C}->{A}->{C,A}->{B,A}->{C,A,B}->{B,C,A}->{C,B,A}
- Sequence 2:
- {A,C,B}->{A,B,C}->{B,A,C}->{A,B}->{A,C}->{A}->{C,A}->{B,A}->{C,A,B}->{C,B,A}->{B,C,A}
- Sequence 3:
- {A,B,C}->{A,C,B}->{B,A,C}->{A,C}->{A,B}->{A}->{B,A}->{C,A}->{C,A,B}->{B,C,A}->{C,B,A}
- Sequence 4:
- {A,C,B}->{A,B,C}->{B,A,C}->{A,C}->{A,B}->{A}->{B,A}->{C,A}->{B,A,C}->{C,B,A}->{B,C,A}

Work center B

- Sequence 1:
- {B,A,C}->{B,C,A}->{A,B,C}->{B,A}->{B,C}->{B}->{C,B}->{A,B}->{C,B,A}->{A,C,B}->{C,A,B}
- Sequence 2:
- {B,C,A}->{B,A,C}->{A,B,C}->{B,A}->{B,C}->{B}->{C,B}->{A,B}->{C,B,A}->{C,A,B}->{A,C,B}
- Sequence 3:
- {B,A,C}->{B,C,A}->{A,B,C}->{B,C}->{B,A}->{B}->{A,B}->{C,B}->{C,B,A}->{A,C,B}->{C,A,B}
- Sequence 4:
- {B,C,A}->{B,A,C}->{A,B,C}->{B,C}->{B,A}->{B}->{A,B}->{C,B}->{C,B,A}->{C,A,B}->{A,C,B}

Work center C

- Sequence 1:
- {C,A,B}->{C,B,A}->{B,C,A}->{C,A}->{C,B}->{C}->{B,C}->{A,C}->{A,C,B}->{A,B,C}->{B,A,C}
- Sequence 2:
- {C,B,A}->{C,A,B}->{B,C,A}->{C,A}->{C,B}->{C}->{B,C}->{A,C}->{A,C,B}->{B,A,C}->{A,B,C}
- Sequence 3:
- {C,A,B}->{C,B,A}->{B,C,A}->{C,B}->{C,A}->{C}->{A,C}->{B,C}->{A,C,B}->{A,B,C}->{B,A,C}
- Sequence 4:

- {C,B,A}->{C,A,B}->{B,C,A}->{C,B}->{C,A}->{C}->{A,C}->{B,C}->{A,C,B}->{B,A,C}->{A,B,C}

In this proposed extended model, besides the previous scenarios related to the two machines job shop sub problems, considered in the Jackson's model, there are further included other job shop scheduling sub problems, with two machines ({A,C},{B,C},{C,A},{C,B}), and job shop sub problems with three machines ({A,B,C},{A,C,B}, {B,A,C},{B,C,A},{ C,A,B},{C,B,A}). These can be solved by using the Johnson's rule for three machines or some other kind of approach, for instance, the Branch-and-Bound (B&B) algorithm by Ignall and Schrage, in 1965 [48], among other approaches, including different kinds of heuristics or meta-heuristics or other AI-based approaches [5,18,45].

As the number of machines/work centers increases, the number of alternative sequences for ordering the sets of jobs for each machine increases too, but fortunately this does not necessarily increase the complexity of the primary scheduling processes, once the number of sets of jobs remains the same, for each alternative sequence to be considered on each machine or work center. Besides, the complexity related to the sequencing problem inherent to ordering the jobs in each corresponding set, requires an extra effort for establishing the alternative sequences for each machine, which turns out to be another additional operation, requiring the examination of the alternative sequences, and the calculation of the performance measure associated to each sequence for the selection of the best one, for each valid or possible complete schedule for each machine/work center. Therefore, the best final sequence of jobs on each machine has to be validated, regarding its feasibility, for each problem instance, while aiming, for instance, at the minimization of the total completion time of the jobs or makespan.

This model can the extended to solve more complex scheduling problems, occurring in job shops with more than three machines or work centers, by using a similar general logic as it was illustrated for the case of a classical job shop with three machines/work centers. Therefore, in these, more complex job shop scheduling environments, the underlying sub-problems to be solved turn out to be increasingly more complex too, with the appearance of more complex underlying flow shop problems, including a higher number of machines/work centers (4, 5, etc.), thus requiring appropriate algorithms, which tend to be more complex too, and this complexity continues to rise when the number of jobs increases, as well as the number of possible alternative sequences for processing the sets of jobs to be further evaluated to reach a final solution for each machine/work center. Thus, with the increase in complexity of the problems it becomes more important to explore different heuristics or meta-heuristics, along with other kinds of approaches, for instance, based on varying kind of AI based ones, to approach corresponding sub-problems [5,18,45].

SCHEDULING CASE STUDY IN A JOB SHOP ENVIRONMENT UNDER THREE DIFFERENT SCENARIOS

The proposed model for supporting CMS can be implemented through diverse kind of scenarios, considering different priorities attributed to the so-called internal (scenario 1, Sc1) and external (scenario 2, Sc2) performance measures, for evaluating the quality of the solutions obtained, varying from purely or 100% internal or external, to intermediate situations that consider different weights attributed to the internal versus external measures, namely by considering the same importance associated to both kind of measures (scenario 3, Sc3, with 50%–50% for each kind of internal and external performance measure).

Table 2. Scheduling problem (instance 5) data

WCj\Ji	J1	J2	J3	J4	J5	J6	J7	J8	J9	J10
Op.1	4| WC2	7| WC2	4| WC1	6| WC2	2| WC2	6| WC3	5| WC1	4| WC2	5| WC1	2| WC3
Op.2	2| WC3	3| WC3	5| WC2	7| WC1	8| WC3	2| WC2	8| WC2	-	-	-
Op.3	6| WC1	9| WC1	-	-	-	4| WC1	6| WC3	-	-	-
di	28	32	27	19	33	34	26	35	31	28

Table 3. Scheduling problem (instance 27) data

WCj\Ji	J1	J2	J3	J4	J5	J6	J7	J8	J9	J10
Op.1	3 |WC2	8| WC3	6 WC1	4| WC2	7| WC2	9| WC1	9| WC1	3| WC1	2| WC1	6| WC3
Op.2	1| WC1	4| WC2	4 WC2	6| WC1	5| WC1	4| WC2	5| WC2	-	-	-
Op.3	3| WC3	3| WC1	7| WC3	-	-	5| WC3	-	-	-	-
di	34	33	36	31	38	32	39	36	32	39

In the Table 2 and Table 3 is shown the data from a clothing company about two scheduling problem instances (5 and 27), among a set of thirty analyzed, which include the deadlines (di) and the processing times of the operations of a set of ten jobs (Ji) that belong to a same family of products, and are executed in the corresponding work centers (WCj: WC1, WC2, and WC3), being the operations measured in time units (t.u.).

Internal Performance Oriented Approaches–Scenario 1

In the case of an absolute importance or priority is given to the satisfaction of internal performance measures, such as the typical total or maximum completion time of a set of jobs to be processed in the manufacturing system (makespan) and/or other production time-oriented measures, like the sum or the mean flow time of jobs, through appropriate optimization algorithms selected, available from the whole set of CSS's scheduling algorithms.

External Performance Oriented Approaches–Scenario 2

In the case of an absolute importance or priority being given to the satisfaction of external performance measures, typically based on the accomplishment of deadlines or due dates for the jobs, namely measures through the number or tardy jobs (Nt), and/or through other more or less closely related performance measures, such as the maximum tardiness of jobs (Tmax), among others, namely the mean lateness of the jobs, also appropriate optimization methods that have to be selected, from the whole set of scheduling algorithms put available through the CSS of the IMSS to solve them.

Combined Performance Oriented Approaches–Scenario 3

In the case of the same importance or priority is given to the satisfaction of internal and external performance measures, thus oriented to jobs' production times and deadlines, by using a 50–50% weighting that has to be attributed to the corresponding solving methods selected from the whole set of scheduling algorithms available through the CSS of the IMSS.

SCHEDULING MODEL APPLICATION ANALYSIS AND DISCUSSION

In Figure 5 are expressed the performance measure results obtained for the thirty problem instances that were run under the corresponding application scenarios previously described.

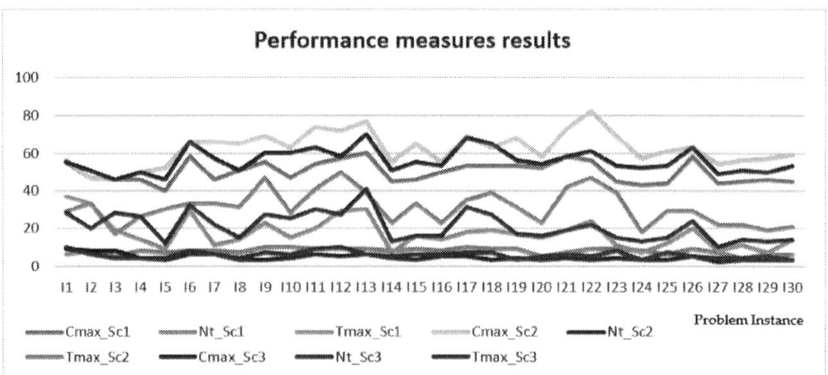

Figure 5. Performance measures' values of the thirty scheduling problem instances from scenarios 1, 2 and 3.

These results are thus organized in three groups, from the upper to the lower level, associated to the scenarios 1, 2 and 3 (Sc1, Sc2, and Sc3) about: the maximum completion time of jobs (Cmax), the maximum tardiness of jobs (Tmax), and the number of tardy jobs (Nt), correspondingly. The mean values obtained through the execution of the thirty problem instances under the scenarios Sc1, Sc2, and Sc3, for the Cmax, Nt, and Tmax performance measures, correspondingly, are expressed in Figure 6.

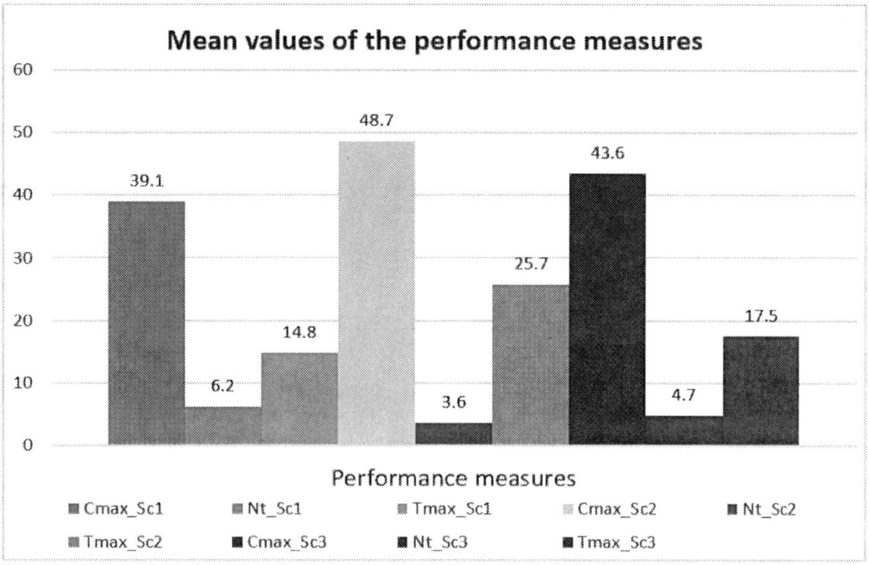

Figure 6. Mean performance measures' values of the scheduling solutions from scenarios 1, 2 and 3.

The analysis of this Figure 6 permits to realize that the best mean value of the makespan (Cmax) about the thirty problem instances run was obtained in the scenario Sc1, by applying the Shorted Processing Time (SPT) rule to the sets of jobs with just one operation, along with the Johnsons rule for the sets of jobs with two operations, to be processed in corresponding two work centers flow shops, and the B&B algorithm from Ignall & Schrage, for the sets of jobs integrating three operations, to be processed in three work centers flow shops [5,16].

Regarding the Nt, the best mean value about the thirty problem instances run was obtained in the scenario Sc2, by applying the Earliest Due Date (EDD) rule to the sets of jobs with just one operation, along with a modified version of the Hodgson's algorithm [5] for solving the sets of jobs with two operations, to be processed in two work centers flow shops, and an adapted version of the Ignall & Schrage's B&B algorithm to the set of jobs with three operations, to be processed in three WorkCentre flow shops, for minimizing the number of tardy jobs.

In terms of the Tmax the best mean value was reached for the scenario Sc1, by also applying the SPT rule to the sets of jobs with one operation, along with the Johnson's rule for solving the sets of jobs to be processed in two work centers flow shops, and an adapted version of the Ignall & Schrage's B&B algorithm to the set of jobs with three operations, to be processed in three work center flow shops, for minimizing the maximum tardiness of the jobs.

In the Figure 7, Figure 8 and Figure 9, are shown the Gantt charts about the best solutions found for the scenarios Sc1, Sc2, and Sc3, correspondingly, after the application of the proposed scheduling model for the compilation of the complete sequence of the jobs to be processes in the corresponding work center, and once selected the best one.

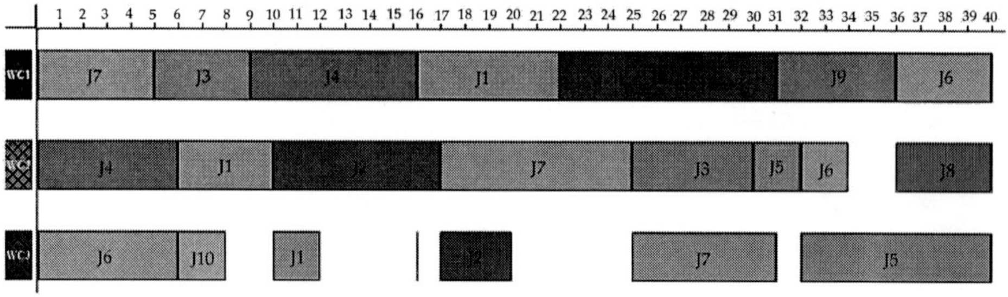

Figure 7. Gantt chart about the best solution found for scenario 1 (about problem instance 5).

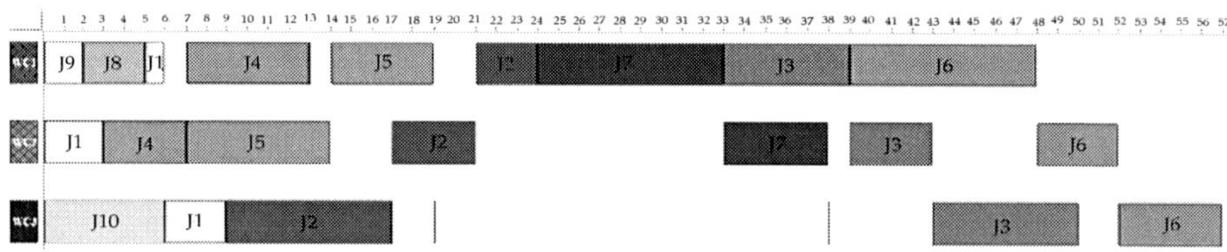

Figure 8. Gantt chart about the best solution found for scenario 2 (about problem instance 27).

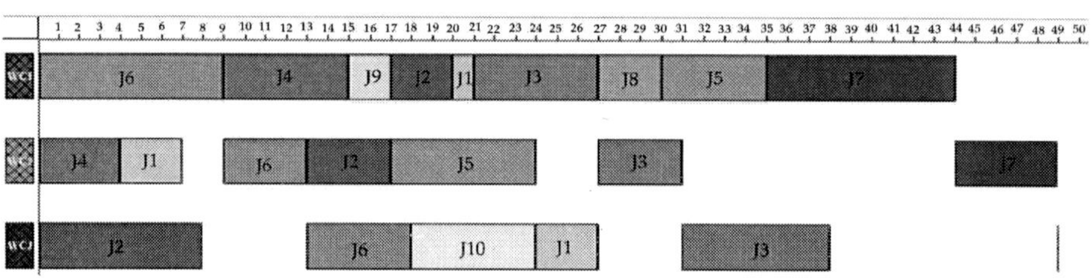

Figure 9. Gantt chart about the best solution found for scenario 3 (about problem instance 27).

As it can be realized by analyzing the Gantt charts about the best solutions obtained for each application scenario, in the Figure 7 it is visible that a more compact solution was reached, which enables a shorter total completion time of the whole set of jobs to be processed in the corresponding three work centers, thus further enabling its most favorable utilization rate, as just the work centers 2 and 3 (WC2, and WC3) present some relatively reduced idle time, in opposite to what happens to the work centers in the scenarios 2 and 3, on which the three work centers present idle times, being more significant ones.

Although, by further analyzing the summarized results about the performance measures values obtained for the three scenarios about Cmax, Nt, and Tmax for these corresponding best solutions, as expressed in the Table 4, it is possible to perform additional analysis.

Table 4. Best scheduling problems results

Scenario (Sc_k)	Cmax	Nt	Tmax
Sc1 (problem instance 5)	40	7	9
Sc2 (problem instance 27)	57	2	25
Sc3 (problem instance 27)	49	4	10

It is possible to realize that the best solution found about the minimization of the Cmax–maximum completion time of the jobs, did occur in the scenario Sc1 (of 40 t.u.), but the total number of tardy jobs (Nt) does correspond to the worst value among the three best solutions, with 7 late jobs in the whole set of ten jobs to be processes. Contrarily, the best (minimum) value for the Nt was obtained in the scenario Sc2, with 2 late jobs, but this Sc2 did obtain the worst value for the makespan (Cmax = 57 t.u.), and also the worst value for the maximum tardiness of the jobs (Tmax = 25 t.u.), among the three best solutions.

Besides, in terms of the minimization of the Tmax, the best value was also reached in scenario Sc1, of 9-time units, very closely followed by the value obtained in the scenario Sc3 (10 t.u.). Moreover, it can be seen that this scenario Sc3 does further enable to reach a better balance between the values obtained for the three performance measures among the best three solutions reached, with a Cmax of 49-time units, and a Nt of 4 late jobs, besides the Tmax with 10-time units. Therefore, although this balance can, in general, be seen as a good solution to be adopted, once it is always visible a trade-off situation between the quality of the solutions obtained, regarding the corresponding set of internal, external, and a mix of internal and external performance measures considered, through the three application scenarios explored, clearly an indication of priorities or preferences is required, by an experienced manufacturing management decision-maker, while selecting a considered best final solution, regarding each specific manufacturing management conditions verified at a given scheduling moment.

CONCLUSIONS

In this paper a proposed collaborative scheduling model was presented that consists of an extension of the Jackson's job shop scheduling model, and its results obtained were analyzed through an industrial example of application, consisting of a set of thirty industrial problem instances from a clothing company. The model was explored under three different application scenarios, about internal, external, and combined performance measures, with the same weight, related to the total completion time of the jobs, the number of late jobs and the tardiness of the jobs being executed in a job shop environment with three work centers. The resolution of the problem instances was carried out through the selection of alternative algorithms put available through a developed interoperable scheduling system, which enables to jointly process scheduling data from a historical repository and information arising from clients, along with incomplete and uncertain data processing. Through the study carried out, it was possible to realize the benefits associated with the use of the presented scheduling system and underlying problem-solving model. One main benefit is related to the possibility of decomposing complex scheduling problems, occurring in job shop manufacturing environment in simpler sub-problems that can be solved individually and then the partial solutions combined to obtain complete alternative solutions for the whole problem to be further analyzed in order to select the one considered best suited in a concrete manufacturing management situation. Moreover, the scheduling algorithms can be selected from a set of varying kind of algorithms put available through the interoperable scheduling system, which range from simple dispatching rules up to more complex ones, for instance, based on branch-and-bound, among other optimization methods and underlying techniques, along with other solving methods, namely a set of heuristics, meta-heuristics, along with other AI-based approaches, including machine learning and clustering algorithms.

The application of different kind of scheduling algorithms was explored, and through the results obtained it was possible to realize that the selection of a certain final solution, will much depend on the priorities or preferences defined by the decision maker, based on each particular conditions underlying a given specific manufacturing and management situation, as each potential possible alternative solution selected will have some drawback and benefit. Although, it was possible to recognize that there are visible general or overall benefits when some weights are attributed to the different kind of performance measures to be considered, namely by using a considered 50-50 performance measures weighting or third scenario, as the alternative solutions tend to present trade-offs, while tending to the optimization of some performance measures, according to the corresponding solving algorithm used, which in this case, were divided in two main subsets, intending the optimization of the so-called internal and external performance measures.

This is a novel contribution, as far as our knowledge, existing contributions do not explore a widened range of alternative methods combinations to solve a given scheduling problem, while decomposing it into simple ones, to further enable different alternatives to concatenate them, in order to permit a wider range of alternative final or complete solutions to be evaluated for reaching a final decision about a considered best suited global solution for a specific problem to be solved. This is considered a relevant contribution for the state of the art in this domain, as it enables a set of entities (decision-makers and/or machines) to collaborate for jointly exploring alternative solutions for solving a given scheduling problem, by running different kind of scheduling algorithms for solving the sub-problems integrating the global one.

As future work, it is planned to further analyze the potential of the proposed extended scheduling model, regarding its potential additional benefits and limitations for carrying out the collaborative manufacturing scheduling in other kind of manufacturing environments, for instance, in the context of distributed manufacturing systems subject to additional constraint, namely about the sets of jobs and their processing units.

ACKNOWLEDGMENTS

This work has been supported by national funds through the FCT—Fundação para a Ciência e Tecnologia through the R&D Units Project Scope: UIDB/00319/2020 and EXPL/EME-SIS/1224/2021.

REFERENCES

1. Putnik, G.D.; Putnik, Z.; Shah, V.; Varela, L.; Ferreira, L.; Castro, H.; Catia, A.; Pinheiro, P. Collaborative Engineering definition: Distinguishing it from Concurrent Engineering through the complexity and semiotics lenses. IOP Conf. Ser. Mater. Sci. Eng. 2021, 1174, 012027.
2. Putnik, G.D.; Putnik, Z.; Shah, V.; Varela, L.; Ferreira, L.; Castro, H.; Catia, A.; Pinheiro, P. Collaborative Engineering: A Review of Organisational Forms for Implementation and Operation. IOP Conf. Ser. Mater. Sci. Eng. 2021, 1174, 012028.
3. Eijnatten, F.M.; Putnik, G.D. Chaos, Complexity, Learning, and the Learning Organization: Towards a Chaordic Enterprise; Emerald Group Publishing: Bingley, UK, 2004.

4. Lou, P.; Ong, S.K.; Nee, A.Y.C. Agent-based distributed scheduling for virtual job shops. Int. J. Prod. Res. 2010, 48, 3889–3910.
5. Vieira, G.; Varela, M.L.R.; Putnik, G.D. Technologies integration for distributed manufacturing scheduling in a virtual enterprise. In International Conference on Virtual and Networked Organizations, Emergent Technologies, and Tools; Springer: Berlin/Heidelberg, Germany, 2012; pp. 337–347.
6. Canadas, N.; Machado, J.; Soares, F.; Barros, C.; Varela, L. Simulation of cyber physical systems behaviour using timed plant models. Mechatronics 2018, 54, 175–185.
7. Kays, H.M.E.; Karim, A.N.M.; Daud, M.R.C.; Varela, M.L.R.; Putnik, G.D.; Machado, J.M. A collaborative multiplicative Holt-Winters forecasting approach with dynamic fuzzy-level component. Appl. Sci. 2018, 8, 530.
8. Putnik, G.D.; Ferreira, L.G.M. Industry 4.0: Models, tools and cyber-physical systems for manufacturing. FME Trans. 2019, 47, 659–662.
9. Deloitte, 2012. Retail Globalization. Deloitte Touche Tohmatsu Limited. Available online: https://www.deloitte.com/global/en.html (accessed on 17 October 2022).
10. Hankel, M.; Rexroth, B. The reference architectural model industrie 4.0 (rami 4.0). ZVEI 2015, 2, 4–9.
11. Kagermann, H. Change through digitization—Value creation in the age of Industry 4.0. In Management of Permanent Change; Springer Gabler: Wiesbaden, Germany, 2015; pp. 23–45.
12. Li, L. China's manufacturing locus in 2025: With a comparison of "Made-in-China 2025" and "Industry 4.0". Technol. Forecast. Soc. Chang. 2018, 135, 66–74.
13. Sony, M.; Naik, S.S. Ten lessons for managers while implementing Industry 4.0. IEEE Eng. Manag. Rev. 2019, 47, 45–52.
14. Jackson, J.R. An extension of Johnson's results on job lot scheduling. Nav. Res. Logist. Q. 1956, 3, 201–203.
15. Arrais-Castro, A.; Varela ML, R.; Putnik, G.D.; Ribeiro, R.A.; Machado, J.; Ferreira, L. Collaborative framework for virtual organisation synthesis based on a dynamic multi-criteria decision model. Int. J. Comput. Integr. Manuf. 2018, 31, 857–868.
16. Reddy, M.S.; Ratnam, C.; Agrawal, R.; Varela, M.L.R.; Sharma, I.; Manupati, V.K. Investigation of reconfiguration effect on makespan with social network method for flexible job shop scheduling problem. Comput. Ind. Eng. 2017, 110, 231–241.
17. Alves, F.; Varela, M.L.R.; Rocha, A.M.A.; Pereira, A.I.; Leitão, P. A human centered hybrid MAS and meta-heuristics based system for simultaneously supporting scheduling and plant layout adjustment. FME Trans. 2019, 47, 699–710.
18. Azevedo, B.F.; Varela, M.L.R.; Pereira, A.I. Production Scheduling Using Multi-objective Optimization and Cluster Approaches. In Proceedings of the International Conference on Innovations in Bio-Inspired Computing and Applications, Online, 16–18 December 2021; pp. 120–129.
19. Shen, W.; Wang, L.; Hao, Q. Agent-based distributed manufacturing process planning and scheduling: A state-of-the-art survey. IEEE Trans. Syst. Man Cybern. Part C 2006, 36, 563–577.
20. Manupati, V.K.; Gokula Krishnan, M.; Varela, M.L.R.; Machado, J. Telefacturing based distributed manufacturing environment for optimal manufacturing service by enhancing the interoperability in the hubs. J. Eng. 2017, 2017, 9305989.
21. Fu, Y.; Wang, H.; Huang, M. Integrated scheduling for a distributed manufacturing system: A stochastic multi-objective model. Enterp. Inf. Syst. 2019, 13, 557–573.
22. Cheng, Y.; Bi, L.; Tao, F.; Ji, P. Hypernetwork-based manufacturing service scheduling for distributed and collaborative manufacturing operations towards smart manufacturing. J. Intell. Manuf. 2020, 31, 1707–1720.

23. Zhou, R.; Chen, G.; Yang, Z.H.; Zhang, J.B. Distributed manufacturing scheduling using a novel cooperative system. In Proceedings of the 2008 IEEE International Conference on Service Operations and Logistics, and Informatics, Beijing, China, 12–15 October 2008; Volume 1, pp. 256–260.

24. Baker, K.R.; Trietsch, D. Safe scheduling: Setting due dates in single-machine problems. Eur. J. Oper. Res. 2009, 196, 69–77.

25. Pinedo, M.; Chao, X. Operations Scheduling with Applications in Manufacturing and Services; McGraw Hill: New York, NY, USA, 1999.

26. Pinedo, M.L. Scheduling Theory, Algorithms and Systems, 4th ed.; Springer: Berlin/Heidelberg, Germany, 2012.

27. Mishra, N.; Singh, A.; Kumari, S.; Govindan, K.; Ali, S.I. Cloud-based multi-agent architecture for effective planning and scheduling of distributed manufacturing. Int. J. Prod. Res. 2016, 54, 7115–7128.

28. Zhang, X.; Liu, X.; Tang, S.; Królczyk, G.; Li, Z. Solving scheduling problem in a distributed manufacturing system using a discrete fruit fly optimization algorithm. Energies 2019, 12, 3260.

29. Mao, X.; Li, J.; Guo, H.; Wu, X. Research on Collaborative Planning and Symmetric Scheduling for Parallel Shipbuilding Projects in the Open Distributed Manufacturing Environment. Symmetry 2020, 12, 161.

30. Zijm, W.H.M. The integration of process planning and shop floor scheduling in small batch part manufacturing, Ann. CIRP 1995, 44, 429–432.

31. Shen, Y.J.; Wang, M.S. Broadcast scheduling in wireless sensor networks using fuzzy Hopfield neural network. Expert Syst. Appl. 2008, 34, 900–907.

32. Madureira, A.; Ramos, R.; Carmo Silva, S. Using Genetic Algorithms for Dynamic Scheduling. In Proceedings of the 14th Annual Production and Operations Management Society Conference (POMS'2003), Savannah, GA, USA, 4–7 April 2003.

33. Alves, C.; Putnik, G.D.; Varela, M.L.R. How environment dynamics affects production scheduling: Requirements for development of CPPS models. FME Trans. 2021, 49, 827–834.

34. Goren, S.; Sabuncuoglu, I. Robustness and Stability Measures for Scheduling: Single Machine Environments. IIE Trans. 2008, 40, 66–83.

35. Ouelhadj, D.; Petrovic, S. A Survey of Dynamic Scheduling in Manufacturing Systems. J. Sched. 2009, 12, 417–431.

36. Aytug, H.; Lawley, M.A.; McKay, K.; Mohan, S.; Uzsoy, R. Executing production schedules in the face of uncertainties: A review and some future directions. Eur. J. Oper. Res. 2005, 161, 86–110.

37. Shen, W. Distributed manufacturing scheduling using intelligent agents. IEEE Intell. Syst. 2002, 17, 88–94.

38. Saeidlou, S.; Saadat, M.; Amini Sharifi, E.; Jules, G.D. Agent-based distributed manufacturing scheduling: An ontological approach. Cogent Eng. 2019, 6, 1565630.

39. Ramakurthi, V.B.; Manupati, V.K.; Machado, J.; Varela, L. A hybrid multi-objective evolutionary algorithm-based semantic foundation for sustainable distributed manufacturing systems. Appl. Sci. 2021, 11, 6314.

40. Guo, Z.; Ngai, E.; Yang, C.; Liang, X. An RFID-based intelligent decision support system architecture for production monitoring and scheduling in a distributed manufacturing environment. Int. J. Prod. Econ. 2015, 159, 16–28.

41. Varela, M.L.R.; Putnik, G.D.; Manupati, V.K.; Rajyalakshmi, G.; Trojanowska, J.; Machado, J. Integrated process planning and scheduling in networked manufacturing systems for I4.0: A review and framework proposal. Wirel. Netw. 2021, 27, 1587–1599.

42. Chiu, C.; Yih, Y. A learning-based methodology for dynamic scheduling in distributed manufacturing systems. Int. J. Prod. Res. 1995, 33, 3217–3232.

43. Varela, M.L.R.; Ribeiro, R.A. Distributed Manufacturing Scheduling Based on a Dynamic Multi-criteria Decision Model. In Recent Developments and New Directions in Soft Computing; Zadeh, L., Abbasov, A., Yager, R., Shahbazova, S., Reformat, M., Eds.; Studies in Fuzziness and Soft Computing; Springer: Cham, Switzerland, 2014; p. 317.

44. Vafaei, N.; Ribeiro, R.A.; Camarinha-Matos, L.M.; Varela, L.R. Normalization techniques for collaborative networks. Kybernetes 2019, 49, 1285–1304.

45. Santos, A.S.; Madureira, A.M.; Varela, M.L.R. An ordered heuristic for the allocation of resources in unrelated parallel-machines. Int. J. Ind. Eng. Comput. 2015, 6, 145–156.

46. Putnik, G.D.; Pabba, S.K.; Manupati, V.K.; Varela, M.L.R.; Ferreira, F. Semi-Double-loop machine learning based CPS approach for predictive maintenance in manufacturing system based on machine status indications. CIRP Ann. Manuf. Technol. 2021, 70, 365–368.

47. Varela, M.L.R.; Amaral, G.; Pereira, S.; Machado, D.; Falcão, A.; Ribeiro, R.; Sousa, E.; Santos, J.; Pereira, A.F. Interoperable Decision Support System based on Multivariate Time Series for Setup Data Processing and Visualization. In Proceedings of the 19th International on Intelligent Systems Design and Applications (ISDA 2019), Auburn, WA, USA, 3–5 December2019; Advances in Intelligent Systems and Computing. Springer: Cham, Switzerland, 2019; pp. 550–560.

48. Ignall, E.; Schrage, L. Application of the branch and bound technique to some flow-shop scheduling problems. Oper. Res. 1965, 13, 400–412.

4

Dynamic Allocation of Manufacturing Resources in IoT Job Shop Considering Machine State Transfer and Carbon Emission

Xuan Su [1], Wenquan Dong [2], Jingyu Lu [1], Chen Chen [1] and Weixi Ji [1,3]

[1]School of Mechanical Engineering, Jiangnan University, Wuxi 214122, China

[2]Department of Industrial and Systems Engineering, The University of Tennessee, Knoxville, TN 37996, USA

[3]Key Laboratory of Advanced Manufacturing Equipment Technology, Jiangnan University, Wuxi 214122, China

ABSTRACT

The optimal allocation of manufacturing resources plays an essential role in the production process. However, most of the existing resource allocation methods are designed for standard cases, lacking a dynamic optimal allocation framework for resources that can guide actual production. Therefore, this paper proposes a dynamic allocation method for discrete job shop resources in the Internet of Things (IoT), which considers the uncertainty of machine states, and carbon emission. First, a data-driven job shop resource status monitoring framework under the IoT environment is proposed, considering the real-time status of job shop manufacturing resources. A dynamic configuration mechanism of manufacturing resources based on the configuration threshold is proposed. Then, a real-time state-driven multi-objective manufacturing resource optimization allocation model is established, taking machine tool energy consumption and tool wear as carbon emission sources and combined with the maximum completion time. An improved imperialist competitive algorithm (I-ICA) is proposed to solve the model. Finally, taking an actual production process of a discrete job shop as an example, the proposed algorithm is compared with other low-carbon multi-objective optimization algorithms, and the results show that the proposed method is superior to similar methods in terms of completion time and carbon emissions. In addition, the practicability and effectiveness of the proposed dynamic resource allocation method are verified in a machine failure situation.

Keywords: *IoT, Low-Carbon Manufacturing, Multi-Objective Optimization, Dynamic Allocation, Manufacturing Resource*

INTRODUCTION

As the lifeblood of the national economy, the manufacturing industry needs to maintain a relatively fast development speed to meet the growing needs of human beings [1]. However, in the face of the energy and resource crisis, global ecological and environmental deterioration [2], climate warming, and other issues, the manufacturing industry is facing a contradiction between development and environmental protection [3], and the pressure on energy conservation is increasing [4]. Therefore, it is of great significance to study the modern production model that takes into consideration both production capacity and environmental protection [5].

At the same time, with the extensive cross-application of various high and new technologies in the manufacturing industry, a new industrial technology revolution is taking place, bringing new opportunities for the sustainable development of the manufacturing industry [6]. Manufacturing enterprises need to absorb and utilize emerging technologies such as the IoT to explore low-carbon, efficient, and low-cost sustainable production models [7].

As the realization carrier of the enterprise production model, resource allocation has become an essential part of actual production. It significantly impacts the manufacturing efficiency, cost and energy consumption [8]. Reasonable resource allocation can continue to bring economic growth to the enterprise. However, current resource allocation research mainly considers production-efficiency-related indicators, such as maximum processing time [9,10], production delay and machine load [11,12], as optimization objectives. These studies cannot meet the actual needs of sustainable manufacturing because they do not consider processing energy consumption such as electric energy [13,14]. Green manufacturing is a modern model that considers manufacturing efficiency, environmental impact, and economic and social benefits. Its ultimate goal is to achieve the sustainable development of the manufacturing industry [15].

Green manufacturing can improve energy efficiency and reduce carbon emissions in the manufacturing process. Therefore, more and more scholars consider green and low-carbon indicators [16] to optimize multi-objective resource allocation because improving the energy utilization rate can effectively increase financial revenue [17]. Zhang et al. [18] and Li et al. [19] studied the resource allocation of the hybrid flow shop and distributed displacement flow shop with the target completion time and energy consumption, respectively; Rifai et al. [20] also considered the cost target to study the resource allocation of distributed reentrant permutation job shop; Feng et al. [21] studied the resource allocation of flexible job shop with quality as one of the goals; Nouiri et al. [22] and Sun et al. [23] proposed a rescheduling method (GRM) that considered energy saving; Wang et al. [24] established a two-stage optimization model for flexible job shop scheduling evaluating energy and operational dynamic characteristics; Liu et al. [25] combined the green scheduling optimization of flexible job shop with crane transportation, paying attention to the workshop's total energy consumption and expanding the research scope of the energy consumption. In terms of solving the resource allocation problem, Salimifard et al. [26] proposed a dual-objective integer linear programming model with task segmentation and resource constraints to study the resource allocation problem in the injection moulding process. Wu et al. [27] applied the improved NSGA-II algorithm to solve the problem of job shop resource allocation, aiming at energy consumption. Lei et al. [28] designed a two-stage metaheuristic algorithm based on the imperialist competitive algorithm (ICA) and the variable neighborhood search algorithm to solve multi-objective problems with total energy consumption constraints. However, the above research mainly focuses on the configuration model and algorithm under the condition that the manufacturing resource status remains unchanged. It does not establish the relationship between the proposed method and the actual production, and cannot guide the actual production.

In the actual production process, production disturbances occur from time to time [29], such as material delays, equipment failures [30], quality fluctuations, etc., and the above static job-shop-based configuration methods will fail [21]. Real-time status information and its use in guiding the resource allocation process is crucial. With the rapid development of IoT technology, it is gradually possible to obtain real-time production information from the discrete production workshop [31]. Chen et al. [32] proposed an energy efficiency monitoring and management system supported by emerging IoT technology to monitor machine status and scheduling plans; Singh et al. [33] developed a new framework based on big data cloud computing technology; Tao et al. [34] introduced the life cycle of manufacturing data; Dong et al. studied the state space modeling method [35]; Qiu et al. [36] discussed the role of data analysis in manufacturing. Singh et al. [37] proposed an integrated approach based on DEMATEL-MMDE-ISM to analyze the barriers to the implementation of the Internet of Things in manufacturing; Zhang et al. [6] studied the construction of a real-time data acquisition network in the workshop and proposed an energy-aware cyber physical system (E-CPS) used for energy extensive data analysis and hidden production anomaly detection. In addition, energy-saving strategies for CNC machine tools to achieve real-time and accurate control is also researched [38,39]; Syafrudin, et al. [40] proposed a real-time monitoring system for automobile manufacturing based on IoT sensors, big data processing and machine learning models; Trakadas et al. [41] studied artificial intelligence based collaboration in industrial IoT manufacturing method and proposed an architectural extension of the manufacturing IoT; Ayvaz et al. [42] developed a predictive maintenance system for manufacturing lines through a machine learning approach that uses IoT data in real-time. The above research shows that the real-time status information of production can be obtained through the IoT in the workshop and can guide the further optimization of production management and control. Studying the optimal allocation of low-carbon resources for IoT discrete vehicles which take into consideration the dynamic real-time state of the machine is of great value.

However, there are two major gaps in current research. First, there is a lack of systematic methods for real-time data collection and analysis serving the optimal configuration of manufacturing resources. Secondly, there is a lack of dynamic optimal methods in manufacturing resources allocation based on real-time status. Therefore, based on the research of real-time state data collection and analysis of manufacturing resources, this paper proposes a real-time state-driven dynamic configuration method of manufacturing resources to achieve low-carbon manufacturing in the IoT discrete job shop. The contributions of this paper are summarized as:

- A real-time data-driven job shop status monitoring framework is proposed to realize real-time collection and packaging modelling of resource status data and energy consumption data. The proposed framework improves the knowledge system of manufacturing process monitoring.

- Taking into consideration the real-time state constraints of manufacturing resources, job shop carbon emission targets and maximum completion time goals, a low-carbon resource allocation method of discrete manufacturing job shop driven by real-time states of manufacturing resources is proposed.
- An improved multi-objective empire competition optimization algorithm is proposed for solving the allocation problem, and the concept of external population invasion is introduced to enhance the local optimization ability of the algorithm. This method can provide a reference for the evolutionary algorithm to function outside of the local optimum.

A FRAMEWORK FOR DYNAMIC CONFIGURATION OF IOT DISCRETE JOB SHOP RESOURCES

Due to the existence of unforeseen factors, the original production plan in the actual production process often deviates from the actual processing situation, which reduces the production efficiency of the job shop. Therefore, real-time monitoring of job shop production is carried out with the help of IoT.

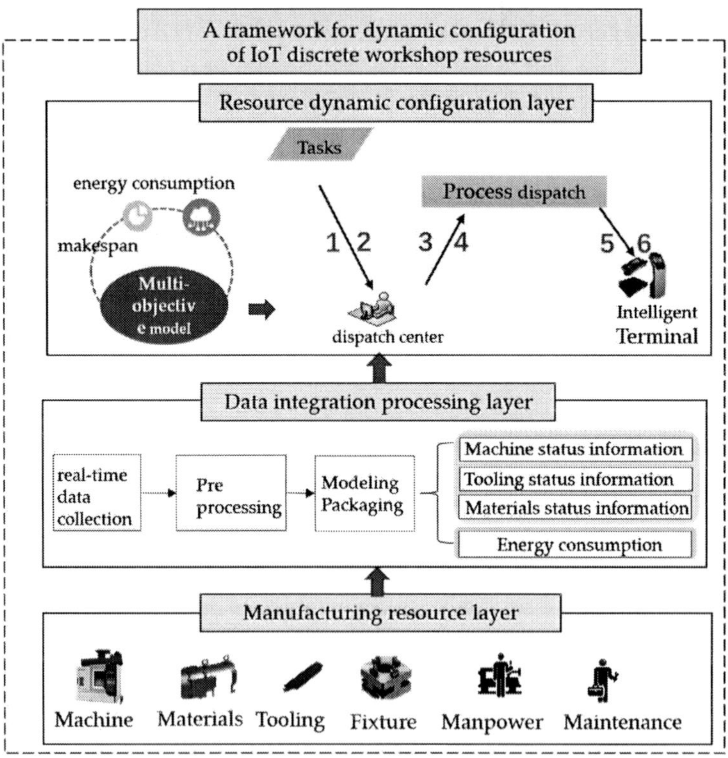

Notes: 1—Routing; 2—Craft document; 3—Resource status;4—Equipment capacity; 5—Process flow card; 6—NC program.

Figure 1. Real-time data-driven configuration framework for IoT discrete job shop resources.

The data obtained is converted into intuitive production events to guide managers to accurately handle abnormal events in the actual production process. At the same time, the manufacturing data acquired is input into the production scheduling in real-time to adjust the production plan and keep it consistent with the actual production situation so that the production plan can meet the production efficiency index and the optimal energy saving and emission reduction index as much as possible. Thereby, an important guarantee for the business-decision-making of enterprises can be provided because the management level and production efficiency is improved and the energy consumption and carbon emissions in the production process is reduced.

To realize the real-time state-driven job shop low-carbon scheduling of manufacturing resources, a real-time data-driven IoT discrete job shop resource dynamic configuration framework is constructed, as shown in Figure 1. This framework includes a real-time data acquisition layer, a data integration processing layer and a resource dynamic configuration layer. The real-time data collection layer implements data collection for job shop manufacturing resources including workers, machine tools, fixtures, workpieces, etc., with the help of RFID equipment or directly using the serial port and network port of the machine tool. The data integration processing layer processes the data collected, including cleaning invalid data and filtering redundant data, modeling and encapsulating the pre-processed data to obtain an effective job shop data model. The resource dynamic configuration layer converts the encapsulated data model into a job shop abnormal event using the abnormal event knowledge base and complex event processing technology. The events acquired are converted into real-time job shop status information and input into the job shop scheduling system after being uploaded to the database.

Real-Time Data Collection of Workshop Manufacturing Process

A real-time data acquisition scheme based on Cyber-Physical Systems (CPS) is designed to realize the real-time acquisition of manufacturing process data. It includes three parts: production planning data acquisition, manufacturing process data acquisition and material status data acquisition, as shown in Figure 2.

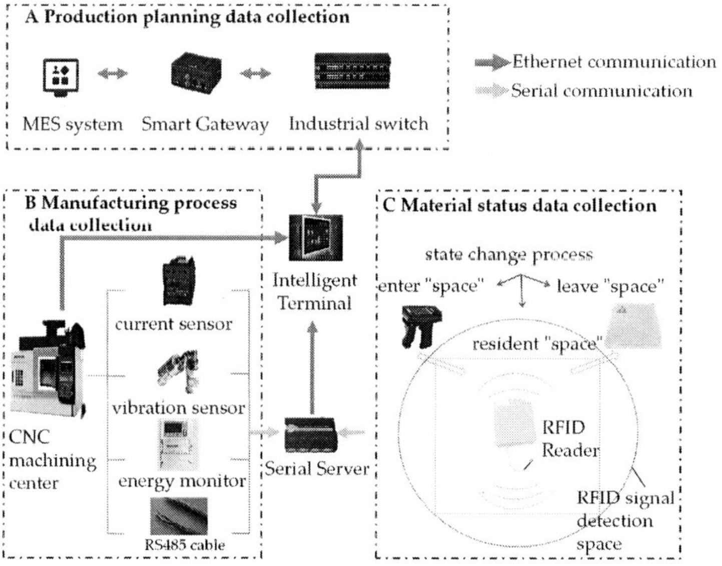

Figure 2. Real-time data collection of manufacturing process.

The job shop equipment realizes regular communication between the equipment and the intelligent terminal through a unified local network. It uses the data interface of the CNC machine tool to obtain the data collected by its monitoring module. The measures of adding auxiliary sensing devices are adopted for the problem of incomplete data collection from machine tool status. Radio frequency identification equipment, a current sensor, a temperature sensor, a vibration sensor and other commonly sensing devices are used to collect corresponding status data; Using RFID technology to sense material status data, the reader can automatically read the RFID signal to detect the data in the space and upload the read data to the intelligent terminal through the serial port server. The energy consumption data is collected by deploying electric energy sensors on each machine tool. And at the same time, the consumption of energy-consuming working fluids (such as cutting fluid) in the machining process is monitored by gas/liquid flow sensors. The data acquisition devices and their main parameters are shown in Table 1.

Table 1. Data collection devices and their main parameters

Device Name	Device Type	Collection Object	Interface
Sensor	PCB356A03	Vibration signal	RS485
Data acquisition card	NI9234	Acoustic signal Vibration signal	RS485
Machining center	KF5608	Processing parameters Spindle load, etc.	FOCAS
High-frequency reader	ALR-F800	RFID Label	RS232
ALR-8696 antenna	ALR-8696-C	RFID Label	RS232
Smart meter	YG194E-9SY	Current, Voltage, Power	RS485

Modeling and Encapsulation of Real-Time Data

The data processing of the IoT discrete job shop includes two main elements: energy consumption data and resource status data. Energy consumption data is collected by deploying power sensors on each machine tool; resource status data consists of machine tool, tooling and material data.

(1) Processing energy consumption data model

For energy-saving production in job shop, it is first necessary to collect relevant electrical energy data, and the consumption data model is:

$$EC = \{ECID, MID, V\langle a_1, a_2, \cdots a_n\rangle, T_1\} \tag{1}$$

where ECID is the identification code of the processing energy consumption data; MID is the identification code of the machine tool; V and T_1 are the collected energy consumption data and collection time, respectively. The data collection frequency is twice per second, and the collected data will be stored in a temporary database.

(2) Machine tool state data model

$$MS = \left\{MID, S\left\langle s_{on}, s_{off}\right\rangle, WID, P\langle p_{id}, p_{name}, \cdots p_t\rangle, H\langle h_1, h_2, \cdots, h_n\rangle, B\langle b_1, b_2, \cdots, b_n\rangle, T_2\right\} \tag{2}$$

where S represents the switch of the machine tool; WID represents the identified cation code of the processed material; P represents the processing information; H represents the tooling used; B represents the fault information of the machine tool.

(3) Tooling state model

$$TS = \{TID, PID, W\langle w_1, w_2, \cdots w_n\rangle, T_3\} \tag{3}$$

where TID represents the identification code of the tooling; PID represents the position information of the tooling; W represents the wear condition.

(4) Material state model

$$WS = \{WID, PID, PW\langle p_1, p_2, \cdots p_n\rangle, T_4\} \tag{4}$$

where PW and T_4 represent the processing status data and corresponding time of the material. The frequency of the RFID reader is five times per second, and the change data of the workpiece status will be stored in the database.

Dynamic Resource Allocation Mechanism

Cycle-driven, event-driven and hybrid-driven mechanisms are often used in reconfiguring job shop resources to ensure the smooth progress of production planning. Event-driven mechanisms have become popular among them due to their ability to respond to explicit production anomalies quickly. However, when the exception occurs frequently, it causes frequent resource reconfigurations, making production impossible. In addition, event-driven mechanisms cannot react to implicit disturbances. Therefore, this paper proposes a state-driven resource allocation mechanism which is driven by the real-time state of manufacturing resources, and combines this mechanism with a cycle-driven mechanism to form a hybrid-driven mechanism to respond to the cumulative impact of invisible disturbances. In addition, a method to evaluate the effects of anomalies using dynamic configuration thresholds is proposed to avoid production shutdowns caused by frequent reconfigurations. The proposed hybrid driving mechanism can give full play to the advantages of the event-driven and cycle-driven mechanisms, as shown in Figure 3. It can design corresponding configuration strategies for different state transitions to accurately and respond to dynamic changes in the job shop in a timely manner, improve job shop production capacity and reduce costs. Specifically, according to the degree of impact of state changes on the production process, this paper divides them into two categories: emergency state changes and ordinary state changes. Emergency state changes refer to changes that must be dealt with immediately after they occur, including job shop equipment failures and emergency work order insertion; common state changes refer to hidden disturbances in the job shop. Generally, these disturbances have little impact on job shop production or may be automatically resolved after they occur, including personnel leaving their posts, processing overtime, etc. A few ordinary state changes have little effect on the overall scheduling scheme, but if gradually accumulated, they will increase the deviation between the initial scheduling and the actual production. The change of the emergency state of the job shop is handled by completely rescheduling the configuration. The change of the ordinary state, firstly based on the above-mentioned earliest and latest starting time scheduling Gantt chart, is determined whether the cumulative delay of the event will affect the latest starting time of the next process of the machine.

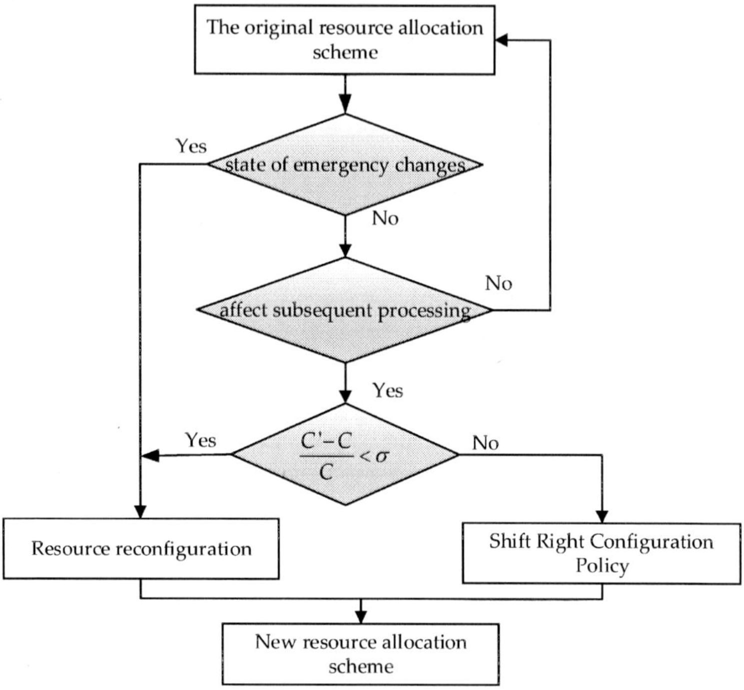

Figure 3. Dynamic resource allocation mechanism.

If there is an impact, the workpiece delay completion threshold is set based on the workpiece delivery date. If the point is not exceeded, the right-shift rescheduling method is used. If the threshold is exceeded, the entire rescheduling method is used. The threshold σ is obtained by the Formula (5), taking into consideration the two factors processing time and energy consumption.

$$\sigma = \frac{\sum_{i=1}^{N_k} T_{ik}}{\sum_{i=1}^{N_k} A_{ik}} + \frac{\sum_{i=1}^{N_k} C_{ik}}{\eta_1 \sum_{i=1}^{N_k} W_{ik}} \quad (5)$$

where N_k is the number of product types processed by the machine k; N_i is the number of processes included in part i; T_{ik} is the maximum acceptable processing time of the i-th product in machine k; A_{ik} is the planned processing time of i-th product in the machine k; C_{ik} is the maximum acceptable carbon emission of the i-th product in the machine k; W_{ik} is the planned energy consumption of the i-th product in the machine k, and η_1 is the carbon emission factor of electric energy.

MODELS AND ALGORITHMS

Multi-Objective Resource Optimal Allocation Model

The real-time state-driven dynamic allocation of manufacturing resources problem can be described as: at time 0, there are m parts $\{J_1, J_2, \ldots, J_m\}$ in n pieces of equipment

$\{M_1, M_2, \ldots, M_n\}$ wait on add work, part i contains l operations $\{O_{i0}, O_{i1}, O_{i2}, \ldots, O_{il}\}$. The primary sources of carbon emissions caused by the production and processing of discrete manufacturing job shop are power consumption and cutting fluid consumption when the machine tool is running. The machine tool operation's power consumption includes standby and processing power. There may be abnormal conditions on the shop floor, causing the affected workpiece processes and machine tools to wait for abnormal processing before they can be put into production. In this paper, machine tool energy consumption and cutting fluid consumption are used as sources of carbon emissions. A multi-objective optimization model is combined with the classical optimization objective-maximum completion time.

$$F_T = \min(\max\sum_{i=1}^{N_k}\sum_{j=1}^{N_i}\left(n_{ijk}\left(1+f_{ijk}\right)t_{ijk}+d_{ijk}\right)+C_k(t)) \tag{6}$$

where n_{ijk} is the quantity required to be processed in the machine k of the j-th process of the i-th product; f_{ijk} is the unqualified product rate of the j-th process of the i-th product in the machine k; t_{ijk} is the i-th product. The unit processing time required by the j-th process of the product in the manufacturing unit k; d_{ijk} is the production preparation time of the j-th process of the i-th product in the machine k; $C_k(t)$ is the time variation of the production demand of the machine k caused by the change of the real-time working conditions.

$$F_C = \min\left[\sum_{k=1}^{n}(C_{ek}+C_{lk})\right] \tag{7}$$

where c_{ek} is the energy consumption of the machine tool, and c_{lk} is the carbon emission of the cutting fluid.

$$C_{ek} = \eta_1\sum_{i=1}^{N_k}\left(\sum_{j=1}^{N_i} n_{ijk}\left(1+f_{ijk}\right)t_{ijk}\, p_{ijk}+o_k v_k\right) \tag{8}$$

where p_{ijk} is the processing power of the j-th process of the i-th product in the machine k, o_k is the standby time of the machine k, v_k is the standby power of the machine k, and η_1 is the carbon emission factor of electricity.

$$C_{lk} = \eta_2\frac{Q_k}{T_k}\sum_{x-k} t_{ijk} \tag{9}$$

where Q_k is the volume of cutting fluid; T_k is the use time of cutting fluid; η_2 is the carbon emission factor of electric energy.

Improved Empire Competition Algorithm

In this section, an improved imperial competition algorithm (I-ICA) is used to solve the low-carbon resource allocation problem in a discrete manufacturing job shop. The imperial competition algorithm (ICA) is a socially inspired random optimization search algorithm, which has certain advantages in large-scale combinatorial optimization problems [9]. The initial solution generated by the ICA algorithm is, however, unevenly distributed in the solution space, and will make the final solution prone to bias towards the local optimum. Therefore, this paper introduces the concept of foreign empire invasion, and proposes an invasion mechanism to expand the search breadth of the solution and improve the convergence speed. Figure 4 shows the specific flow of the improved algorithm.

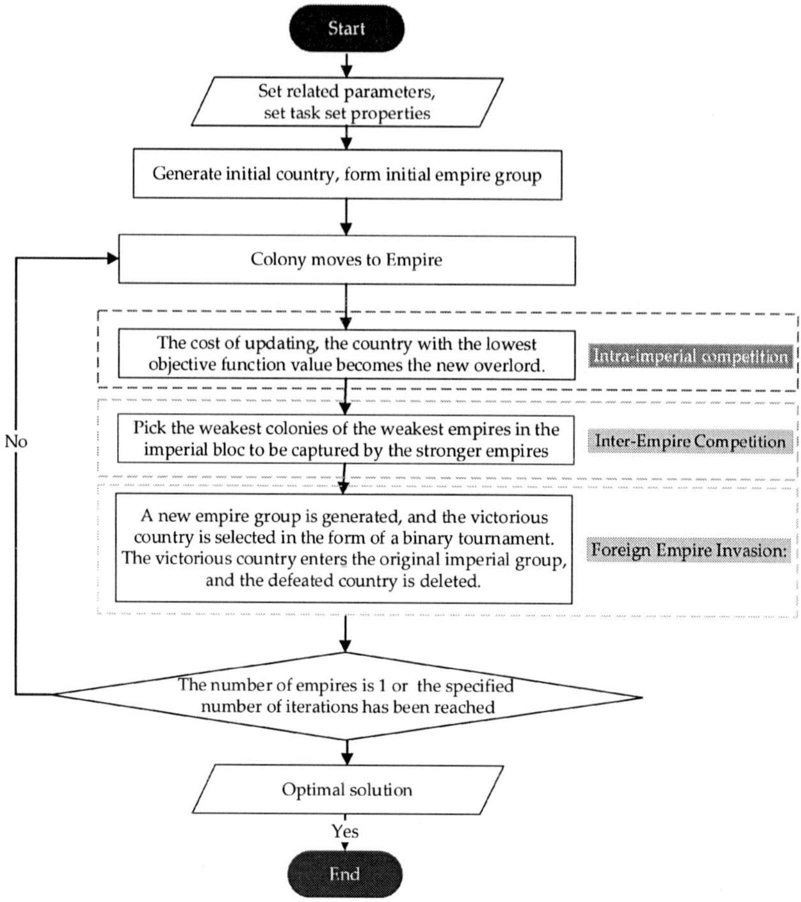

Figure 4. Improved Empire Competition Flowchart.

Encoding and Decoding

In the ICA, each segment of code represents a country, that is, a feasible solution. However, the problem of resource allocation should not only consider the processing sequence of the workpiece, but also select the corresponding processing equipment for the process. Therefore, the process sequence and the machine sequence are placed in two dimensions, and two-stage coding is used. The process code and the machine code are shown in Figure 5. The process code represents the processing sequence of each process and consists of the workpiece number. The number of occurrences of the workpiece number in the process code represents the process number of the workpiece. The first number 4 in the process code represents the first process of workpiece 4 (process O_{41}). The machine code represents the processing machine of each process, and each digit is arranged in the order from the first process of the first workpiece to the last process of the last workpiece, representing the sequence number of the optional processing machine set, the first number 2 is the second machine of the optional machine set {M5, M8} of the process processed by the machine, that is, M8. We introduce the concept of machine sets when encoding machine codes, so that no infeasible solutions are generated.

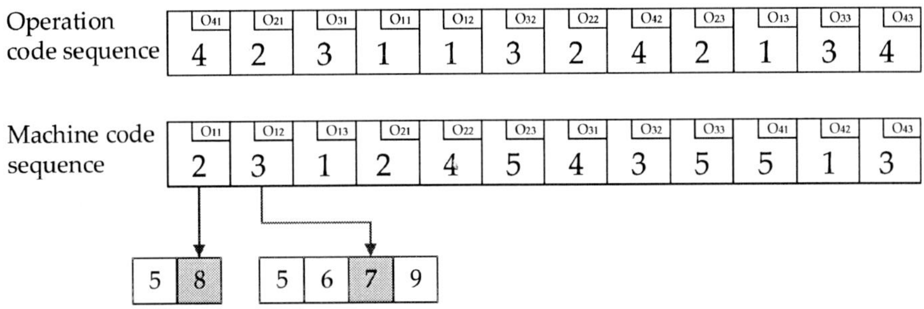

Figure 5. Coding Format of I-ICA Algorithm.

When decoding the individual country, first decode the process code from left to right, and decode it into the sequence of process processing; then decode the machine code in turn, decode it into the machine corresponding to the process, and determine the processing start of each process on the corresponding machine, and the end time.

This paper takes the minimum completion time and the lowest energy consumption as the optimization goals, taking into consideration that dynamic configuration requires faster response time and uses the index weighting method to construct the fitness function, as shown in the Formula (10). β is the penalty factor, and the value in this paper is 0.1:

$$\min\hat{E} = F_T + \beta F_C \tag{10}$$

Assimilation and Revolution

Among the initialized N countries, the country with the smallest fitness function Ê of M is selected as the imperialist state, and the remaining N-M countries are regarded as colonial countries, and are allocated to M imperial countries according to a certain probability. The imperialist countries and all their colonial countries jointly form an empire, and several empires form an imperial group. The assimilation operation is divided into two parts: process sequence assimilation and machine sequence assimilationÿÿÿ The selection part of the machine adopts the method of multi-point crossover mutation. The specific operation is as follows: randomly select r positions, replace the information of the r positions of the colonial country with the corresponding positions in the colony, and keep the rest of the position information unchanged; the process sorting part adopts. In the method of workpiece exchange, the processing part of the colony is exchanged with the processing part of the colonial country, and the processing part of the colony is updated.

The revolutionary operation is also divided into the machine selection part and the process sequence part. In the machine selection part, select a processing machine, and then select any other machine in the corresponding machine set to replace it. In the process sequence part, select two processes for location information exchange. When the colony has been assimilated and revolutionized, compare the cost of the imperialist country with all the colonies: if the cost of a colony is lower than that of the imperialist country, the colony replaces the imperialist country as the new imperialist country within the empire; otherwise, the colonial state does not change.

Imperial Rivalry and Foreign Imperial Invasions

Release the most expensive colony among the weakest empires and let other empires compete. Generally, the stronger the empire, the higher the probability of acquiring the colony. The competition process is as shown in Figure 6.

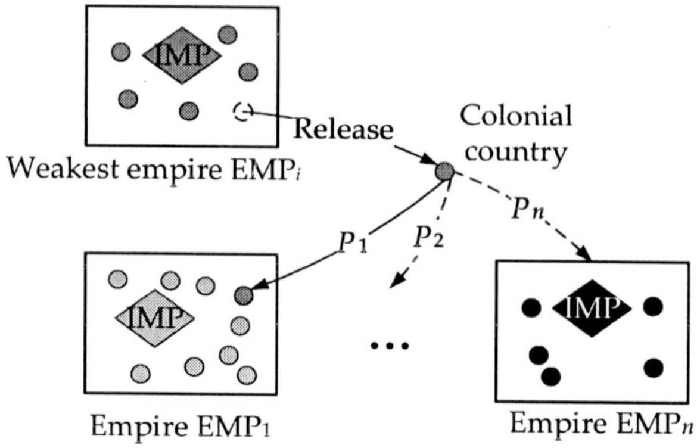

Figure 6. The process of imperial competition.

Step 1: Calculate the total cost of the empire. Empires are differentiated by their total cost value. The smaller the total cost of the empire, the stronger the empire's power. Therefore, the total cost value of each empire needs to be calculated before the competition. Its value is composed of the cost of the colony and the cost of the overlord, and the two have different influences on the empire's power. Therefore, it is necessary to construct the total cost objective function of the empire to measure its power, as shown in Equation (11).

$$TC_{emp,i} = C_{imp,i} + \alpha \times \frac{\sum_{col=1}^{\tau} C_{col,i}}{\tau}, i, \tau = 1, 2, \cdots, \tag{11}$$

where $TC_{emp,i}$ represents the total cost of the i-th empire group, $C_{imp,i}$ represents the total cost of the i-th imperial, $C_{col,i}$ represents the total cost of the i-th colony, τ represents the number of colonies owned by imperialist countries, and α is the colony impact factor, $0 < \alpha < 1$. Next, carry out normalization processing, as shown in Formula (12).

$$ETC_{emp,i} = 2 \times \max\{TC_{imp,1}, TC_{imp,2}, \cdots, TC_{imp,\tau}\} - TC_{imp,i}, i, \tau = 1, 2, \cdots, \tag{12}$$

where $ETC_{emp,i}$ denotes the normalized cost of the i-th empire group.

Step 2: Calculate the probability that each empire occupies a weak colony, as shown in Equation (13).

$$p_n = \left| ETC_{imp} \Big/ \sum_{i=1}^{\gamma} ETC_i \right| \tag{13}$$

Step 3: the strongest imperialist country gains the freed colonies.

The original algorithm only iterates in randomly generated initial countries. Considering that the initial solutions developed are not uniformly distributed in the solution space, the algorithm is prone to fall into local optimum. In this paper, referring to real society, the invasion of solid external forces will aggravate the evolution of the conflict. The surviving parties will quickly become stronger through the survival of the fittest. Based on this phenomenon, an invasion strategy of foreign imperial groups is proposed to enhance the search breadth of solutions. It improves the quality and convergence speed of the country; the intrusion process is shown in Figure 7.

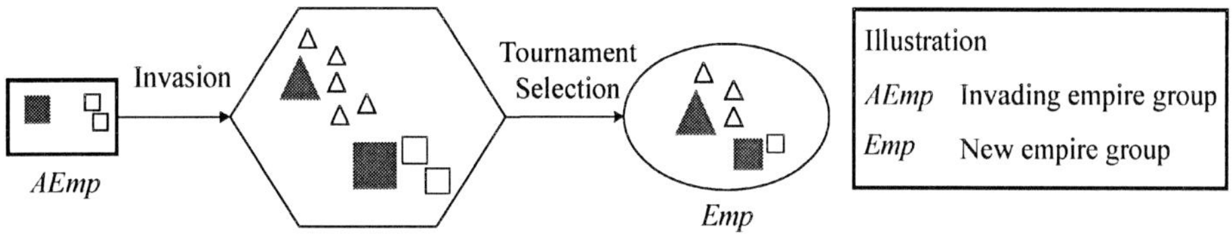

Figure 7. Intrusion process.

Stage 1: Generate a random country group to form a group of foreign invasion empire groups.

Stage 2: In the form of a binary tournament, the original empire group and the invading empire group are used to run for the victorious country.

Stage 3: The victorious nation will select outstanding colonies with the same number of colonies as the original empire to form a new empire group and enter the original empire group to compete.

Fall of the Empire and the End of the Algorithm

In the algorithm iteration process, other empires will compete for the colonies of the weakest empire in the empire group with a certain probability. When the number of colonies owned by an empire is less than or equal to the specified threshold (the threshold in this paper is zero), it means that the empire destroyed and the overlord in that empire was demoted to the colony to be competed for by other empires. As the iteration progresses, weak empires are continuously deleted, and eventually only one empire remains or, when the algorithm iterates to the specified maximum number of iterations, the algorithm terminates. The imperialist country in the most powerful empire is used as the optimal output of the algorithm.

RESULTS

This method is applicable to most discrete production plants targeting low carbon. Elevator parts have a wide range of application scenarios and are typical representatives of mechanical parts processed in a discrete job shop. Therefore, the effectiveness of the method was verified by taking the intelligent low-carbon resource allocation in the elevator parts processing job shop as an example. This is a virtual simplified model from a manufacturing company in Jiangsu Province, China, whose main products are various elevator parts, including traction machines, etc.

Data Preparation

The job shop was equipped with transfer equipment such as a mechanical arm, slide rail and roller table for the transportation, loading and unloading of materials, tooling and work in progress. By equipping various sensors, numerical control systems, industrial personal computers and other manufacturing IoT equipment, the workshop had the ability to monitor materials, equipment and other manufacturing elements in real time. The actual environment of the job shop is shown in Figure 8. The production process studied was the processing of the brake disc, output shaft, and traction wheel. The processing equipment involved includes drilling and milling center (TC-R2B), precision machine tool (BNC427C), CNC lathe (L200E-M), face turning center (LT2000EX), and machining center (LJ-650), etc. In this discrete job shop, fine-grained status data of processing equipment are collected using CNC machine tools and sensor networks, while the position of workpieces is located using RFID equipment (Alien ALR-H450). The production process can be simplified as a 9 ×× 8 discrete job shop resource optimization problem. The average processing power (kWh), average standby power (kWh), and cutting fluid consumption per unit time (ml/min) corresponding to each equipment are shown in Table 2. The values in the table are all dimensionless quantities, in which "-" indicates that the process cannot be processed on this equipment.

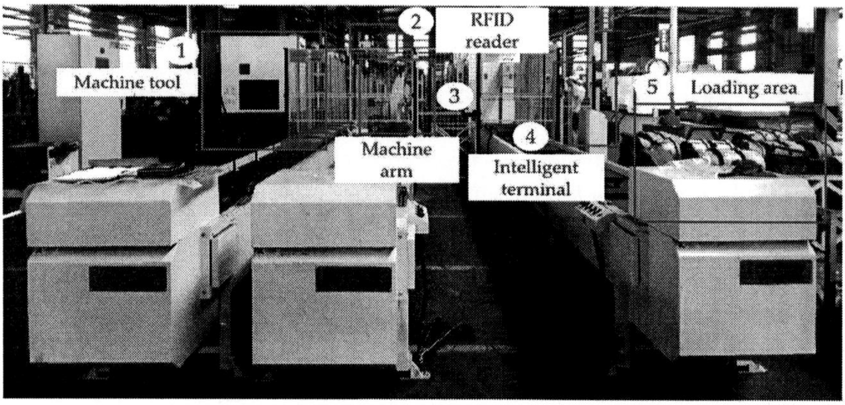

Figure 8. The actual environment of the job shop.

Table 2. Processing time and energy consumption data sheet of machines

Part	**Process**	**Machine Time/Energy Consumption**							
		M1	**M2**	**M3**	**M4**	**M5**	**M6**	**M7**	**M8**
Part 1	O_{11}	6/9.6	6/7.8	-	9/13.5		11/12.8	4/3.9	5/8.5
	O_{12}	2/15	4/4.9	-	-	7/10	2/8.4	2/12.1	7/5.7
	…	…	…	…	…	…	…	…	…
Part 2	O_{21}	9/4.4	9/8.4	3/5.2	7/7	-	5/14.6	6/9.3	7/7.4
	O_{22}	5/10.9	7/15.2	8/11	-	-	5/8.4	3/16.4	9/7.2
	…	…	…	…	…	…	…	…	…
Part 3	O_{31}	9/12				6/6.5	10/5.4	10/11.1	
	O_{32}	10/4.7	9/12.9	7/16.3	-	-	9/10.2	5/11	2/5.2
	…	…	…	…	…	…	…	…	…
Part 4	O_{41}	8/13.9	-	3/12.7	7/10.2	6/6.5	-	10/9.4	5/15.1
	O_{42}	-	-	4/14.6	3/5.7	4/16.4	-	-	-
	…	…	…	…	…	…	…	…	…

Part 5	O_{51}	-	11/12.6	4/3.4	8/8.7	6/10.2	6/9.9	11/13	9/7.9
	O_{52}	5/7.7	-	11/8.6	6/11.8	5/13.7	-	9/9.8	10/9.6
	...	...	...	...	...	...	...	...	...
Part 6	O_{61}	6/7.1	4/8.9	10/11.2	-	7/7.9	11/14.9	10/8.2	7/13.5
	O_{62}	5/5.6	8/7.7	-	-	-	7/8.7	8/13.7	-
	...	...	...	...	...	...	...	...	...
Part 7	O_{71}	10/2.2	7/7.8	7/13.6	-	-	9/10.1	-	-
	O_{72}	9/15.2	6/11.8	-	6/14.3	11/8.2	-	7/13.8	4/15
	...	...	...	...	...	...	...	...	...
Part 8	O_{81}	7/8	-	-	4/10.3	-	9/15.1	-	-
	O_{82}	6/12.5	5/10.8	-	-	10/13.5	9/14.5	4/5.9	9/11
	...	...	...	...	...	...	...	...	...
Part 9	O_{91}	8/11.1	9/12	8/15.2	-	4/6.8	-	6/7.3	-
	O_{92}	-	4/10.4	9/13.9	-	5/12.3	7/15.4	6/13.2	8/13.5
	...	...	...	...	...	...	...	...	...
P_{id}	-	1.2	2.3	3.5	3.6	3.7	1.6	1.8	2.9
r_k	-	11.8	6.1	5.6	6.5	5.6	7.1	5.0	11.6

Algorithm Verification

Performance Comparison of the Proposed Method with Other Multi-Objective Optimization Methods

The production task sets PTS1-PTS9 of different scales shown in Table 3 were used to compare I-ICA with traditional ICA and the current relatively advanced non-dominated genetic algorithm NSGA-III. The above algorithm was implemented using MATLAB R2016a programming. The operating environment of the test computer was the Windows10 operating system, the CPU frequency was 1.90 GHz, 2.11 GHz, and the memory was 16 GB. Numerical simulation experiments were carried out under the same conditions. The parameters of each algorithm are shown in Table 4:

Table 3. Production task sets at different levels

Small Scale		**Middle Scale**		**BIG SCALE**	
PTS1	[P1,P5,P8]	PTS4	[P1,P4,P5,P7,P8,P9]	PTS7	[P2,P3,P4,P6,P7,P8,P9,P10,P11]
PTS2	[P2,P3,P10]	PTS5	[P2,P3,P4,P5,P6,P10]	PTS8	[P1,P2,P3,P5,P7,P8,P9,P10,P11]
PTS3	[P4,P6,P9]	PTS6	[P1,P3,P6,P8,P10,P11]	PTS9	[P1,P2,P3,P4,P5,P6,P7,P8,P9]

Table 4. Algorithm parameter details

Algorithm	**Parameter Settings**
I-ICA	Revolution Prob: 0.3, Assimilation Prob: 0.7, Invasion Prob: 0.29
NSGA-II	The crossover rate is 0.9 and the mutation rate is 0.1
NSGA-III	The crossover rate is 0.9 and the mutation rate is 0.1

Each algorithm ran 10 times independently to solve nine production task sets and calculates the average completion time value and carbon emissions. According to the relevant literature, η1 = 0.7478 $kgCO_2/kWh$, and η2 = 29.6 $kgCO_2/L$. The statistical results are shown in Table 5. Through analysis, it can be found that there is little difference between the optimal solutions obtained by the ICA algorithm and the NSGA-III algorithm. However, the optimal values obtained by the former were more concentrated on multiple targets, indicating that the algorithm is effective for multiple targets. The uniformity of the objective solution was better. The optimal values and average values of all indicators obtained by the I-ICA were superior to the ICA and the NSGA-III, indicating that the I-ICA algorithm has better local and global search capabilities. The bolded values in the table were better. When solving small-scale problems, NSGA-III obtains three better values, ICA obtains two better values, and I-ICA obtains five better values. When solving large-scale problems, the values obtained by I-ICA were all the better than that of NSGA-III and ICA.

Table 5. Algorithm performance comparison table

T a s k Set	NSGA-III		ICA			I-ICA		
	F_C/kg	**F_T/min**	**F_C/kg**	**F_T/min**	$\hat{E}$	**F_C/kg**	**$F_{.T.}$/min**	$\hat{E}$
PTS1	**7.09**	21	10.97	21	22.10	**7.28**	21	21.73
PTS2	8.01	**20**	**7.58**	**20**	20.96	**7.43**	**20**	20.74
PTS3	**7.64**	21	9.82	21	21.98	**6.27**	**19**	19.63
PTS4	25.72	**39**	27.82	40	42.78	**22.93**	**37**	39.29
PTS5	**22.46**	40	26.88	40	42.69	**21.26**	**35**	37.13
PTS6	**20.24**	40	**24.03**	**39**	41.40	**18.93**	**35**	36.89
PTS7	40.51	57	37.24	59	62.72	**29.2**	**48**	50.92
PTS8	40.97	58	40.51	66	70.05	**31.5**	**52**	55.15
PTS9	39.04	56	40.15	64	68.02	**27.6**	**46**	48.76
Average	10.71	25.8	10.86	25.9	-	10.66	25.3	-

In contrast to the single-objective problem, evaluating the multi-objective situation cannot only stop at comparing the values of each optimization objective function, but also needs to consider the spatial distribution of the solution. Therefore, the spacing and H.V. indexes are selected to evaluate different aspects of the algorithm performance. In particular, since the ICA algorithm normalizes multiple targets through a weighting method, the optimal solution within a specific range is selected to form a solution set for analysis.

The spacing index can reflect the uniformity of the individual distribution in the non-dominated solution set, which is specifically defined as follows:

$$Spacing = \sqrt{\frac{1}{N-1}\sum_{l=1}^{N}(\bar{d}-d_l)^2} \tag{14}$$

where d_l is the shortest distance from individual l to other individuals, $\bar{d}$ is the average value of all dl, and N is the solution set size. The lower the index value, the better the distribution and diversity of individuals in the solution set. The value of 0 means that all individuals are equally spaced. The H.V. index was used to measure the volume of a target space, which can comprehensively reflect the convergence and diversity of the algorithm. The specific definition is as follows:

$$HV = \delta(\cup_{l=1}^{N} v_l) \tag{15}$$

where δ represents the Lebesgue measure, which is used to measure the volume, N is the size of the non-dominated solution set, and v_l represents the hypervolume formed by the reference point and the l-th individual in the solution set. The reference point is to be dominated by all individuals in the non-dominated solution set. In this paper, the point corresponding to the maximum value of each optimization objective function value is selected as the reference point in the H.V. index.

Figure 9 shows the comparison box plot of the algorithm spacing index. It can be seen that the spacing value of the I-ICA is the lowest, and the gap with the other two algorithms increases with the increase of the solution scale, indicating the uniformity of the algorithm solution. Diversity is better than the two algorithms and has more advantages in solving large-scale problems. In addition, the NSGA-III algorithm's box is more comprehensive, meaning that the data volatility was relatively high and the data stability was rather poor. Figure 10 is a box plot of the algorithm H.V. index comparison, from which it can be seen that the H.V. values of the I-ICA algorithm are the highest, indicating that the algorithm's overall performance was better than the other two algorithms. As the scale of the problem increased, although the algorithm's advantages were weakened, the box remains within a narrow range, indicating that the algorithm's stability was better than the ICA and NSGA-III algorithms.

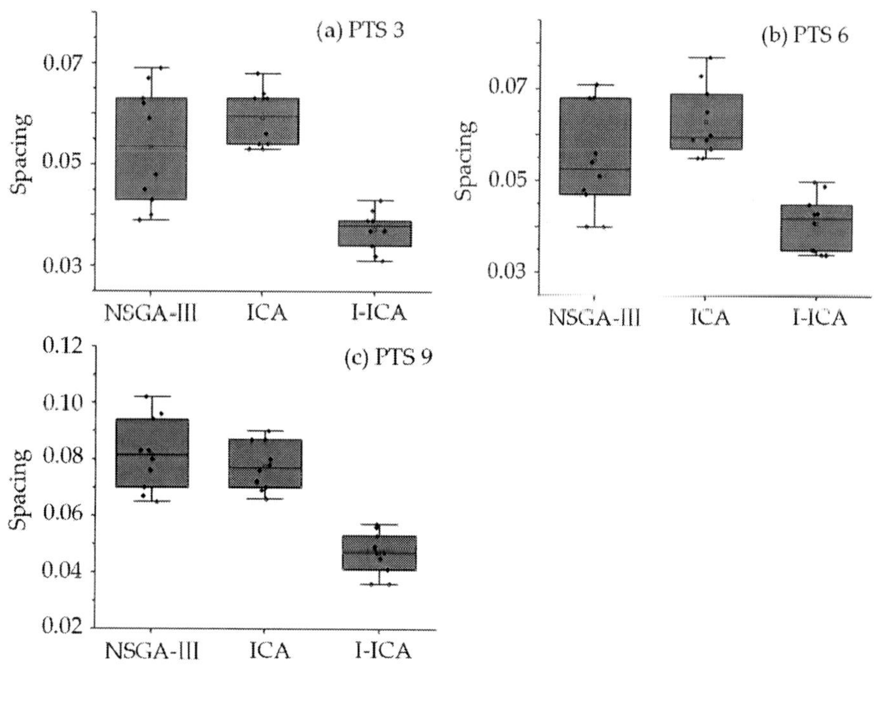

Figure 9. Algorithm Spacing Indicator Comparison Box Plot.

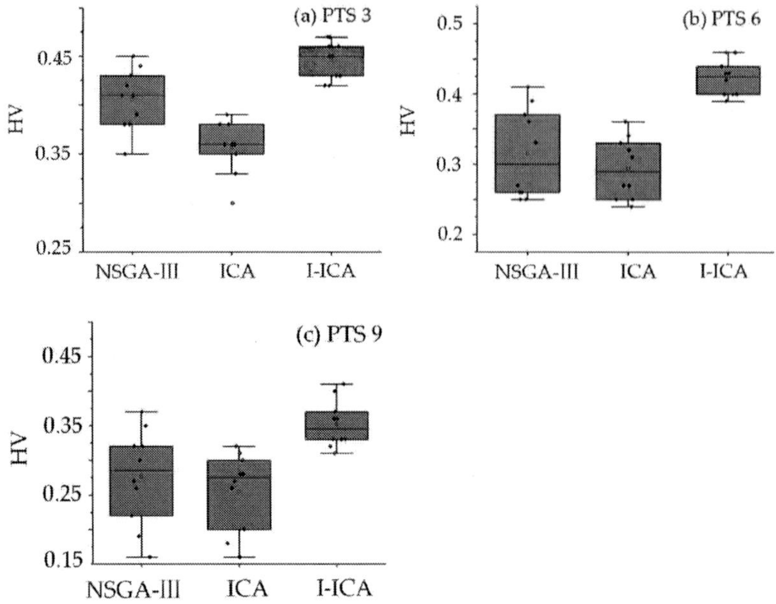

Figure 10. Box plot of algorithm HV index comparison.

On the whole, the upper and lower limits of the box plot of the algorithm in this paper were lower, the overall distribution was more concentrated, and it was closer to the optimal value. It shows that in the comparison experiment, the solution set obtained by the I-ICA algorithm has little difference between the spacing index and the H.V. index. In other words, the proposed algorithm is better than the comparison algorithm in terms of convergence, uniformity and diversity.

Validation of the Proposed Method under Disturbance

In uncertain disturbances, machine failures occur frequently and significantly impact the production process. Therefore, this paper selected the scene of machine failures to verify the effectiveness of the proposed method in solving the problem of dynamic resource allocation in a flexible job shop. The real-time state-driven low-carbon resource allocation strategy proposed in this paper was compared with the results of traditional shift-right scheduling and ADSM [9] to verify its effectiveness. The original configuration scheme remained unchanged in the specific strategy of right-shift processing. The workpiece process directly affected and the available time of the machine tool then directly delayed the time it takes to deal with the exception, and the indirectly affected process delayed the corresponding time according to the constraints of the process and the machine tool.

First, the I-ICA algorithm was called to configure the production tasks mentioned above without considering the abnormality of the job shop, and the initial configuration scheme was obtained. Figure 11 shows the Gantt chart of the iterative optimal solution. The same color represents the same workpiece. The numbers on the color block are expressed as follows: the first number is the workpiece number, and the last two digits represent the process number, such as '1-1' for the first process of workpiece 1, '4-2' Indicates the second process of workpiece 4. Machine 3 failed at 8:28, and the fault repair time was 8:44. Perform right-shift processing on all initial scheduling schemes to obtain the right-shift configuration scheme, as shown in Figure 12. Reconfigure the manufacturing resources after the machine failure through method ADSM, and obtain the configuration scheme as shown in Figure 13. Perform dynamic resource allocation on all initial scheduling schemes to obtain the reconfiguration scheme, as shown in Figure 14.

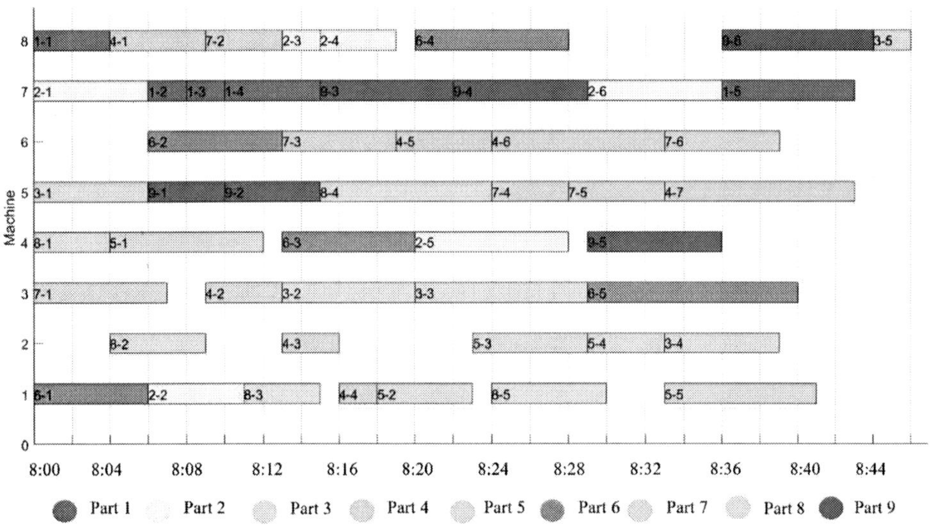

Figure 11. Initial Resource Configuration Gantt Chart.

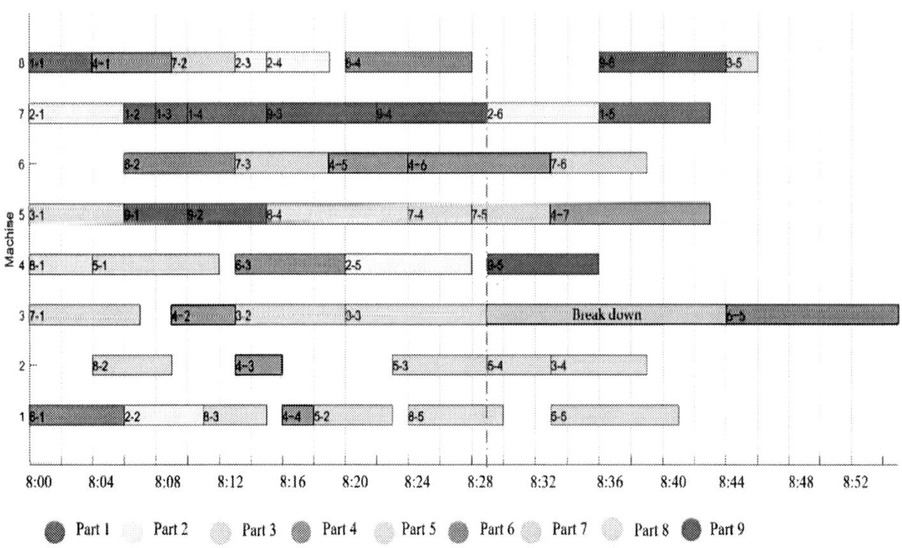

Figure 12. Gantt chart of resource configuration after right-shift processing.

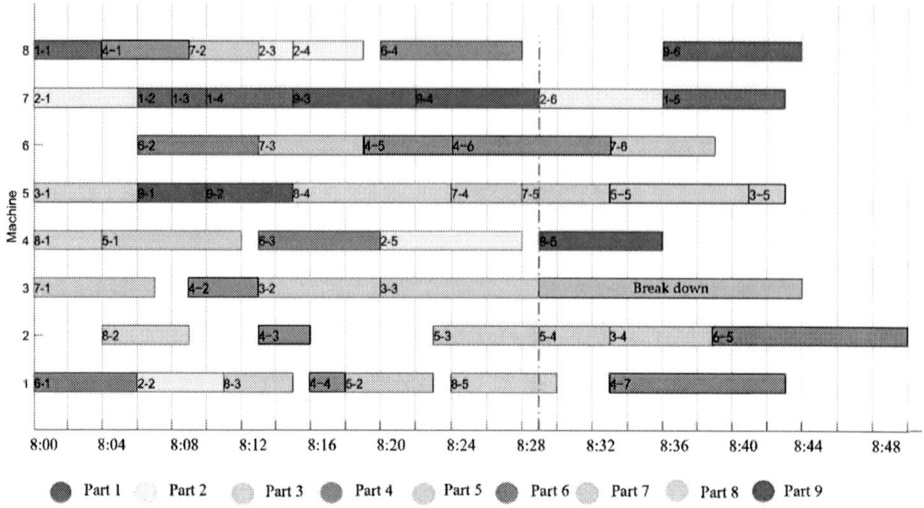

Figure 13. Gantt chart of resource configuration using ADSM.

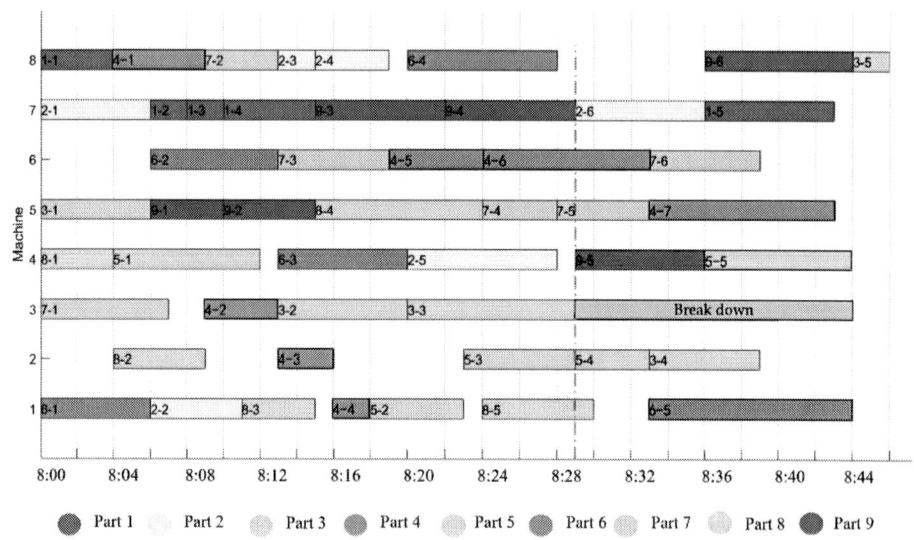

Figure 14. Gantt chart of resource configuration driven by real-time state of manufacturing resources.

The comparison shows that since the traditional model does not consider the real-time state of manufacturing resources, processing can only be performed after the abnormality is resolved when an abnormal situation occurs. The model in this paper used manufacturing resources as constraints through real-time state monitoring so that the processes affected could be reasonably adjusted. For example, process 5 of the workpiece 6 on the faulty machine 3 was arranged on other machines for processing, and the final result was obtained. Compared with the traditional strategy, the scheduling scheme reduced the maximum completion time and carbon emissions by 16.36% and 9.36%, respectively. Compared with the ADSM method, the maximum completion time and carbon emissions were reduced by 8% and 5.27%, respectively.

Discussion

In terms of algorithm performance, without considering the machine state transition, it can be seen from Table 4 that the I-ICA can comprehensively consider the processing time and processing energy consumption. When the completion time is short, the carbon emission is relatively tiny. The mean and optimal value of the genetic algorithm are larger than those of the proposed method, so the latter runs stably and has an excellent solution. With the increase in the problem size, the advantages are more prominent. In addition, the method can couple the two objectives through the fitness function so that they both approach the optimal solution. Combined with the comparison results of spacing and H.V. indicators, it can be seen that the proposed algorithm performs better in the spatial distribution, diversity and convergence of the solution. The main reasons for this are as follows:

- The traditional NSGA-III algorithm has limitations in terms of initial population quality, crossover mutation rate, retention strategy, etc., making the algorithm search effect poor and prone to falling into local optimum.
- The improved external empire invasion strategy optimizes the multiple objectives of the initial empire collaboratively, preventing the empire from moving to a certain target direction so that the initial empire is to a certain extent better than the comparison algorithm in all target dimensions, in speeding up the algorithm convergence;
- Regarding solution speed, NSGA-III is a single-structure algorithm, and ICA and I-ICA are multi-structure algorithms. The distribution of the latter in the solution space is more uniform, making the multi-structure algorithm closer to the optimal solution. When the scale of the problem is small, the distance between the initial solution and the optimal solution is relatively small, and the difference between the algorithms of the two structures is not obvious. However, the advantages of multi-structure algorithms gradually become more prominent as the problem scale increases.

In addition, when the machine state changes, compared with the right-shift strategy and ADSM method, the proposed dynamic allocation strategy can detect the sudden change of the machine state in time and perform low-carbon reconfiguration to respond to the sudden change of the machine state to the original configuration. The scheme's impact can be more comprehensively considered by examining the processing time and energy consumption, and the optimal solution can be found. This proves the necessity and importance of intelligent monitoring and diagnosing machine states. In addition, the low-carbon resource allocation, considering the uncertainty of machine states, has excellent practical application value.

CONCLUSIONS

This paper introduces a low-carbon resource allocation method for discrete manufacturing job shop driven by the real-time status of manufacturing resources. Considering the two objectives of job shop carbon emissions and maximum completion time, a low-carbon resource allocation model for discrete manufacturing job shop was established, and an improved multi-objective I-ICA algorithm was proposed to solve the model. Finally, the algorithm performance comparison and example verification proved that the proposed method runs stably, performs well and has great practical value. The main contributions of this paper are as follows:

(1) The framework of discrete job shop resource dynamic configuration in the IoT environment is proposed, and the real-time data collection and encapsulation modeling of manufacturing resource are realized;

(2) A calculation model of the dynamic allocation threshold of manufacturing resources based on delivery date is established and a dynamic allocation mechanism of manufacturing resources based on allocation threshold is proposed;

(3) The hybrid evolutionary algorithm was improved in order to solve the resource optimization allocation model. A new cost normalization formula was proposed to solve the problem of losing some colonial countries during initialization; the intrusion mechanism is proposed to help the algorithm function outside of the local optimal solution, which improves the speed and quality of the algorithm.

With the increasingly severe environmental situation, enterprises should shoulder the responsibility of environmental protection, improve their awareness of environmental protection, and put reducing carbon emissions in the production process in an important position while pursuing benefits. At the same time, various countries have proposed different carbon emission limitation measures. In the future, manufacturing enterprises in various countries will actively or passively enter the carbon emission quota market and undertake the task of quantifying and reducing carbon emissions. It is found that the proposed method can be used to guide the manufacturing resource allocation process, and both the completion time and energy consumption goals can be considered. In addition, the framework proposed in this paper can provide reference for the real-time carbon emission perception quantification of a manufacturing job shop.

In future research, the carbon emission tooling model (such as cutting tools, etc.) can be established and added to the objective function. In addition, the threshold value of the machine tool switch can be studied, and the reasonable operation mode of the machine tool can be explored to further reduce the energy consumption in the manufacturing process. A dynamic resource allocation evaluation system can be established to guide the allocation process, including the stability of the allocation scheme and the allocation cost.

AUTHOR CONTRIBUTIONS

Conceptualization, X.S.; methodology, X.S. and W.D.; software, J.L.; validation, C.C.; formal analysis, W.D. and C.C.; investigation, J.L. and X.S.; resources, W.J.; data curation, X.S.; writing—original draft preparation, X.S.; writing—review and editing, W.J.; funding acquisition, W.J. All authors have read and agreed to the published version of the manuscript.

ACKNOWLEDGMENTS

This work was supported by the Major Scientific and Technological Innovation Project of Shandong Province, grant number (2019JZZY020111).

REFERENCES

1. Su, X.; Lu, J.; Chen, C.; Yu, J.; Ji, W. Dynamic Bottleneck Identification of Manufacturing Resources in Complex Manufacturing System. Appl. Sci. 2022, 12, 4195.

2. Sun, K.; Xiao, H.; Liu, S.; You, S.; Yang, F.; Dong, Y.; Wang, W.; Liu, Y. A review of clean electricity policies—From countries to utilities. Sustainability 2020, 12, 7946.
3. Feng, Y.; Gao, Y.; Tian, G.; Li, Z.; Hu, H.; Zheng, H. Flexible process planning and end-of-life decision-making for product recovery optimization based on hybrid disassembly. IEEE Trans. Autom. Sci. Eng. 2018, 16, 311–326.
4. Dos Santos, P.H.; Neves, S.M.; Sant Anna, D.O.; de Oliveira, C.H.; Carvalho, H.D. The analytic hierarchy process supporting decision making for sustainable development: An overview of applications. J. Clean. Prod. 2019, 212, 119–138.
5. Wang, H.; Wang, X.; Zhang, X.; Liu, G.; Chen, W.; Chen, S.; Du, T.; Shi, L. The coupling between material footprint and economic growth in the "Belt and Road" countries. J. Clean. Prod. 2022, 359, 132110.
6. Zhang, C.; Wang, Z.; Ding, K.; Chan, F.T.; Ji, W. An energy-aware cyber physical system for energy Big data analysis and recessive production anomalies detection in discrete manufacturing workshops. Int. J. Prod. Res. 2020, 58, 7059–7077.
7. Liang, Y.; Cai, W.; Ma, M. Carbon dioxide intensity and income level in the Chinese megacities' residential building sector: Decomposition and decoupling analyses. Sci. Total Environ. 2019, 677, 315–327.
8. Xiao, H.; Sun, K.; Pan, J.; Li, Y.; Liu, Y. Review of hybrid HVDC systems combining line communicated converter and voltage source converter. Int. J. Electr. Power 2021, 129, 106713.
9. Qiu, Y.; Ji, W.; Zhang, C. A hybrid machine learning and population knowledge mining method to minimize makespan and total tardiness of multi-variety products. Appl. Sci. 2019, 9, 5286.
10. Zhang, G.; Hu, Y.; Sun, J.; Zhang, W. An improved genetic algorithm for the flexible job shop scheduling problem with multiple time constraints. Swarm Evol. Comput. 2020, 54, 100664.
11. Deng, J.; Wang, L. A competitive memetic algorithm for multi-objective distributed permutation flow shop scheduling problem. Swarm Evol. Comput. 2017, 32, 121–131.
12. Shao, Z.; Pi, D.; Shao, W. A multi-objective discrete invasive weed optimization for multi-objective blocking flow-shop scheduling problem. Expert Syst. Appl. 2018, 113, 77–99.
13. Sun, K.; Qiu, W.; Dong, Y.; Zhang, C.; Yin, H.; Yao, W.; Liu, Y. WAMS-based HVDC Damping Control for Cyber Attack Defense. IEEE Trans. Autom. Sci. Eng. 2022. Early Access.
14. Sun, K.; Qiu, W.; Yao, W.; You, S.; Yin, H.; Liu, Y. Frequency injection based HVDC attack-defense control via squeeze-excitation double CNN. IEEE Trans. Autom. Sci. Eng. 2021, 36, 5305–5316.
15. Bhowmik, S.; Paul, A.; Panua, R.; Ghosh, S.K.; Debroy, D. Artificial intelligence based gene expression programming (GEP) model prediction of Diesel engine performances and exhaust emissions under Diesosenol fuel strategies. Fuel 2019, 235, 317–325.
16. Safarzadeh, H.; Niaki, S.T.A. Bi-objective green scheduling in uniform parallel machine environments. J. Clean. Prod. 2019, 217, 559–572.
17. Sun, K.; Li, K.; Zhang, Z.; Liang, Y.; Liu, Z.; Lee, W. An integration planning for renewable energies, hydrogen plant and logistics center in the suburban power grid. IEEE Trans. Ind. Appl. 2021, 58, 2771–2779.
18. Zhang, B.; Pan, Q.; Gao, L.; Li, X.; Meng, L.; Peng, K. A multiobjective evolutionary algorithm based on decomposition for hybrid flowshop green scheduling problem. Comput. Ind. Eng. 2019, 136, 325–344.
19. Li, Y.; Pan, Q.; Gao, K.; Tasgetiren, M.F.; Zhang, B.; Li, J. A green scheduling algorithm for the distributed flowshop problem. Appl. Soft Comput. 2021, 109, 107526.
20. Rifai, A.P.; Mara, S.T.W.; Sudiarso, A. Multi-objective distributed reentrant permutation flow shop scheduling with sequence-dependent setup time. Expert Syst. Appl. 2021, 183, 115339.

21. Feng, Y.; Hong, Z.; Li, Z.; Zheng, H.; Tan, J. Integrated intelligent green scheduling of sustainable flexible workshop with edge computing considering uncertain machine state. J. Clean. Prod. 2020, 246, 119070.

22. Nouiri, M.; Bekrar, A.; Trentesaux, D. An energy-efficient scheduling and rescheduling method for production and logistics systems. Int. J. Prod. Res. 2020, 58, 3263–3283.

23. Sun, K.; Xiao, H.; Pan, J.; Liu, Y. VSC-HVDC interties for urban power grid enhancement. IEEE Trans. Autom. Sci. Eng. 2021, 36, 4745–4753.

24. Wang, H.; Jiang, Z.; Wang, Y.; Zhang, H.; Wang, Y. A two-stage optimization method for energy-saving flexible job-shop scheduling based on energy dynamic characterization. J. Clean. Prod. 2018, 188, 575–588.

25. Liu, Z.; Guo, S.; Wang, L. Integrated green scheduling optimization of flexible job shop and crane transportation considering comprehensive energy consumption. J. Clean. Prod. 2019, 211, 765–786.

26. Salimifard, K.; Li, J.; Mohammadi, D.; Moghdani, R. A multi objective volleyball premier league algorithm for green scheduling identical parallel machines with splitting jobs. Appl. Intell. 2021, 51, 4143–4161.

27. Wu, X.; Sun, Y. A green scheduling algorithm for flexible job shop with energy-saving measures. J. Clean. Prod. 2018, 172, 3249–3264.

28. Lei, D.; Li, M.; Wang, L. A two-phase meta-heuristic for multiobjective flexible job shop scheduling problem with total energy consumption threshold. IEEE Trans. Cybern. 2018, 49, 1097–1109.

29. Hong, Z.; Feng, Y.; Li, Z.; Wang, Y.; Zheng, H.; Li, Z.; Tan, J. An integrated approach for multi-objective optimisation and MCDM of energy internet under uncertainty. Future Gener. Comput. Syst. 2019, 97, 90–104.

30. Zhao, J.; Mili, L. A framework for robust hybrid state estimation with unknown measurement noise statistics. IEEE Trans. Ind. Inform. 2017, 14, 1866–1875.

31. Zhang, Y.; Wang, J.; Liu, Y. Game theory based real-time multi-objective flexible job shop scheduling considering environmental impact. J. Clean. Prod. 2017, 167, 665–679.

32. Chen, X.; Li, C.; Tang, Y.; Xiao, Q. An Internet of Things based energy efficiency monitoring and management system for machining workshop. J. Clean. Prod. 2018, 199, 957–968.

33. Singh, A.; Kumari, S.; Malekpoor, H.; Mishra, N. Big data cloud computing framework for low carbon supplier selection in the beef supply chain. J. Clean. Prod. 2018, 202, 139–149.

34. Tao, F.; Qi, Q.; Liu, A.; Kusiak, A. Data-driven smart manufacturing. J. Manuf. Syst. 2018, 48, 157–169.

35. Dong, Y.; Ma, J.; Wang, S.; Liu, T.; Chen, X.; Huang, H. An Accurate Small Signal Dynamic Model for LCC-HVDC. IEEE Trans. Appl. Supercon. 2021, 31, 0603606.

36. Qiu, Y.; Sawhney, R.; Zhang, C.; Chen, S.; Zhang, T.; Lisar, V.G.; Jiang, K.; Ji, W. Data mining—Based disturbances prediction for job shop scheduling. Adv. Mech. Eng. 2019, 11, 753307422.

37. Singh, R.; Bhanot, N. An integrated DEMATEL-MMDE-ISM based approach for analysing the barriers of IoT implementation in the manufacturing industry. Int. J. Prod. Res. 2020, 58, 2454–2476.

38. Zhang, C.; Jiang, P. RFID-driven energy-efficient control approach of CNC machine tools using deep belief networks. IEEE Trans. Autom. Sci. Eng. 2019, 17, 129–141.

39. Zhang, C.; Jiang, P. Sustainability Evaluation of Process Planning for Single CNC Machine Tool under the Consideration of Energy-Efficient Control Strategies Using Random Forests. Sustainability 2019, 11, 3060.

40. Syafrudin, M.; Alfian, G.; Fitriyani, N.L.; Rhee, J. Performance analysis of IoT-based sensor, big data processing, and machine learning model for real-time monitoring system in automotive manufacturing. Sensors 2018, 18, 2946.

41. Trakadas, P.; Simoens, P.; Gkonis, P.; Sarakis, L.; Angelopoulos, A.; Ramallo-González, A.P.; Skarmeta, A.; Trochoutsos, C.; Calvo, D.; Pariente, T. An artificial intelligence-based collaboration approach in industrial iot manufacturing: Key concepts, architectural extensions and potential applications. Sensors 2020, 20, 5480.

42. Ayvaz, S.; Alpay, K. Predictive maintenance system for production lines in manufacturing: A machine learning approach using IoT data in real-time. Expert. Syst. Appl. 2021, 173, 114598.

5

Micromachining of Advanced Materials

Wayne N.P. Hung[1] and Mike Corliss[2]

[1]Texas A&M University, College Station, Texas, USA

[2]KGSBO, Katy, Texas, USA

ABSTRACT

Market needs often require miniaturized products for portability, size/weight reduction while increasing product capacity. Utilizing additive manufacturing to achieve a complex and functional metallic part has attracted considerable interests in both industry and academia. However, the resulted rough surfaces and low tolerances of as-printed parts require additional steps for microstructure modification, physical and mechanical properties enhancement, and improvement of dimensional/form/surface to meet engineering specifications. Micromachining can (i) produce miniature components or microfeatures on a larger component, and (ii) enhance the quality of additively manufactured metallic components. This chapter suggests the necessary requirements for successful micromachining and cites the research studies on micromachining of metallic materials fabricated by either traditional route or additive technique. Micromachining by nontraditional techniques—e.g., ion/electron beam machining—are beyond the scope of this chapter. The chapter is organized as following: Introduction; Requirement for successful micromachining: cutting tools, tool coating, machine tools, tool offset measuring methods, minimum quantity lubrication, and size effect; Effect of materials: material defects, ductile regime machining, crystalline orientation, residual stress, and microstructure; Micromachining: research works from literature, process monitoring, and process parameters; Micromilling; Microdrilling; Ultraprecision turning; Summary; and References.

Keywords: *Micromilling, Microdrilling, Ultraprecision turning, Minimum quantity lubrication, Additive manufacturing*

INTRODUCTION

Recent technological advancement and market need for product miniaturization demand suitable processes to mass produce three-dimensional (3D) microcomponents. Although microelectronic manufacturing techniques can produce two-dimensional (2D) microdevices using silicon and other semiconducting materials, silicon is neither robust enough for demanding engineering applications nor biocompatible for biomedical applications. Biocompatible materials and superalloys are traditionally fabricated in bulk quantity by forging, casting, or extrusion. The recent explosion of additive manufacturing innovations has led to several revolutionary fabrication methods of engineering devices. Powder bed fusion techniques using energy beams or binding polymers to consolidate powders in sequential layers are commonly used for metals. As in casting and welding, fabrication of a complex product by fusing re-solidified layers would introduce point, line, and volume defects in the part: dislocation entanglement, porosity, solidification shrinkage, microcrack, significant residual stress, anisotropy, rough surface finish, distortion, and undesirable microstructure are among key issues for metallic components fabricated by additively manufacturing route.

Micromachining techniques can be applied to successfully fabricate engineering components—either in meso or micro scales—from robust or biocompatible bulk materials. Micromachining is also among the key post processing techniques to enhance the quality of additively built metallic components [1, 2, 3]. This book chapter provides necessary requirements for micromachining, and cites research studies on micromachining of metallic materials fabricated by traditional or additive techniques.

REQUIREMENT FOR SUCCESSFUL MICROMACHINING

To obtain the same surface speed as in macromachining, a machine tool must:

- Be capable to rotate a workpiece or tool at high rotation speeds at 25,000 rpm or above,
- Control spindle runout to submicron level,
- Have very robust mechanical and thermal structure that does not affect by vibration or thermal drift, and
- Have high resolution tool positioning and feeding mechanisms.

Success of micromachining depends on tool quality and precision of a machine tool. Machine spindle runout, tool concentricity and tool positioning accuracy must be in the neighborhood of 1/100 of a microtool diameter or less for successful operation. Tolerance stack up for spindle runout, tool eccentricity, and wandering of a microtool cause cyclic bending of a tool that leads to a catastrophic failure. At a low rotating speed, the displacement of a spindle can be monitored with a sensitive mechanical indicator. However, this option is not applicable for machines that operates at few thousands rpm or above. Other non-contact techniques using capacitance, magnetism, or light would be more appropriate. A laser beam can be focused on a rotating precision plug gage. The spindle displacement is then recorded on a computer for further analysis and is displayed in either frequency or time domain. Commercial laser systems can provide displacement reading to ±10 nm resolution.

Size Effect

The parameters for machining and tooling that are successfully applied in macromachining do not necessarily scale down linearly for micromachining. It is relatively easy to have a rigid turning or facing microtool, but it would require careful planning to maintain rigidity of a high aspect ratio micromill or a microdrill. Geometries of macroscale and microscale drilling/milling tools are the same: tool diameter, number of cutting flutes, point included angle for microdrill, helix angle, web thickness, clearance angle, flute length, shank diameter, and overall length. A careful selection of microtools must consider the intended machined features and highest possible tool stiffness. The two most important geometries that affect the microtool stiffness are the tool diameter and flute length assuming the number of flutes have been chosen. It can be shown that the torsional stiffness of a mill/drill is proportional to (tool diameter)^4 and (flute length)$^{-2}$. For a specific mill/drill tool dimension, we must adjust the milling/drilling strategy accordingly to avoid tool breakage.

If we select a drill diameter of 0.2 mm instead of 0.5 mm, then such 60% reduction of diameter will result in a reduction in torsional stiffness ΔE of:

$$\Delta E = \frac{(D_2)^4 - (D_1)^4}{(D_1)^4} = \frac{0.2^4 - 0.5^4}{0.5^4} = -97\% \tag{1}$$

Similarly, if we choose the flute length of 1.2 mm instead of 1.0 mm, this 20% change in flute length will lead to a decrease in torsional stiffness ΔE of:

$$\Delta E = \frac{(L_2)^{-2} - (L_1)^{-2}}{(L_1)^{-2}} = \frac{1.2^{-2} - 1.0^{-2}}{1.0^{-2}} = -30\% \tag{2}$$

Machining parameters that are successfully used in macromachining are not necessarily applicable for micromachining. A published literature recommends milling speed of 178 m/min and chip load of 0.1 mm/tooth for end milling 316L stainless steel using uncoated carbide tool.[1]

- Macromachining: to have the said surface speed for an Ø25.4 mm end mill, the required spindle speed is:

$$N = \frac{V}{\pi D} = \frac{178\ (\text{m/min})}{\pi(\text{rad/rev}) \times 25.4\ (\text{mm})} \times 1000\ (\text{mm/m}) = 2230\ \text{rpm} \tag{3}$$

- Micromachining: using the same surface speed for an Ø0.1 mm micromill, the new spindle speed is:

$$N = \frac{V}{\pi D} = \frac{178\ (\text{m/min})}{\pi(\text{rad/rev}) \times 0.1\ (\text{mm})} \times 1000\ (\text{mm/m}) = 555,600\ \text{rpm} \tag{4}$$

A machine tool with spindle speed exceeding 500,000 rpm is rare or simply not commercially available at this time. Applying the recommended macro chip load of 0.1 mm/tooth for an Ø0.1 mm micromill would break the fragile tool since the feed/tooth is as large as the microtool diameter.

Tool Sharpness

The tool edge radius is critical in micromachining. If the depth of cut (or chip load) is too shallow, the tool simply plows the material and pushes it away elastically. This elastic material layer just springs back after the tool passing. If the depth of cut (or chip load) is substantial, then a chip is formed and a new machined surface is generated. Typical fine grain carbide tools are first sintered from submicron carbide particles in a cobalt matrix, and then ground and lapped to final geometry. Optimal edge radii of 1–4 μm are typically designed for sintered tools to balance edge sharpness and edge strength. Only single crystalline diamond tools can be ground and lapped to form edge radii within nanometer range. The threshold depth has been investigated theoretically and verified experimentally by many researchers. It varies from 5 to 40% of the tool edge radius depending on the workpiece material and original rake angles. A depth of cut (or chip load), therefore, can be conservatively set to be 50% of the tool edge radius. When machining below this threshold, a microtool just rubs the surface and deforms it elastically during the first pass. When machining with depth of cut below the critical level, the material is then being plowed at negative effective rake angle. This results in high cutting force, high specific energy, fast tool wear, rough surface finish, and significant burr [4]. In subsequent passes when the cumulative depth is above the critical depth of cut, then a tool can remove materials as chips and the cycle repeats.

It is crucial to verify the tool edge radius before deciding on cutting parameters. Measuring of tool edge radius, however, is not trivial. A tool edge radius can be estimated from a scanning electron microscopic picture when the cutting edge is parallel to the electron beam axis [5], or scanning probe microscopic picture using a probe to scan the neighborhood of a cutting edge (Figure 1), or by scanning the edge on an optical microscope profiler in different views to reconstruct a 3D image of an tool edge before finding its radius.

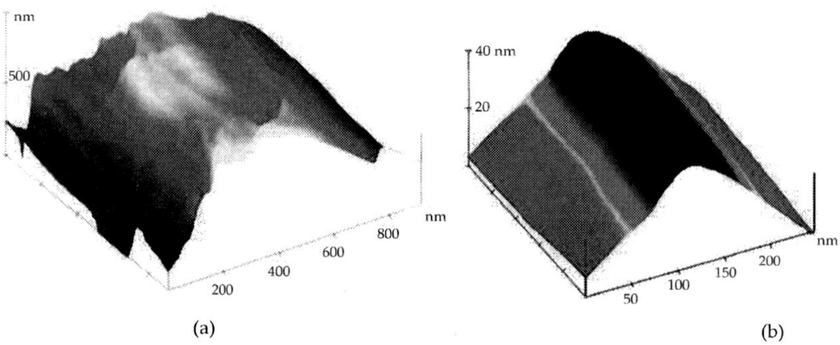

Figure 1. Tool edge radii of (a) 750 nm on a new polycrystalline diamond tool and (b) 10 nm on a new single crystalline diamond tool.

Tool Materials

Having the right microtool is essential for micromachining. A microtool that successfully drills through holes on a plastic printed circuit board does not necessarily be able to drill deep blind holes on titanium alloys. Understand the requirement and select the right microtool for each condition would save time, money, and frustration.

It has been theoretically derived and experimentally proven that the smaller the chip is, then the higher the required stress will be. Microcutting tools, therefore, have to be designed for higher stress with extreme geometrical constraints. When depth of cut is smaller than the average grain size of a workpiece, each grain with different orientation generates different stress on a cutting edge and eventually fatigues the tool.

Microtools as small as 25 μm are commercially available. Common tool materials are high speed steel (HSS), cermet, carbide, cubic boron nitride (CBN), polycrystalline diamond (PCD), and single crystalline diamond (SCD). The HSS is not used in micromachining of metal since it does not have required hardness and strength to resist plastic deformation. A SCD tool is available for microturning, but not for microdrilling or micromilling. Carbide and cermet, having properties between HSS and diamond, are most suitable for microcutting tools. They are sintered from random abrasive grains in either cobalt or nickel binder with a small addition of molybdenum or chromium. A higher binder content increases the tool toughness and crack resistance, but reduces the bulk tool hardness. Having ultra-fine grain (submicron size) abrasives in a lesser amount of binder is the optimal solution since a tool with a submicron carbide grains can maintain a high hardness while improving its crack resistance against chattering, interrupted cut, or cyclic deflection due to spindle runout.

Microtool failure modes include shearing, chipping, and wear. To minimize shearing and catastrophic tool failure, a tool should be made from a high hardness substrate and its geometry would be suitable for micromachining, i.e., large included angle and sharp cutting edge. A tool with smaller than minimum included angle will be deformed and fractured in service.

Coating of microtool is still a technical challenge due to conflicting constraints for tool performance. Chemical or physical vapor deposition (CVD or PVD) techniques have been developed to coat cutting tools with mono/multiple layers of intermetallic or ceramic compounds (Table 1). Criteria for acceptable tool coating are numerous: uniformity of coating thickness, high hardness, high toughness, low friction, high wear resistance, surface smoothness, high chemical/diffusion resistance, and high temperature stability at a reasonable cost [6]. Although a coating thickness of 2–4 μm is acceptable for a macrotool, coating thickness on a microtool should be thinner, in the range 1–2 μm, to minimize fracture and peeling of the coating (Figure 2). Both CVD and PVD processes not only add the coating thickness to an edge radius, but they also increase the radius due to extra coating at a sharp corner. This is unfortunate since the thicker coating reduces the tool sharpness by enlarging the tool edge radius and causes an unfavorable plowing effect with negative effective rake angle. An uncoated microtool might perform satisfactorily, but the same machining parameter can be devastating to an over-coated microtool. Although the Calo destructive test can be used to measure coating thickness on a large object [8], it is more practical and convenient to measure coating thickness on an expensive microtool nondestructively. Commercial instruments are available for coating thickness measurement using x-ray, magnetism, Eddy current, or ultrasound. A thin coating less than 1.5 μm following by an edge sharpening process would improve the tool performance, however, at the expense of higher tool cost. Published data indicate that micrograin carbide tools with 1.5 μm-TiN coating is the best for micromilling of H13 tool steel that has been hardened to 45 HRc.

Table 1. Commercial coating for microtools

Coating	Structure	Hardness (GPa)	Coefficient of friction	Coating thickness (μm)	Maximum temperature (°C)
TiN	Monolayer	24	0.55	1–5	600
TiCN	Gradient	37	0.20	1–4	400
TiAlCN	Gradient	28	0.30	1–4	500
TiAlN	Multilayer	28	0.60	1–4	700
AlTiN	Gradient	38	0.70	1–3	900

ZrN	Monolayer	20	0.40	1–4	550
CrN	Monolayer	18	0.30	1–4	700
Diamond like	Gradient	20	0.15	0.5–1.5	400
$AlTiN/Si_3N_4$	Nanocomposite	45	0.45	1–4	1200
$AlCrN/Si_3N_4$	Nanocomposite	42	0.35	1–5	1100

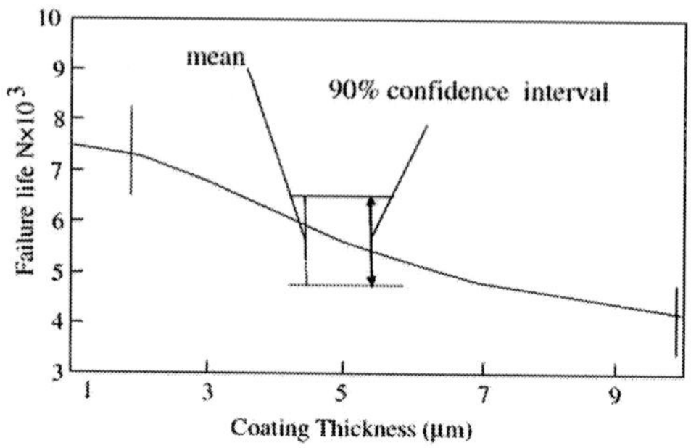

Figure 2. Effect of tool coating thickness on tool life. TiC coated WC tool in interrupted cut [7].

Tool Offset and Positioning

Tool offset and tool positioning are crucial in micromilling and microdrilling since a high aspect ratio tool is small and extremely vulnerable. Selection of a suitable sensor for tool offsetting and tool positioning depends at least on following criteria:

- The sensor has better resolution compared to that of machine tool axis.
- The sensor should have a small working zone to cover a microtool.
- The sensor can perform at fast sampling rate for intended tool speed.

Contact techniques must be used with care for positioning a microtool. Common shop practices to find tool offsetting and positioning often damage a microtool or workpiece.

- A mechanical edge finder is adequate for most macromachining setup, but it is not suitable for micromachining especially with small and pliable part.
- Measuring resistance or current flow when a tool touching a conductive workpiece has been used with moderate success. A pulsed current might spark and damage the sharp edges of a microtool.
- An accelerometer can be mounted on either a workpiece or tool spindle housing. The difference in vibration signals indicates contact of tool and workpiece. The vibration signal, however, depends on the material of workpiece and tool, their surface roughness and detection threshold [9].

Non-contact techniques, although are generally more expensive, can provide a satisfactory accuracy and repeatability.

- Commercial laser displacement sensor with 20 μs sampling rate (50 kHz) would be sufficient for most cases. Submicron accuracy and be achieved, but the sensor's repeatability depends on the repeatability of multiple axes of a machine tool. Both lateral and axial tool offsets have been successfully used with this technique.
- Other non-contact techniques using magnetism, capacitance, ultrasound… could be used depending on the required accuracy and the workpiece materials.

Tool Damage

Tool damage can be categorized by the relative size of the damage, ranging from submicron to hundreds of microns (Table 2). The tool failure mechanisms include damages due to mechanical, thermal, chemical effects, or adhesion.

Table 2. Categories of tool damage

Microtool damage	Damage size (μm)	Mechanism
Abrasion	<1	Mechanical, thermal
Attrition	1–3	Mechanical, thermal
Peeling	1–3	Mechanical, chemical
Microchipping	3–10	Mechanical, adhesion
Chipping	10–30	Mechanical
Fracture	>100	Mechanical

Mechanical effect is the most common source of tool damage. Abrasive wear is caused by low speed sliding of hard particles from workpiece or tool against the cutting tool surface (Figure 3). At a high cutting speed and lack of sufficient coolant/lubricant, the high temperature at tool cutting edge accelerates the tool wear due to increasing rate of diffusion and/or chemical reaction at the coating layer and the substrate below. Figures 5a and 5b compare the wear of PVD coated TiAlN/TiN layer on WC tool when machining at 180 m/min; the material contrast in scanning electron microscopy highlights the faster wear rate of the coating layer when machining 3D printed titanium alloy [10].

Attrition wear is larger than abrasion wear. This happens when one for few grains of the tool are weakened at their grain boundaries and dislodged from the tool.

- Microchipping and chipping happen when larger chunks of tool being removed due to mechanical or thermal shocks upon loading and unloading (Figure 4). Machining at optimal parameters and rigid setup would reduce vibration, shock, and mechanical damage to a microtool. Chipping can occur due to high stress when machining at excessive cutting speed and feed [11]. Tool chipping also starts with microcracks due to chemical reaction among tool coating material, workpiece material, and coolant/lubricant.

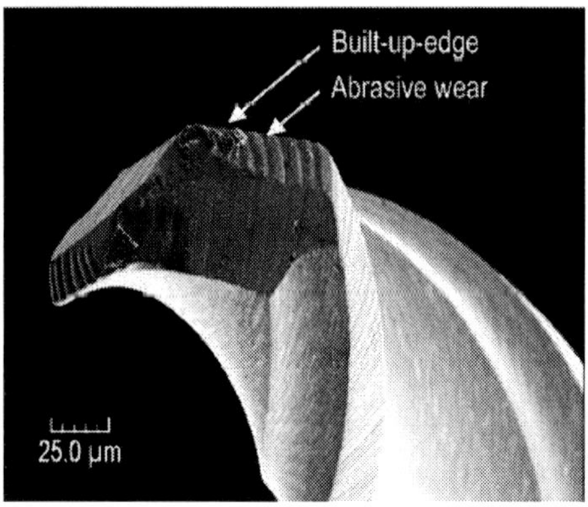

Figure 3. Abrasive wear on a WC microdrill.

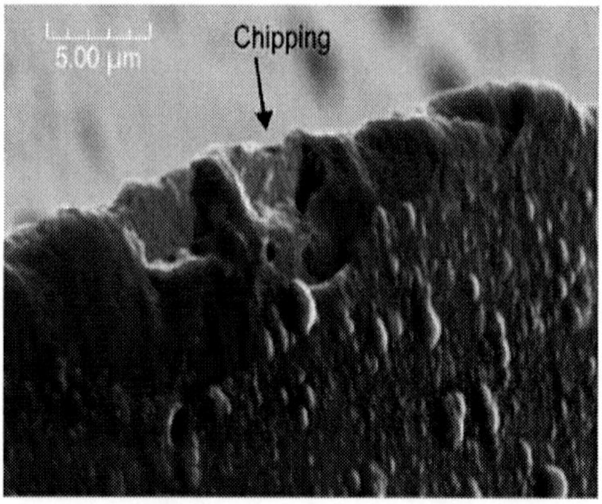

Figure 4. Chipping of cutting edge. AlTiN coated micromilling tool.

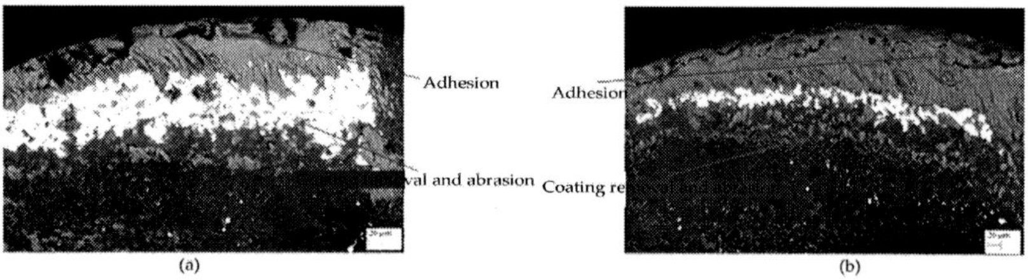

Figure 5. Wear of coating tool after machining Ti 6Al 4V at 180 m/min on (a) wrought material and (b) selective laser melted material [10].

Thermal effect is the second cause of tool damage. A cutting tool edge is softened at high machining temperature, deformed plastically, and removed from the tool. Both high speed steel tool and carbide tool with high cobalt content are vulnerable to thermal damage. High temperature also promotes diffusion, i.e., atoms from the tool and workpiece move mutually across their interfaces, therefore degrade their properties and cause diffusion wear. Diamond with a carbon-rich matrix, or diamond-like coated tool, cannot be used with low-carbon ferrous alloy like steels or stainless steels since diamond carbonizes at temperature exceeding 600°C and diffuses to steel due to the steel's lower carbon content and its high affinity to carbon. A tool would extend its useful life by applying proper coolant to reduce thermal damage, or having a protective coating that blocks undesirable thermal diffusion from/to a tool surface. At higher cutting speed, the thermal/diffusion wear is the main tool wear mechanism. Combination of abrasive and thermal wear can be present when both high cutting speed and material hardness are combined. After machining at a high cutting speed of 180 m/min, severe coating tool wear (Figure 5b) is observed after cutting the harder selective-laser-melted titanium alloy compared to that when machining the same but softer extruded material (Figure 5a).

Chemical damage of a tool is due to chemical reaction between tool material and its environment like air, cutting fluid, or workpiece material. Tool oxidation is common when cutting in air at high speed. An oxidation reaction is accelerated with temperature, but can be eliminated when using inert gas to shield the cutting tool from surrounding oxygen. A chain reaction can also occur and further degrade a tool. For example, iron in steel is first oxidized at high cutting temperature to form iron oxide; this iron oxide then weakens the aluminum oxide coating of a tool and leads to peeling and chipping of the coating.

Adhesion tool damage happens when a built-up-edge (BUE) welds strongly to a tool surface and then breaks away with a minute amount of tool material. Some of the BUE deposits on the back of a chip, but some can be on the machined surface thus degrading the workpiece quality (Figure 6). When machining soft materials, a chip tends to adhere to the tool and grows in size (Figure 7). When such cumulative BUE is large and becomes unstable, it is removed with chip while shearing off part of the cutting tool due to the higher adhesion strength of BUE and tool interface than the inter-grain binding strength. Stainless steel, nickel and titanium alloys are known for causing adhesion wear on carbide microtools (Figure 8). Adhesion damage can be reduced by using proper lubricant to reduce friction between chip and tool, by coating tool with a smooth and low friction layer, by reducing tool edge radius, or by increasing cutting speed to raise tool surface temperature and soften BUE while reducing its weldability to tool surface.

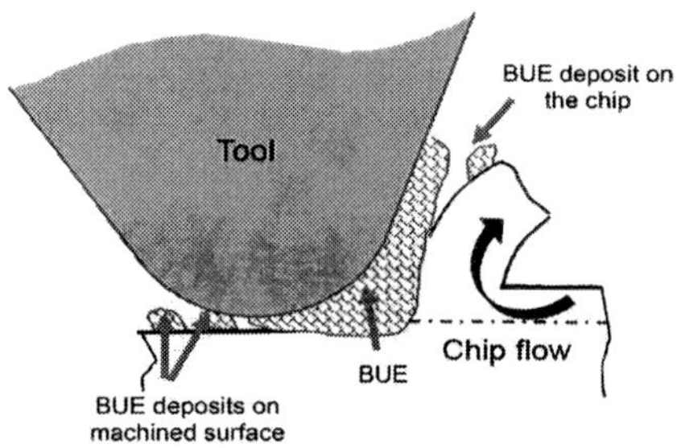

Figure 6. Built-up-edge and its effects [12].

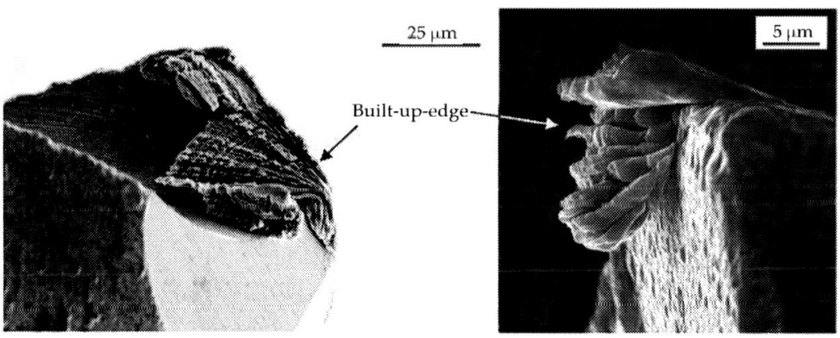

Figure 7. Built-up-edge at the cutting edge on a microdrilling tool (left) and micromilling tool (right).

A thick tool coating, although possessing a thicker diffusion barrier, can fail prematurely due to excessive shear stress at the interface (Figure 9). A 5 μm thick coating is common for large carbide insert, but 1–2 μm thin coating is recommended for microtools (Figure 2). Failure of microtools can happen due to combination of the above mechanisms. For example, peeling of tool coating might be due to coating defects or mechanical mechanism when a large gradient of stress exists across a thick coating layer; the loosen coating particles then rub and cause mechanical abrasive wear on a tool. Thermal mechanism may cause workpiece atoms to diffuse, weaken, and dislodge several tool grains as microchipping. The quenched and tempered 4140 steel fails tools by abrasion, the 304 stainless steel causes adhesion tool wear, while the nickel supper alloy Inconel 718 damages tools by all wear mechanisms [13]

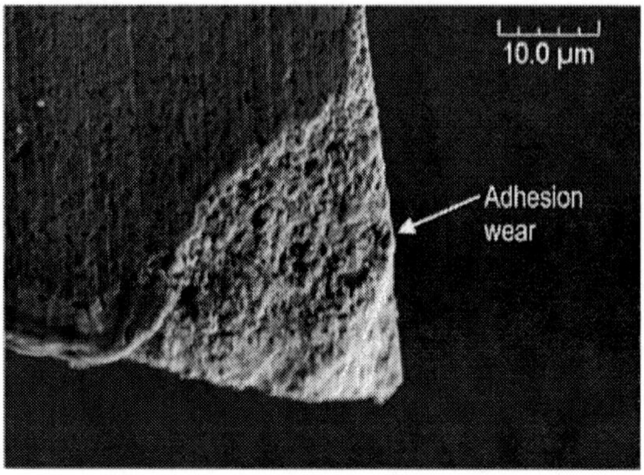

Figure 8. Adhesion wear of a micromilling tool.

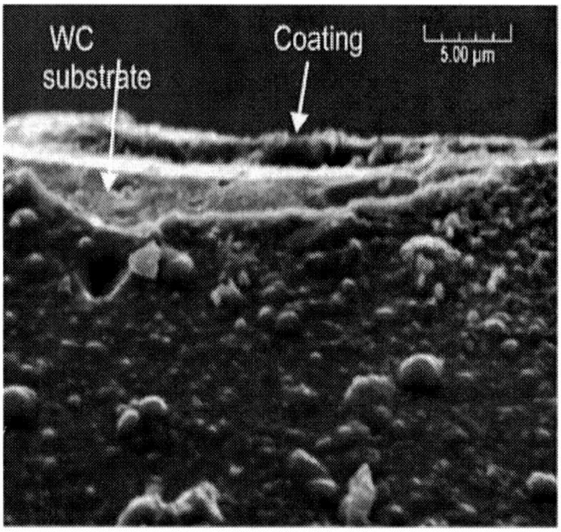

Figure 9. Delamination of $AlTiN/Si_3N_4$ coating on a WC microdrilling tool.

Cutting Fluid

Shearing of workpiece material and relative motion between tool and chip generate a significance of heat during machining. This thermal energy could change the microstructure, plastically deform the subsurface, degrade the part quality and wear a cutting tool quickly. Cutting fluids, either oil based for lubrication or water based for cooling, should be applied appropriately for effective micromachining while evacuating tiny chips from the machined surface.

- Dry machining. Although simple, dry machining is not appropriate since it neither reduce the heat, extend tool life, nor removing chips that may interfere with machining action.

- Flood cooling. A large amount of fluid can cover a tool and workpiece, but it is not effective since the bulk liquid cannot penetrate the air boundary layer surrounding a rapidly rotate micro drilling/milling tool-typically in the range of 30,000–120,000 rpm. Increasing the flood cooling pressure, as in jet cooling, simply deflect a fragile microtool and affect the machining quality.
- Minimum quantity lubrication (MQL). A mixture of oil and compressed air is very effective for micromachining when operating at high pressure above 4 bars (400 kPa, 60 psi). The micron-sized oil droplets can be propelled at high speed to penetrate the air boundary layer, adhere to workpiece/tool zones, spread out by surface tension to effectively cool and lubricate the tool/chip interface. Correct applications of MQL extend tool life while reducing burr as reported in published literature. Advanced MQL systems include additives (lignin, nano-sized diamond particle, graphene, etc.) can further enhance the effectiveness of MQL [14].
- Cryogenic cooling. Rapid freezing of most metals at liquid nitrogen temperature (−196°C) would embrittle the materials, reduce the required energy for machining and burr formation at the expense of tool wear [15]. This expensive technique, however, requires proper insulation of tooling and fixture surrounding a workpiece.

EFFECT OF MATERIALS

Micromachining is often utilized to fabricate components for miniaturized sensors, medical, optical, and electronic devices. Common engineering materials for these applications include stainless steel, aluminum, titanium, copper, and tool steel for miniature molds and dies.

Workpiece materials must meet certain conditions for successful micromachining. Unlike in macromachining, a micromachining tool is subjected to fluctuating cutting force when encounters each grain since microtool size is comparable to material grain size. A microtool is more vulnerable to fatigue fracture and the resulted surface—if the tool survives—would be rough due to different spring-back protrusion from each grain due to different crystallographic orientations of the grains, and direction-dependent properties of the material. Homogenous workpiece materials with very fine and uniform grain sizes should be chosen for micromachining. Inclusions and large precipitates should be minimized to avoid damage to a fragile tool edge.

Ductile Regime Micro/Nano Machining

The concept of ductile-regime machining has been investigated since 1960s for amorphous brittle materials such as glasses. Silicon, germanium, and glasses have become strategic materials that are widely used to fabricate intricate components in microelectronics, optics, defense industries, and recently as micro optical-electrical-mechanical systems. Silicon and other brittle materials are known for their low machinability unless they are machined in the ductile-regime conditions. When utilized at the optimal machining conditions, only minimum effort is required for the subsequent etching, grinding, or polishing to remove the damaged subsurface. This section summarizes the theory and provides practical guidance for ductile-regime machining. The mechanism of ductile-regime machining has been studied by many researchers. Using fracture mechanics approach, it can be shown that there is a threshold below which ductile regime prevailed:

$$d_c = \frac{\text{plastic flow energy}}{\text{fracture energy}} = A\left(\frac{E}{H}\right)\left(\frac{K_c}{H}\right)^2 \tag{5}$$

where d_c: critical depth of cut (m); A: constant. $A = 0.15$ for microscratching, $A = 0.60$ for micromachining; E: Young modulus (Pa); K_C: surface fracture toughness (Pa $m^{0.5}$); H: surface microhardness (Pa).

A shallow depth of cut, therefore, would energetically promote plastic flow rather than brittle fracture in the substrate and the chips. Table 3 tabulates properties of some brittle materials and their experimental critical depths of cut.

Table 3. Properties of selected brittle materials

Materials	Young modulus (GPa)	Fracture toughness (MPa $m^{0.5}$)	Knoop hard-ness (GPa)	Critical depth of cut (μm)
α-Al_2O_3	275–393	3.85–5.90	19.6–20.1	1.0
SiC	382–475	2.50–3.50	24.5–25.0	0.2
Silicon	168	0.6	10	0.5

The constant A in Eq. (5) varies in the range 0.1–0.6 due to measuring uncertainty of surface toughness K_c, elastic modulus E, and microhardness H in a testing environment. These properties depend on crystalline orientation of the materials, surface conditions, and tool geometry. An example of ductile regime machining on single crystal silicon wafer is shown in Figure 10.

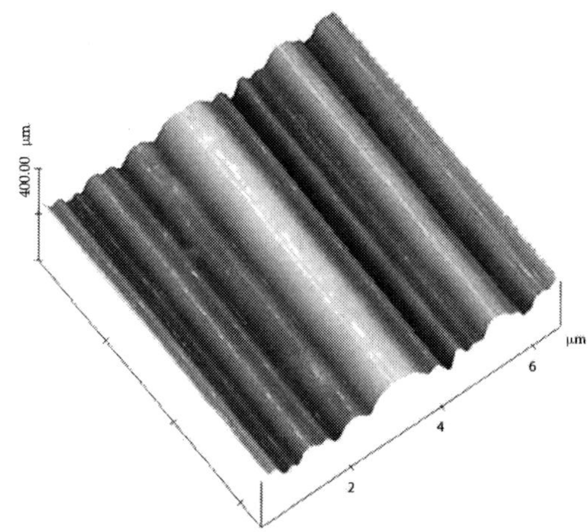

Figure 10. Perfect ductile regime machining of (001) silicon [16].

- The critical resolved shear stress, on a crystalline plane due to the cutting action, is directly proportional to the Schmid factor (cosλ)(cosϕ), where ϕ and λ are the orientations of the slip plane and slip direction. An ideal ductile mode machining would happen when the cutting shear stress is parallel to both the slip plane and the slip direction, otherwise a pseudo ductile mode with micro cleavages occurs. True ductile-regime machining happens only along certain crystalline orientation, but brittle machining occurs at other crystalline orientation. This explains why micromachining a crystalline specimen at the same speed, depth of cut, and coolant produces ductile machined surfaces in one direction but brittle machined surfaces on others.

- Cutting fluid changes the surface properties of materials (K_c, E, and H) and affects conditions for ductile regime micromachining. When micromachining the (100) plane of germanium using a single crystalline diamond tool, the critical depth of cut changes from 0.13 μm with distill water as cutting fluid to 0.29 μm in dry machining.
- Tool geometry also affects the results. Plowing and fracture of material occurs when depth of cut is less than approximately half of the tool cutting edge radius. Tool with negative top rake angle is usually utilized since a negative rake causes compressive zone in the workpiece ahead and below the tool and suppresses microcrack formation.

Additively Manufactured Metals

The evolution of 3D printing allows metallic parts to be printed in different methods.

- Power beam fusion. Laser or electron beam are used to melt either metal wire or powder particles to form layers, then fuse these layers to form a complex shaped part.
- Material jetting. Metal powder is fed at the energy beam focused point to melt and form a part.
- Jet binding. An organic binding material is sprayed and bind metal powder in layers. The "green" part is then sintered to form the final shape.

Using any of the above techniques, an as-built part:

- Is warped due to high thermal induced residual stress, or non-uniform shrinkage during sintering,
- Has very rough surface (typically 15–20 μm Ra), and
- Is filled with surface defects (e.g., microcrack, shrinkage cavity, partially welded powder particles, etc.) as shown in Figure 11, and volume defects (e.g., porosity, inclusion, shrinkage cavity, etc.).

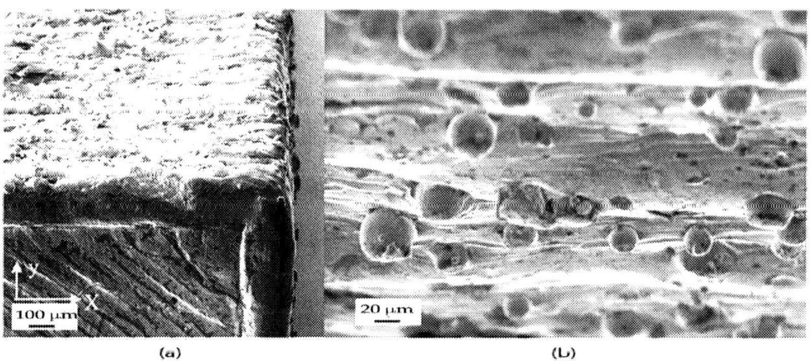

Figure 11. Surface topography of an Inconel 718 block after selective laser melting. (a) Oblique view, and (b) viewing along the building z-axis.

Post processing of the as-built metal parts must be performed so that they can meet required engineering criteria for surface finish or dimensional/form tolerances. Micromachining is the most effective post processing technique to control the surface and dimension of local areas of additively manufactured metals due to its high removal rate and well-established computer numerical controlled (CNC) industry.

MICROMACHINING

Micromachining refers to removal of material subtractively in micron scale. The process can be done by (i) conventional processes, i.e., removing material mechanically with hard tools in contact with a workpiece and removing minute amount of material as chips, or (ii) non-conventional processes, i.e., removing material by other physical mechanisms such as optical, thermal, chemical, electrical, or combinations of these. The following section focuses only on the three major conventional techniques, namely micromilling, microdrilling, and microturning of advanced materials.

Micromilling

Micromilling is among the most versatile microfabrication processes. Although alternative nontraditional processes to produce microfeatures (e.g., laser micromachining, electrical discharge micromachining, electrochemical micromachining, chemical microetching, electron/ion beam micromachining) are available, these processes are either cost prohibitive, or inferior when comparing resulted surface and subsurface integrity, anisotropic aspect ratio, material removal rate, or feature quality. Successful micromilling requires new tool geometry, tool material, machining parameters, and machining skills. It is technically incorrect and costly to perform micromilling by just scaling down a milling cutter, or parameters from macroscale milling.

Tool material. Carbide tools should be sintered from fine grains, and precisely ground to obtain a micron-level cutting edge radius.

Milling direction. Down milling is the preferred mode since a micromill will engages a workpiece and removes a wedge shape chip with decreasing chip thickness. In contrast, a tool in up milling would rub on the workpiece until the effective chip thickness is greater than 0.5 cutting edge radius. Down milling also produces less amount of burr.

Lubrication. Minimum quantity lubrication should be used with all micromachining. A nozzle should be as closed as possible and is positioned to let the cutting flute pulls the mist into the cutting zone. Tool and workpiece should be arranged to avoid stagnant zone, or being blocked or interfered by chips [17].

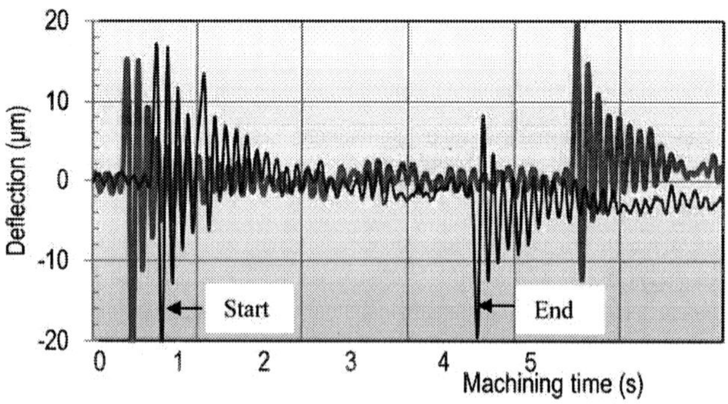

Figure 12. Vibration of a micromill when engaging and disengaging a workpiece. Carbide mill Ø1 mm, 316L stainless steel, 25,000 rpm, 10 µm/tooth feed, 0.348 mm axial depth, 0.558 mm radial depth.

- Tool vibration. Avoid unnecessary disengaging then engaging of microtool and workpiece in a milling program. Vibration and bending of a microtool at starting and ending could fatigue and shorten tool life of a microtool (Figure 12).

Commercial micromills are available for diameter of 25 μm and above. Optional geometries include:

- Flute lengths: standard or extended length (10–80% longer)
- Number of flutes: 2, 3, or 4
- Helix angles: 25°, 30°, 50°
- End configuration: hemisphere or flat.

As mentioned above, the BUEs on a cutting tool surface can break and deposit on a machined surface as shown in Figure 13. Measuring area surface finish Sa would combine the roughness contributed from milling parameters (e.g., speed, feed), tool and machine condition (e.g., vibration), and surface irregularities (e.g., pore and BUE). The BUEs is reduced when an optimal condition of MQL is used, low chip load, and higher speed. In a study of micromilling 316L stainless steel, the amount of BUE is significantly diminished when cutting at speed higher than 30 m/min (Figure 14). Perhaps the high temperature at high cutting speed improves the material plasticity and reduces the weldability of BUEs on cutting tool tip.

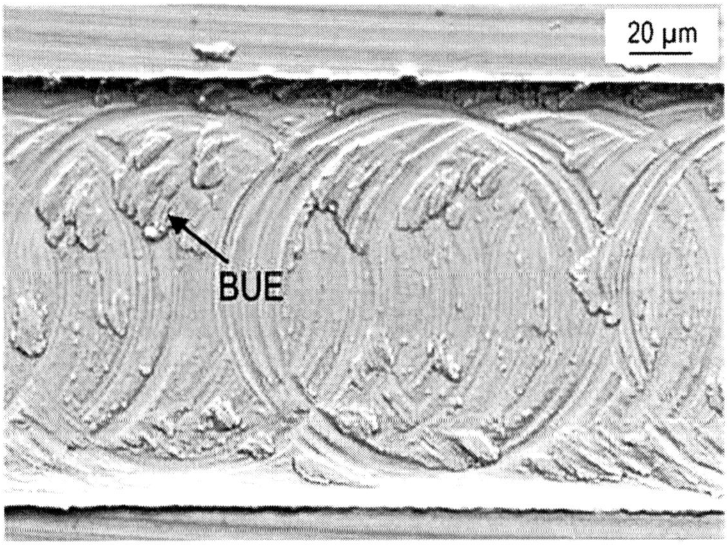

Figure 13. Built-up-edges deposit on machined Ti 6Al 4V surface. Micromilling at 9.6 m/min, 0.1 μm/tooth, 10 μm axial depth. Dry [18].

Lack of BUEs on coated tool also results in better surface finish of micromilled channels on 304/316L stainless steels, NiTi alloy, A36 low carbon steel, 6061-T6 aluminum, and Ti-6Al-4V titanium alloy. The AlTiN coating effectively increases tool life while reducing burrs significantly when micromilling 304 stainless steel. The incompatibility of the coating on specific material workpiece prevent BUE formation, therefore, shear the materials as chips rather than deforming it as burr (Figure 15b). The effect of micromilling mode is also shown when up-milling tends to generate more burr than down-milling (Figure 15a).

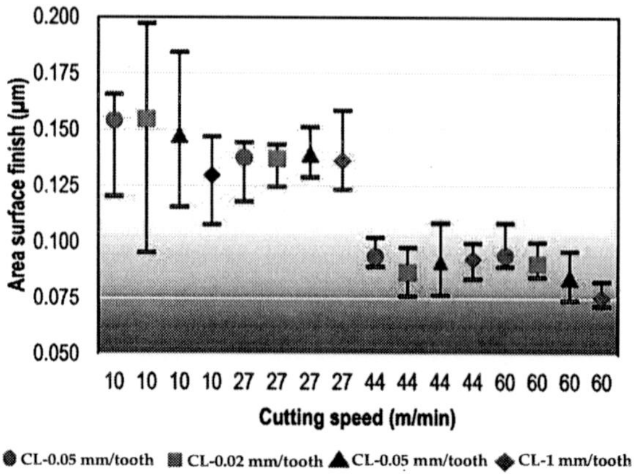

Figure 14. Effect of cutting speed and chip load on area surface roughness Sa. Each range plot shows the maximum, minimum, and average of 15 measurements. Micromilling 316L stainless steel [12].

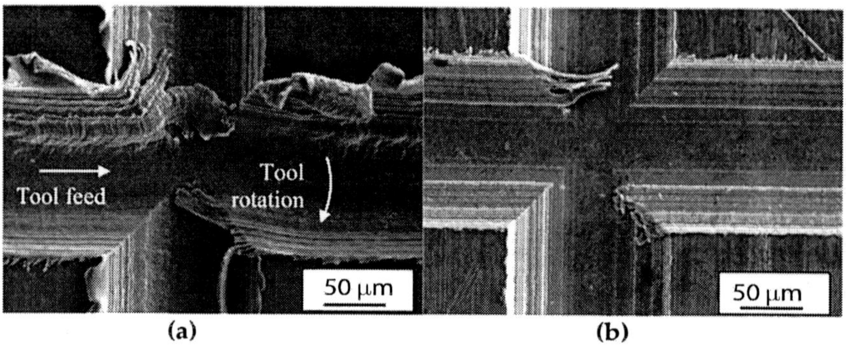

Figure 15. Effect of tool coating on resulting burrs: (a) uncoated ϕ152 µm tool, milling 304 stainless steel, 24 m/min, 0.1 µm/tooth, MQL; and (b) AlTiN coated ϕ198 µm tool, milling 304 stainless steel, 24 m/min, 0.1 µm/tooth, MQL [19].

The theoretical surface finish of machined surface after milling with a flat-end tool can be shown to be:

$$R_a = \frac{5}{18} f_t tan\alpha \tag{6}$$

And that for a ball-end milling tool is:

$$R_a = 0.2423 \frac{f_t^2}{D}. \tag{7}$$

Rearranging Eq. (7) to have:

$$D \cdot R_a = 0.2423 f_t^2 \tag{8}$$

where R_a: average surface finish (µm); f_t: chip load (µm/tooth); D: diameter of ball-end milling tool (µm); α: concavity angle, or end-cutting-edge angle (°).

Both Eqs. (6) and (8) predict the dependent of chip load on surface finish Ra. When plotting Eq. (8) using experimental data from different tool diameters and different chip loads, then Eq. (8) is confirmed with data in macromilling when chip load >100 μm but not with smaller chip load for micromilling (Figure 16). The reason for a higher surface finish is the intermittent BUEs, although small, smear and degrade the machined surface.

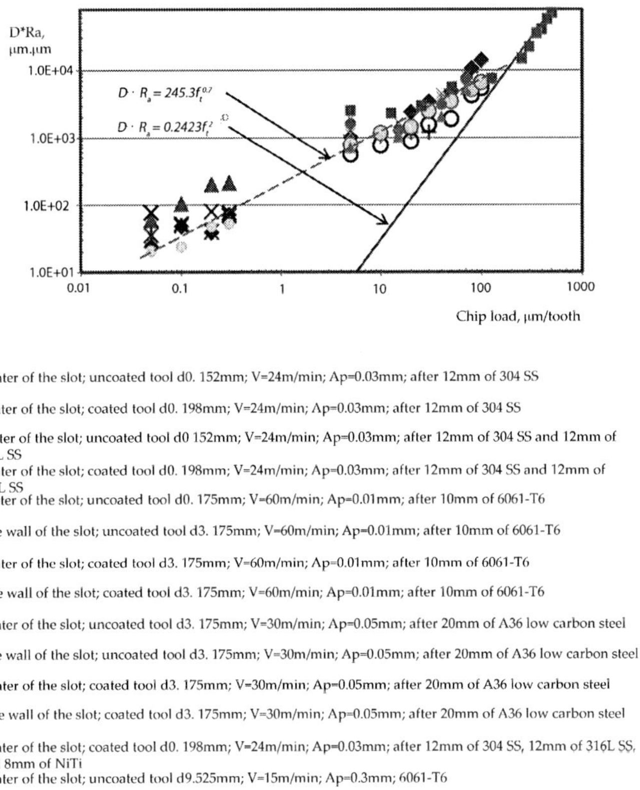

Figure 16. Average surface finish at center of milled microchannels. Ball-end milling tools ϕ152–9525 μm, workpiece materials 6061-T6, A36 steel, NiTi, 304/316L stainless steels, in MQL condition [19].

Similar experimental results is shown in Figure 17 for micromilling of additively manufactured Ti 6Al 4V alloys. At a very low chip load of 0.1 μm/tooth, the presence of significant BUEs on machined surface degrades the surface quality as indicated by high surface roughness R_a. The surface improves at higher chip loads, by reduction of BUEs, but is gradually increased with chip load as predicted by Eq. (6). Similar surface roughness result was reported for machining 7075 aluminum alloy [21].

Post processing by micromachining of additively manufactured metals have been investigated. Few studies have compared machinability of selected metals produced by conventional route (e.g., casting, extrusion, rolling, etc.) and by additive manufacturing route (e.g., powder bed fusion, direct energy deposition, etc.). Limited machining investigations on Inconel 625, Inconel 718, Ti 6Al 4V, H13 tool steel, Ti 48Al 2Nb 2Cr alloy, 17Cr 4Ni stainless steel, and 316L stainless steel have concluded that the AM metals in general have lower machinability compared to the conventional metals.

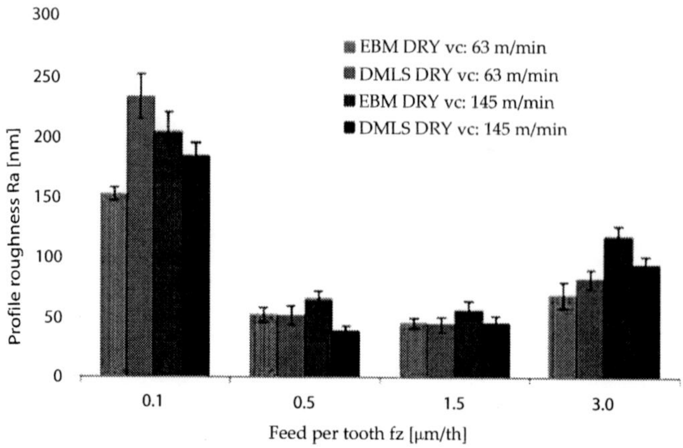

Figure 17. Effect of chip load and cutting speed on surface finish. Micromilling of Ti 6Al 4V fabricated by electron beam melting, and direct metal laser sintering [20].

Machinability is affected by microstructural changes in a material. A quick comparison between the microstructure of extruded and SLM'ed Inconel 718 shows the contrast of the same materials after different manufacturing routes. Uniform microstructure of the extruded specimen is expected (Figure 18). The mechanical properties of extruded specimen could be slightly different in longitudinal and transversal directions due to preferred grain orientation along the extrusion direction. In contrast, the fast heating and cooling rate of SLM'ed Inconel 718 creates alternate layers along the laser paths and hard particles in the microstructure (Figure 19). The obvious changes in microstructure result in different mechanical properties, therefore, affecting machinability. Fast cooling in SLM'ed Inconel 718 also forms brittle Laves particles and traps pores near an edge (Figure 20a). During machining, some particles are broken, smeared along the tool path and probably chipped the cutting tool. Porosity is unavoidable in AM metals. The burr on top of those micron-size pores after micromachining is difficult to remove mechanically (Figure 20b). Although hot isostatic pressing (HIPping) can eliminate porosity, some materials (e.g., Inconel 718) are aged at HIPping temperature; the resulted precipitates increase the material strength but reduce its machinability (Figure 21).

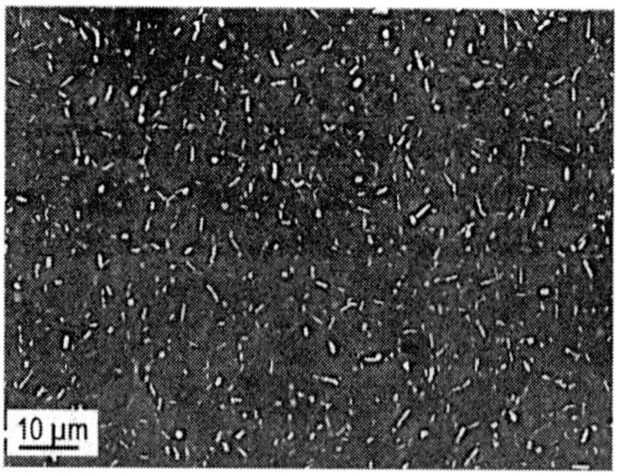

Figure 18. Uniform microstructure of extruded Inconel 718. Viewing along the extruding direction.

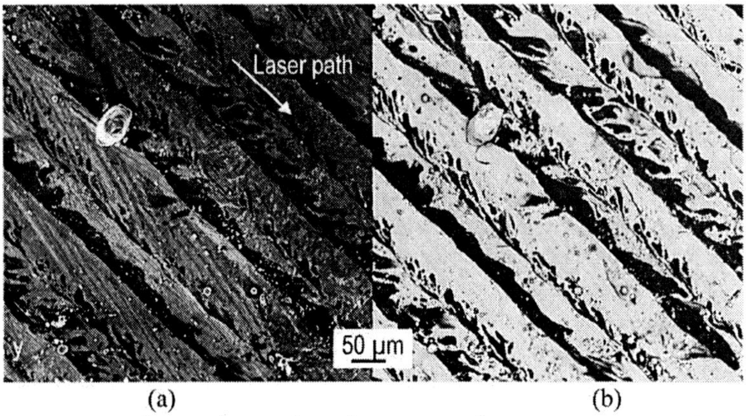

Figure 19. Microstructure of SLM'ed Inconel 718 by scanning electron microscopy in (a) secondary electron mode, and (b) back scattered electron mode. Notice the different layers across the laser scanning paths.

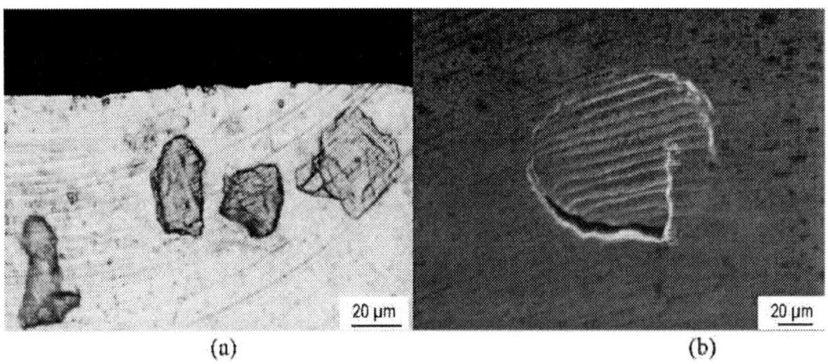

Figure 20. Irregularities in selective laser Inconel 718. (a) Sheared Laves particles after micromilling, (b) A machined micropore with burr.

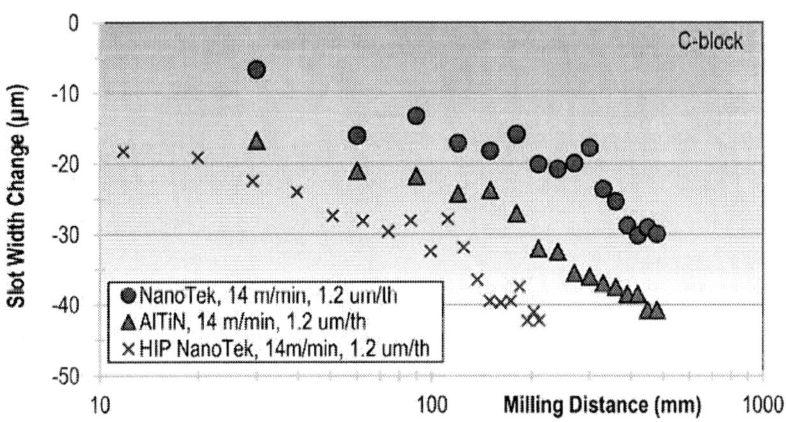

Figure 21. Micromilling of SLM'ed Inconel 718. Change of slot width with milling distance. Minimum quantity lubrication, 50 μm depth of cut [22].

Conflicting literature data are probably due to different process parameters for AM metals and different scanning strategies. For example, the precipitation hardenable 17Cr 4Ni stainless steel was reported to have near fully martensitic structure and high yield strength than the cast alloy, but the opposite conclusion was found in another study.

Advanced cutting fluids and techniques have been applied for micromilling of advanced materials. Poor results are reported when using a pressurized jet to flood cool during micromilling of Ti 6Al 4V. The fragile tool (200 μm diameter, AlTiN coated, 1.25 μm/tooth feed, 30,000 rpm rotating speed, 20 μm depth of cut) being deflected and vibrated under pressurized jet, generates large burr and rough surface (Figure 22a), while cutting a large slot width (Figure 22b). Applying MQL with flow in the feeding direction solves these problems. When using MQL at high air pressure above 5.5 bar, a nozzle with rough internal surface breaks the lubricant into smaller droplets and effectively improves tool life of micromilling tools [24].

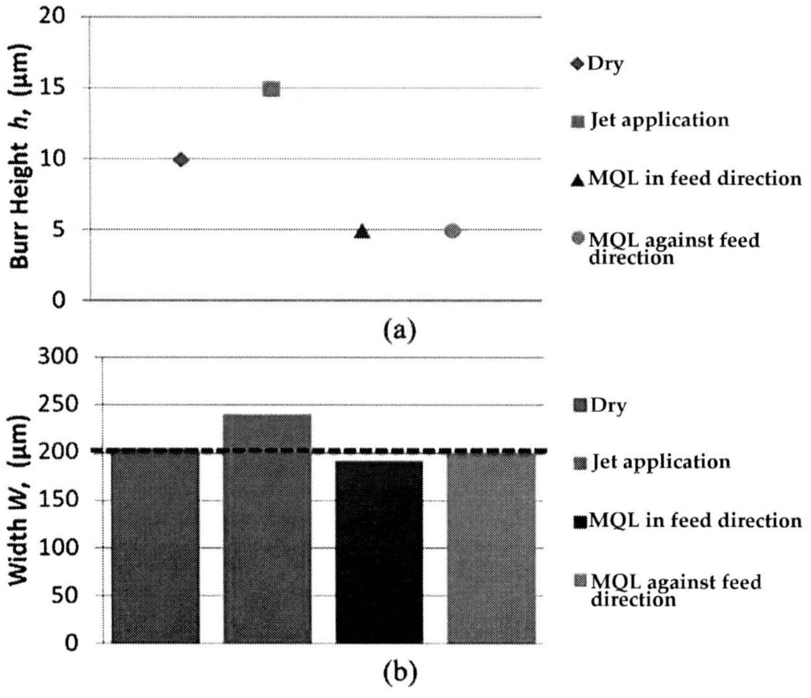

Figure 22. Effect if different cooling methods on (a) burr formation, and (b) resulted slot width. Micromilling of Ti 6Al 4V [23].

Effort was made to produce an environmentally friendly cutting fluid while enhancing the cutting fluid performance. Lignin is a biodegradable product from wood. It can be mixed in alcohol then TRIM water soluble as cutting fluid. Micromilling tests are performed with 396 μm diameter milling tool on 6061 aluminum and 1018 steel. The optimal concentration of 0.015% lignin seems to provide the best lubricating and cooling effects when reducing the cutting forces on both materials (Figure 23).

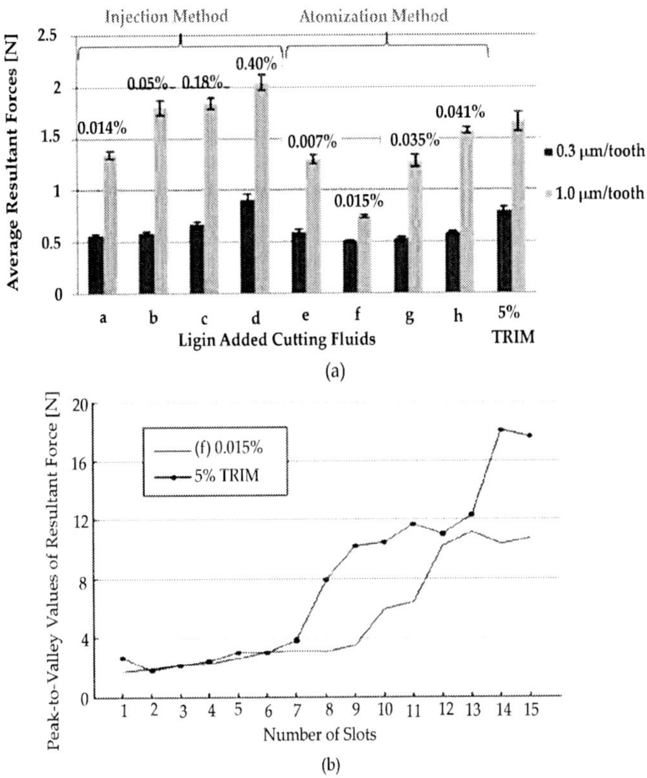

Figure 23. Effect of atomized cutting fluid with lignin on micromilling of (a) 6061 aluminum and (b) 1018 steel [25].

Cryogenic precooling can be used to reduce BUE formation and its effect on part quality. Liquid nitrogen, dispensed in front of a microtool in a micromilling test on Inconel 718. The tool (760 μm diameter, AlCrN coated) is used at 48 m/min speed, 1.25–5 μm/flute chip load, 0.1–0.2 mm depth of cut for a constant distance of 120 mm. The cryogenic condition embrittles the Inconel material so it can be micromilled in brittle mode with minimum plastically deformed burr and BUEs. The result is the low surface roughness at different chip loads (Figure 24a) and depth of cuts (Figure 24b). However, the brittle chip debris are abundant and might interfere with subsequent machining passes. No chip debris is seen when MQL is used.

The positive results of cryogenic cooling on Inconel 718, however, was not confirmed in a similar study on micromilling of electron beam melted Ti 6Al 4V. The 300 μm cutting tools were utilized at 63–145 m/min speed, 0.1–3.0 μm/tooth chip load, and 30 μm axial depth of cut. The temperature of the workpiece was at −155 ± 5°C with liquid nitrogen. No brittle chip debris are seen, ductile burr are visible (Figure 25a), and the surface profile (R_a finish) are similar for dry, MQL, and cryogenic conditions. The machined surface is work-hardened after micromilling at cryogenic condition as shown in the nanohardness results below the surface (Figure 25b). This implies the material is not truly embrittled as planned.

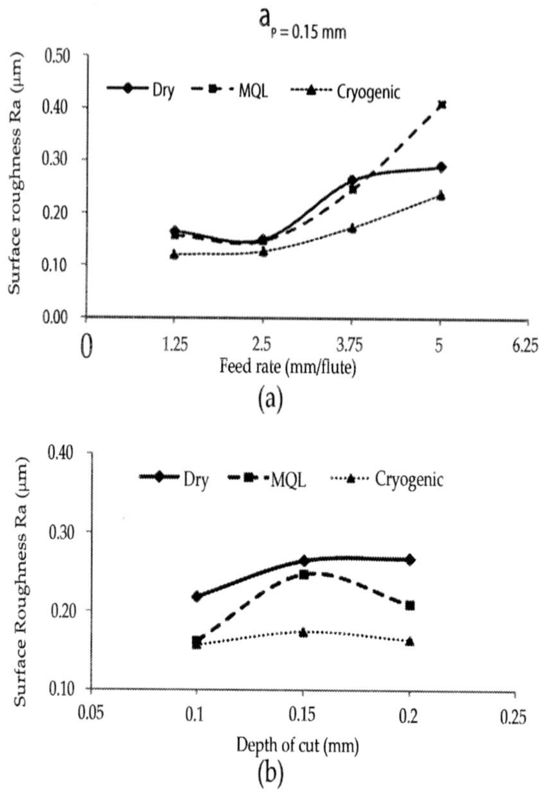

Figure 24. Effect of different cooling strategies on micromilling of Inconel 718 (a) effect of chip loads, and (b) effect of axial cutting depth (Ucun, 2014).

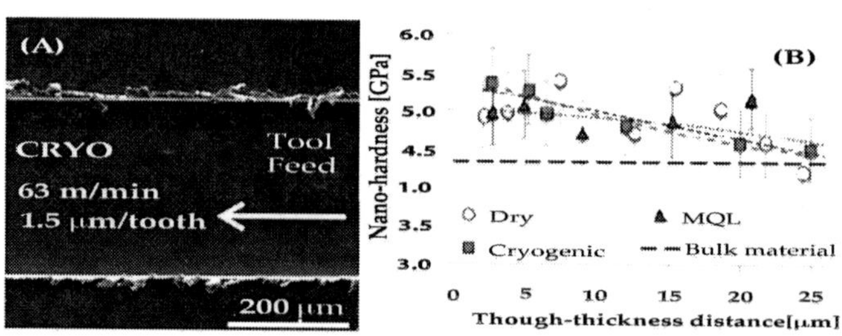

Figure 25. Effect of cryogenic cooling on micromilling of electron beam melted Ti 6Al 4V [26].

Another effective additive in MQL is nano-sized diamond particles. This application, applied to microdrilling, will be presented in the next section.

Microdrilling

Microdrilling is a more complex operation comparing to turning or milling. Chip removal and effectively supplying of cutting fluid are easy with the latter, but not with microdrilling due to extremely limited space around a microdrill.

Tool material. As with a micromill, a carbide microdrill should be sintered from fine grains, and ground to small cutting edge radius.

Hole quality. Spindle runout, tool eccentricity, and wandering of a microdrill cause cyclic bending of a tool and could lead to a catastrophic failure. To control drill wandering, precision pre-drilling of a center hole can be tried, or the workpiece surface must be ground to minimize deflection of a slender drill when starting on an irregular surface.

Micromist with fixed nozzle pointing to the drill tip and making an angle of 60–70° with the tool axis is recommended. This way, the chip is blown away after each pecking cycle and the microdrill is re-lubricated before re-entering into the hole.

High aspect ratio. Pecking is essential for microhole drilling since chips have to be extracted and cutting fluid must penetrate into a small and deep microhole. The pecking depth can be substantial in the beginning, but it must be gradually reduced when drilling at deeper depths. One can start with an initial pecking depth of (2*drill diameter) and gradually reduce it to (0.5*diameter) at the hole depth of (10*diameter). It is convenient to program pecking cycles in microdrilling following the equations below.

$$\frac{P}{D} = \frac{1}{9}(-1.5R + 19.5) \quad \text{for } R \leq 10 \tag{9}$$

$$\frac{P}{D} = 0.5 \quad \text{for } R > 10 \tag{10}$$

where *P*: incremental pecking depth (mm); *D*: drill diameter (mm); *R*: progressive drill aspect ratio = current hole depth/drill diameter.

Although application of MQL in micromachining is necessary, other researchers have found ways to improve its effectiveness. Nanoparticles are mixed in MQL oil to improve its performance in microdrilling. The nano-sized particles of CNT-C60, TiO_2, Al_2O_3, MoS_2, and diamond would increase the thermal conductivity of the fluid thus prolong the tool life while reducing burr. In an experimental microdrilling study, uncoated microdrills of 100–500 μm diameters are used at 10–15 mm/min, 30,000–60,000 rpm spindle speeds, while varying the concentration of 30 nm diamond particles in the range 0–4%. The MQL system is used at 3-bar air pressure to drill a constant 0.3 mm depth. The optimal conditions for low torque and thrust force are experimentally obtained to be 60,000 rpm and 2% concentration.

Inspection of a microdrilled and tapped hole would be difficult. Destructive technique by sectioning a part is time consuming, expensive, and error prone since the internal features might be distorted by releasing of residual stress. X-ray computed tomography (CT) has been utilized to evaluated drilled and tapped Ti 6Al 4V dental implant fabricated by direct metal laser sintering. The best microdrilled hole quality—cylindricity and perpendicularity—is achieved at the lowest testing drill speed of 60 m/min and the lowest chip load of 10 μm/flute. Figure 26a shows the sectional view of the CT image of a drilled and tapped dental implant. Detailed observation and measurement can then be performed (Figure 26b).

Finite element modeling of a microdrill was done to find the limiting drilling parameters that would fracture a microdrill catastrophically. It was assumed that the drill shank is rigid, axial thrust force and torsional torque can fail a drill in either buckling mode or torsional mode. Transverse shear strength in three-point bending test of a sintered carbide tool is estimated to be half of the material tensile strength. This study used commercially pure (CP) titanium, 316L stainless steel, 6061-T6 aluminum, PEEK plastic, and Nitinol

(51 wt% Ni 49% Ti) shape memory alloy. Some surfaces were faced milled on a milling machine, others were milled, hand ground and then finish polished with 1 μm diamond paste. Microdrilling was performed with Ø100–150 μm drill diameter, 135° point angle, 30° rake angle, 40–44° helix angle, 2 flutes, and 1.50–3.50 mm flute length. Some were coated with AlTiN or AlTiN/Si_3N_4 under the trade name Nanotek.

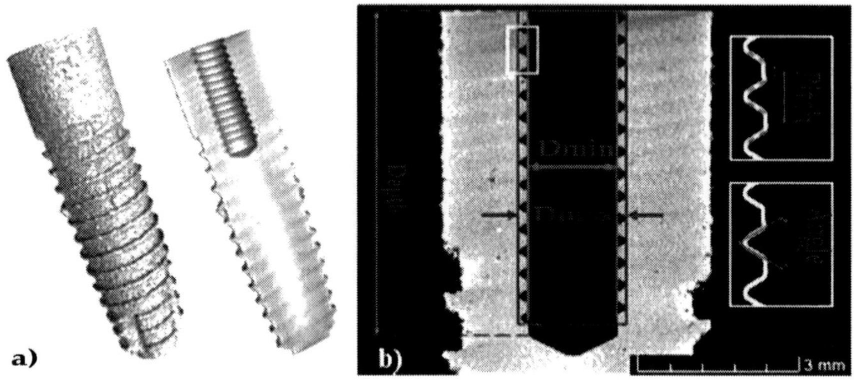

Figure 26. Inspection of drilled and tapped microhole by X-ray computed tomography. Ti 6Al 4V dental implants fabricated by direct metal laser sintering [27].

The classical Taylor's equation has been applied for macromachining, micromachining, and is used for microdrilling to show the effects of chip load and tool coating. For the same cutting speed of 20 m/min and comparable drilling distance of about 35 mm, the CP titanium can be microdrilled 400% faster than 316L stainless steel since the chip load for the former is 0.1 μm and that for the latter is 0.02 μm. Also, AlTiN coated drills improve tool life by at least 122%. This drilling operation is stopped after drilling all possible holes on the test blocks (Figures 27 and 28). Negligible tool wear are observed when drilling 6061-T6 aluminum and PEEK plastic, therefore, no modeling is necessary.

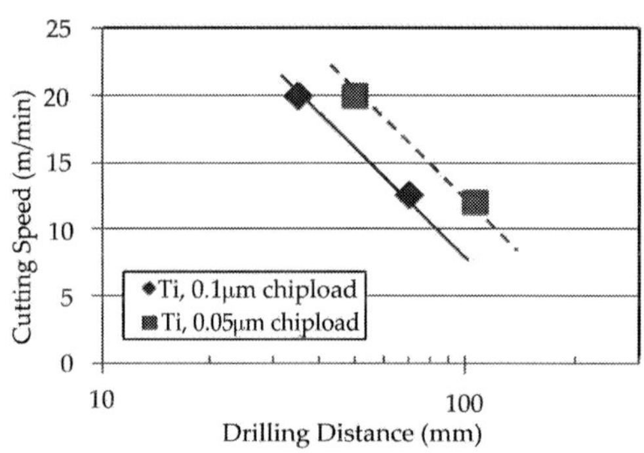

Figure 27. Tool life plot for microdrilling of CP titanium. Progressive pecking, tool life criterion 8 μm [28].

Burr, hole size, hole position, and work hardening around a drilled hole contribute to the hole quality. During the initial engagement of drill and workpiece surface, a slight lateral motion of the drill chisel edge is sufficient to bend and misguide the slender microdrill. Drill wandering refers to the deviation of a drilled hole from its intended position. A machined surface is rough enough to cause wandering of microdrills.

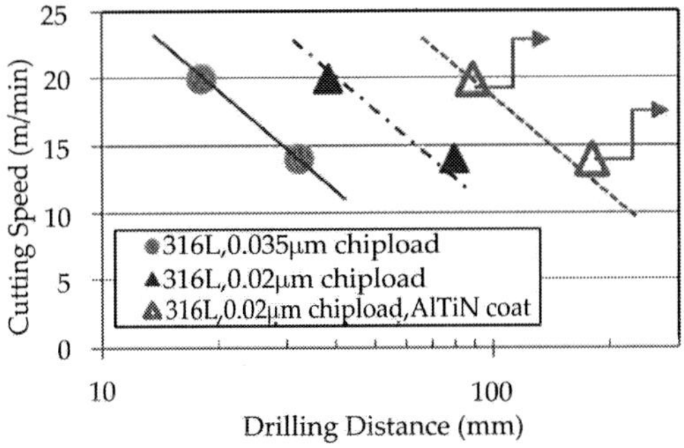

Figure 28. Tool life plot for microdrilling of 316L stainless steel. Progressive pecking, tool life criterion 15 µm. Drilling with AlTiN coated drills were stopped due to shortage of materials [28].

A sloped ridge on a rough surface bends and deviates the drill axis from intended position. Such deviation causes drill wandering, significant burrs, and irregular hole diameters. The hole quality is improved significantly when drilling on a polished surface at the same or more aggressive drilling parameters. An improvement of 27% in hole center deviation is achieved for the polished surface of CP titanium (Figure 29). Similarly, an improvement of 260% on hole deviation is achieved when drilling a polished PEEK block.

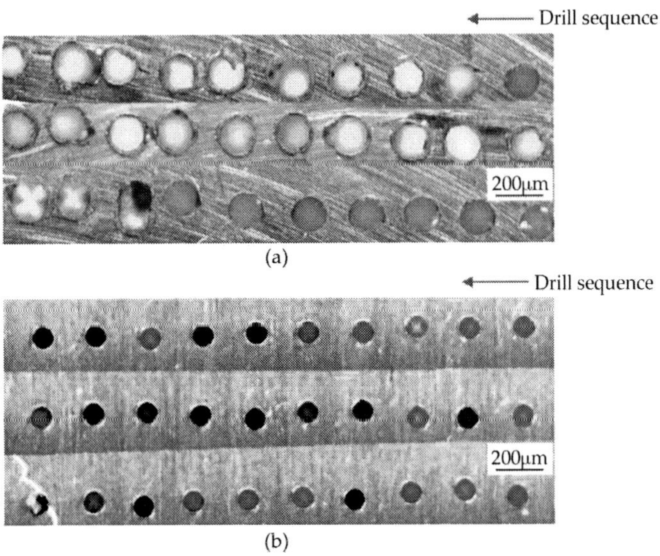

Figure 29. Composite optical images showing drill wandering and hole accuracy on (a) milled CP titanium surface; 4 m/min, 1 µm/flute, 2:1 aspect ratio, and (b) polished CP titanium surface; 12 m/min, 0.05 µm/flute, 10:1 aspect ratio [28].

Vickers microhardness near a drilled surface is obtained to study the level of plastic deformation and work hardening below a drilled surface. The hardness near the drilled surface is found to be 15% higher than those at the unmachined zone (Figure 30). The work hardening effect is caused by plastic deformation of the surface by a worn tool, and smearing of BUE on the drill wall. Similar work hardening effect is reported while drilling austenitic stainless steel leading to a higher resistance near the chisel edge of the drill. Ideally, the drill cutting edges should not shear the workpiece within the work hardened layer from a previous cut. Since the work hardening zone is about 30 μm, it is impractical to microdrill 316L stainless steel at an aggressive chip load more than 30 μm/flute since a fragile microdrill would simply fracture.

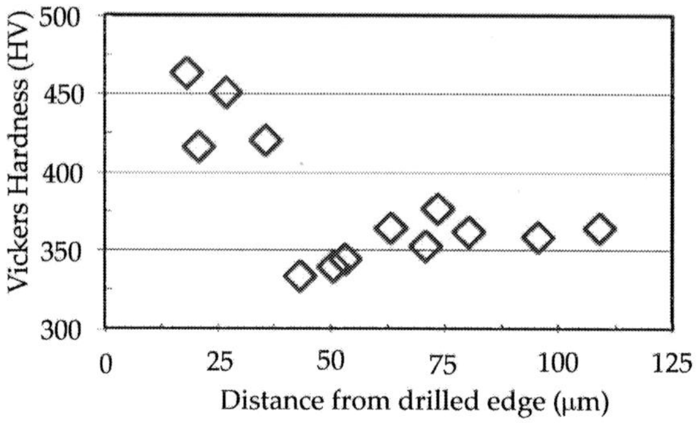

Figure 30. Vickers microhardness below drilled surface of the 10th hole. 12.7 mm drilling distance, 14 m/min, 0.035 μm/flute chip load on 316L stainless steel. Microhardness test at 50 g load, 14 s dwell time [28].

Ultraprecision Turning

Product miniaturization and demand for ultraprecision products drives the rapid development of micro/nano scale turning or ultraprecision turning. This technology produces polished and high quality spherical, aspherical parts from metals, ceramics, semiconductors, and polymers that cannot be economically produced by traditional grinding, lapping, or polishing processes. Micro/nano turning also produces intricate shape with low or no subsurface damage since it operates in the ductile-regime mode.

Commercial lathe systems for ultraprecision machining are available. Although tool and axes motions can be in the nanometer ranges, it is an engineering challenge to control the thermal drift issue of a large system. Having a very compact 200-mm system, however, would compromise the required resolution for precision microturning [29]. Diamonds are commonly used for micro/nano turning. Polycrystalline diamond tools are sintered from micron-sized diamond grains. It is less expensive but with limited capability due to large edge radius (few hundred nanometers) and lower edge strength due to attrition wear. Single crystalline diamond tools are best for micro/nano turning since they:

- Have single crystalline structure that allows a sharp cutting edge as small as few nanometers (Figure 1b),
- Have highest thermal conductivity among all engineering materials,
- Retain high strength and hardness at high temperature,
- Possess high elastic and shear moduli to resist plastic deformation, and
- Exhibit a low coefficient of friction.

A diamond tool, however, is costly and brittle. A tool with zero or negative rake angle (i) improves its edge strength, and (ii) forms a hydrostatic compressive stress field in the material just in front and below a tool, therefore, minimizes crack initiation. The single crystal diamond typically has (110) crystal plane as rake face and is brazed onto a steel shank of different shape and size.

Not any material can be successfully micro/nano turned with a diamond tool. Ferrous alloys and silicon carbide (SiC) are not suitable for diamond turning because of diffusion from highly concentrated carbon in diamond tool to a lower concentration zone of carbon in workpiece materials when the cutting zone is at high temperature during machining. Selected materials that can be successfully machined with a diamond tool are shown in Table 4. These material should be homogeneous and contain few if no impurities. The hard inclusions might either damage a sharp diamond edge or being sheared off and smearing against the machined surface. Figure 31 shows the hard beryllides in beryllium copper CA173 that plow and smear the mirror finish surface.

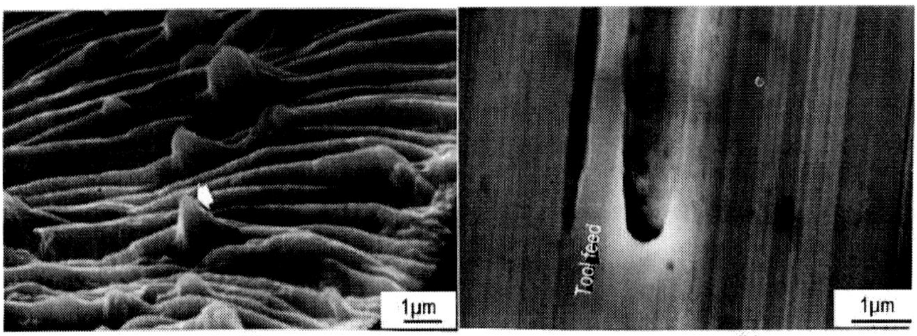

(a) (b)

Figure 31. (a) Microchip from CA 173 showing a beryllide inclusion, (b) deep scratch on machined surface by a broken beryllide.

Table 4. Examples of diamond machinable materials

Semiconductor	**Metal**	**Ceramic**	**Plastics**
Cadmium telluride Gallium arsenide Germanium Lithium niobate Silicon Silicon nitride Zinc selenide Zinc sulphide	Aluminum alloys Copper alloys Electroless nickel Gold Magnesium Silver Zinc	Aluminum oxide Zirconium oxide Optical glasses Quartz	Acrylic Fluoroplastics Nylon Polycarbonate Polymethylmethacrylate Propylene Styrene

Micromist is required to lubricate and cool both tool and machined surface. A micromist nozzle should move with a tool while blowing micro/nano chips away from the machined surface.

An experimental study was done to compare machinability of Ti 6Al 4V produced by casting or selective laser melting. TiAlN coated microturning tools with 8° rake angle, 1.3 μm edge radius were used. Microturning at orthogonal condition was performed at 6–600 m/min, 1–20 μm/rev, and 500 μm depth of cut. The chip morphologies are similar for both materials and there is no significant effect on microstructure; however, the cutting and feeding forces on AM alloy is about 3–24% higher than those for cast alloy when varying the cutting speed (Figure 32a) or changing the feed (Figure 32b). Such higher forces would shorten the tool life and subsequently degrade the surface quality.

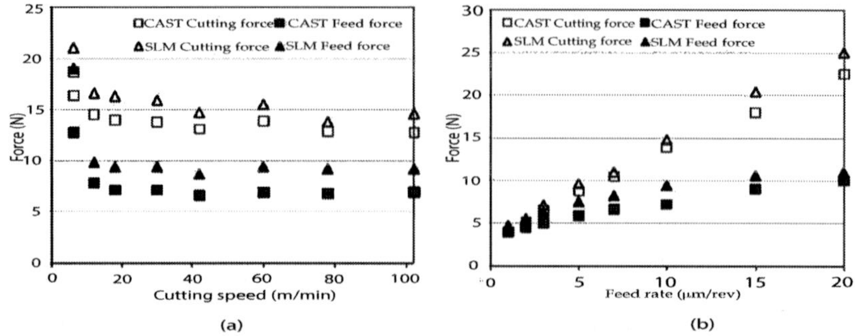

Figure 32. Comparison of cutting forces in orthogonal microturning of cast and selective laser melted Ti 6Al 4V [30].

SUMMARY

The demanding for product miniaturization and increasing part precision has fueled the development of micromachining. Recent explosion of product innovation with printing 3D metal parts also escalate the post processing studies due to inherent defects of 3D printed metals. The synergy of subtractive processes—micromilling, microdrilling, and microturning—with additive processes for metals—power bed fusion, material jetting, binder jetting, and direct energy deposition—will enable the successful manufacturing of complex metal parts to meet strict engineering requirement.

REFERENCES

1. Chu WS, Kim CS, Lee HT, Choi JO, Park JI, Song JH, et al. Hybrid manufacturing in micro/nano scale: A review. International Journal of Precision Engineering and Manufacturing-Green Technology. 2014;1(1):75-92
2. Kaynak Y, Kitay O. The effect of post-processing operations on surface characteristics of 316L stainless steel produced by selective laser melting. Additive Manufacturing. 2019;26:84-93
3. Kaynak Y, Tascioglu E. Finish machining-induced surface roughness, microhardness and XRD analysis of selective laser melted Inconel 718 alloy. Procedia CIRP. 2018;71:500-504
4. Jagadesh T, Samual GL. Investigation into cutting forces and surface roughness in micro turning of titanium alloy using coated carbide tool. Procedia Materials Science. 2014;5:2450-2457
5. Afazov AM, Rachev SM, Segal J. Modelling and simulation of micromilling cutting forces. Journal of Materials Processing Technology. 2010; 210:2154-2162
6. Rahim EA. Tool failure modes and wear mechanism of coated carbide tools when drilling Ti-6Al-4V. International Journal of Precision Technology. 2007;1 (1):30-39
7. Zhou L, Ni J, He Q. Study on failure mechanism of the coated carbide tool. International Journal of Refractory Metals and Hard Materials. 2007;25:1-5
8. Rutherford KL, Hutchings IM. A micro-abrasive wear test, with particular application to coated systems. Surface and Coatings Technology. 1996; 79:231-239
9. Kumar M, Dotson K, Melkote SN. An experimental technique to detect tool–workpiece contact in micromilling. Journal of Manufacturing Processes. 2010;12:99-105

10. Shunmugavel M, Polishetty A, Nomani J, Goldberg M, Littlefair G. Metallurgical and machinability characteristics of wrought and selective laser melted Ti-6Al-4V. Journal of Metallurgy. 2016;2016:1-10. Article ID 7407918. Available from: http://dx. doi. org/10.1155/2016/7407918
11. Gu J, Barber G, Tung S, Gu RJ. Tool life and wear mechanism of uncoated and coated milling inserts. Wear. 1999; 225–229:273-284
12. Wang Z, Kovvuria V, Araujo A, Bacci M, Hung NP, Bukkapatnam STS. Built-up-edge effects on surface deterioration in micromilling processes. Journal of Manufacturing Processes. 2016;24:321-327
13. Klocke F, Maßmann T, Gerschwiler K. Combination of PVD tool coatings and biodegradable lubricants in metal forming and machining. Wear. 2005; 259:1197-1206
14. Nam JS, Kim DH, Chung H, Lee SW. Optimization of environmentally benign micro-drilling process with nanofluid minimum quantity lubrication using response surface methodology and genetic algorithm. Journal of Cleaner Production. 2015;102: 428-436
15. Ucun I, Aslantasx K, Bedir F. The effect of minimum quantity lubrication and cryogenic pre-cooling on cutting performance in the micro milling of Inconel 718. Proceedings of the Institution of Mechanical Engineers, Part B: Journal of Engineering Manufacture. 2015;229 (12):2134-2143
16. Hung NP, Fu YQ. Effect of crystalline orientation in the ductileregime machining of silicon. Journal of Advanced Manufacturing Technology. 2000;16:871-876
17. Kajaria S, Chittipolu S, Adera S, Hung NP. Micromilling in minimum quantity lubrication. Machining Science and Technology. 2012;16:524-546
18. Ziberov M, Bacci da Silva M, Jackson M, Hung NP. Effect of cutting fluid on micromilling of Ti-6Al-4V titanium alloy, NAMRC 44-129. Procedia Manufacturing. 2016;5:332-347
19. Berestovskyi D, Hung NP, Lomeli P. Surface finish of ball-end milled microchannels. Micro- and NanoManufacturing. 2014;2(0411005):1-10
20. Rysava Z, Bruschi S. Comparison between EBM and DMLS Ti6Al4V machinability characteristics under dry micro-milling conditions. Materials Science Forum. 2016a;836-837:177-184
21. Kuram E, Ozcelik B. Multi-objective optimization using Taguchi based grey relational analysis for micro-milling of Al 7075 material with ball nose end mill. Measurement. 2013;46:1849-1864
22. Sadiq M, Hoang MN, Valencia N, Obeidat S, Hung NP. Experimental study of micromilling selective laser melted Inconel 718 superalloy. Procedia Manufacturing. 2018;26:983-992
23. Vazquez E, Gomar J, Ciurana J, Rodríguez CA. Analyzing effects of cooling and lubrication conditions in micromilling of Ti6Al4V. Journal of Cleaner Production. 2015;87:906-913
24. Khan WA, Hoang MN, Tai B, Hung NP. Through-tool minimum quantity lubrication and effect on machinability. Journal of Manufacturing Processes. 2018;34(Part B):750-757
25. Zhang Y, Jun MBG. Feasibility of lignin as additive in metalworking fluids for micro-milling. Journal of Manufacturing Processes. 2014;16: 503-510
26. Bruschi S, Tristo G, Rysava Z, Bariani PF, Umbrello D, De Chiffre L. Environmentally clean micromilling of electron beam melted Ti6Al4V. Journal of Cleaner Production. 2016;133:932-941
27. Rysava Z, Bruschi S, Carmignato S, Medeossi F, Savio E, Zanini F. Microdrilling and threading of the Ti6Al4V titanium alloy produced through additive manufacturing. Procedia CIRP. 2016b;46:583-586

28. Mohanty S, Wells S, Hung NP. Microdrilling of Biocompatible Materials. IMECE2012-87523, Proceedings, ASME International Mechanical Engineering Congress & Exposition; Houston, Texas. 2012

29. Lu Z, Yoneyama T. Micro cutting in the micro lathe turning system. International Journal of Machine Tools and Manufacture. 1999;39:1171-1183

30. Coz GL, Fischer M, Piquard R, D'Acunto A, Laheurte P, Dudzinski D. Micro cutting of Ti-6Al-4V parts produced by SLM process. Procedia CIRP. 2017;58:228-232

6

Machine Translation and the Evaluation of Its Quality

Mirjam Sepesy Maučec and Gregor Donaj

Faculty of Electrical Engineering and Computer Science, University of Maribor, Slovenia

ABSTRACT

Machine translation has already become part of our everyday life. This chapter gives an overview of machine translation approaches. Statistical machine translation was a dominant approach over the past 20 years. It brought many cases of practical use. It is described in more detail in this chapter. Statistical machine translation is not equally successful for all language pairs. Highly inflectional languages are hard to process, especially as target languages. As statistical machine translation has almost reached the limits of its capacity, neural machine translation is becoming the technology of the future. This chapter also describes the evaluation of machine translation quality. It covers manual and automatic evaluations. Traditional and recently proposed metrics for automatic machine translation evaluation are described. Human translation still provides the best translation quality, but it is, in general, time-consuming and expensive. Integration of human and machine translation is a promising workflow for the future. Machine translation will not replace human translation, but it can serve as a tool to increase productivity in the translation process.

Keywords: *Machine translation, Statistical machine translation, Neural machine translation, Evaluation, Post-editing*

INTRODUCTION

Machine translation (MT) investigates the approaches to translating text from one natural language to another. It is a subfield of computational linguistics that draws ideas from linguistics, computer science, information theory, artificial intelligence, and statistics. For a long time, it had a bad reputation because it was perceived as low quality. Especially in the last two decades, we have been witnessing great progress in MT quality, which made it interesting also for the use in the translation industry. Its quality is still lower than human translation, but that does not mean it does not have good practical uses. In the past, translation agencies and other professional translators were the only actors in the translation industry, but, in recent years, we have been faced with the rapidly growing range of machine translation solutions entering the market and being of practical use. There is increasing pressure on the translation industry in terms of price, volume, and turnaround time. The emergence of commercial applications for MT is a welcome change in translation processes. In professional or official circumstances, human translation is inevitable, as humans are essential to making sure a translation is grammatically correct and carries the same meaning as the original text. Machine translation is appropriate in different circumstances, mainly for unofficial purposes or for providing content for a human translator to improve upon it. MT has proved to be able to speed up the whole translation process, but it cannot replace the human translator. The questions that researchers in the translation industry are trying to answer today are: How much can human translators benefit from using MT? How could MT be integrated efficiently into translation processes? If MT is integrated into the translation workflow, will the quality of translation remain at the same level? These questions will not be answered explicitly in this chapter, but an effort will be made to show that MT is worth being part of the translation process, as its quality can be evaluated reliably. MT opens new opportunities for translators through using MT output only as a suggestion and, if necessary, post-editing it to the desired quality. It could be much faster than translation from scratch. This process is further discussed in the penultimate section of the chapter.

MACHINE TRANSLATION

Computer scientists began trying to solve the problem of MT in the 1950s. The first published machine translation experiment was performed by the Georgetown University and IBM. It involved automatic translation of more than 60 Russian sentences into English. The system had only 6 grammar rules and 250 lexical items in its vocabulary. It was by no means a fully featured system. The sentences for translation were selected carefully, as the idea of the experiment was to attract governmental and public interest and funding by showing the possibilities of MT. Many problems of MT had come to light right after, and, consequently, for a long time, MT was present only as a research area in computational linguistics. Overtime, different approaches for MT were defined and gained maturity for practical use today. The history of the development of MT approaches is given in Figure 1 . In [1], it has been shown that 22% of the MT users in the translation industry use rule-based MT systems, 50% use statistical MT systems, and 36% of them use hybrid MT systems.

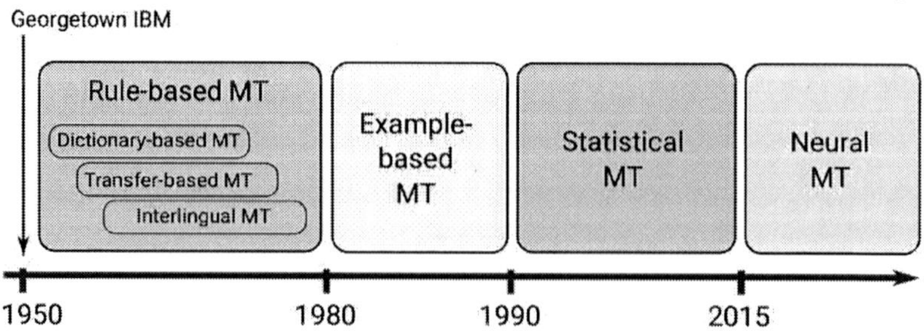

Figure 1. Timeline of MT evolution.

Rule-based Machine Translation

The first approaches for MT were based on linguistic rules that were used to parse the source sentence and create the intermediate representation, from which the target language sentence was created. Such approaches are appropriate to translate between closely related languages. The rule-based machine translation methods include dictionary-based MT, transfer-based MT, and interlingual MT.

Dictionary-based MT uses entries in a language dictionary to find a words equivalent in the target language. Using a dictionary as the sole information source for translation means that the words will be translated as they are translated in a dictionary. As this is, in many cases, not correct, grammatical rules are applied afterwards.

Transfer-based MT belongs to the next generation of machine translation. The source sentence is transformed into an intermediate, less language-specific structure. This structure is then transferred into a similar structure of the target language, and, finally, the sentence is generated in the target language. The transfer uses morphological, syntactic, and/or semantic information about the source and target languages.

In interlingual MT, the source sentence is transformed into an intermediate, artificial language. It is a neutral representation that is independent of any language. The target sentence is then generated out of the interlingua.

To be useful in practice, rule-based MT systems consist of large collections of rules, developed manually over time by translation experts, mapping structures from the source language to the target language. They are costly and time-consuming to implement and maintain. As rules are added and updated, there is the potential of generating ambiguity and translation degradation. Rule-based MT requires linguistic experts to apply language rules to the system.

Example-based Machine Translation

Example-based MT is based on the idea of analogy. It is grounded upon a search for analogous examples of sentence pairs in the source and target languages. Example-based MT belongs to corpus-based approaches because examples are extracted from large collections of bilingual corpora. Given the source sentence, sentences with similar sub-sentential components are extracted from the source side of the bilingual corpus, and their translations to the target language are then used to construct the complete translation of the sentence.

Statistical Machine Translation

Statistical MT is based on statistical methods [2]. It also belongs to corpus-based approaches, as statistical methods are applied on large bilingual corpora. Building a statistical MT system does not require linguistic knowledge. Statistical MT utilises statistical models generated from the analysis of texts, being either monolingual or bilingual. It is called training data. If more training data are available, better and larger MT systems can be built. Statistical MT systems are computationally expensive to build and store. Statistical MT can be adapted easily to a specific domain if enough bilingual and/or monolingual data from that domain are available.

Statistical MT is defined using the noisy-channel model from the information theory:

$$\mathbf{e} = \underset{\mathbf{e}}{\arg\max} P(\mathbf{e}|\mathbf{f}) = \underset{\mathbf{e}}{\arg\max} P(\mathbf{e})P(\mathbf{f}|\mathbf{e}). \quad (1)$$

where f is the source sentence and e is the target sentence. The source sentence consists of words f_j and the target sentence of words e_i . Words f_j belong to the source vocabulary F and the words e_i to the target vocabulary E. In the phrase-based model, the source sentence f is broken down into I phrases $\bar{f}_i$ and each source phrase $\bar{f}_i$ is translated into a target phrase.

Standard phrase-based SMT models consist of three components:

- A translation model of phrases (denoted as $\phi(\bar{f}|\bar{e})$). In practice, both translation directions, with the proper weight setting, are used: $\phi(\bar{f}|\bar{e})$ and $\phi(\bar{e}|\bar{f})$.
- A reordering model (denoted as d). It is based on distance. The reordering distance is computed as $start_i - end_{i-1} - 1$, where $start_i$ is the position of the first word in phrase i, end_{i-1} is the position of the last word of phrase i-1, and d is the probability distribution of reordering.
- A language model (denoted as *pLM* ðeÞ). It makes the output a fluent sequence of words in the target language and is most commonly an *n*-gram language model.

Log-linear models of phrase-based SMT are most commonly used:

$$p(\mathbf{e},a|f) = \exp\left[\lambda_\phi \sum_{i=1}^{I} \log\phi\left(\bar{f}_i|\bar{e}_i\right) + \lambda_d \sum_{i=1}^{I} \log d(start_i - end_{i-1} - 1) + \lambda_{LM} \sum_{i=1}^{N} \log p_{LM}(e_i|e_1 \ldots e_{i-1})\right]. \quad (2)$$

where a is an alignment between source and target sentences and N is the length of the target sentence.

Statistical MT faces many obstacles. Data sparsity of highly inflected languages limits the effectiveness of statistical MT. Advanced statistical MT systems try to overcome the limitations by introducing data preprocessing and data post-processing. In Figure 2 data preprocessing is used, where morphosyntactic tags (MSD) and lemmas are assigned to words and used in translation and language models. Reordering model captures short-term dependencies. The operation sequence model (OSM) is able to capture long-distance dependencies [3]. It models translation by a linear sequence of operations. The operation generates translation, performs reordering, jumps forward and backward, etc. Having morphosyntactic tags and lemmas available, OSM could be constructed based on them, as depicted in Figure 2 .

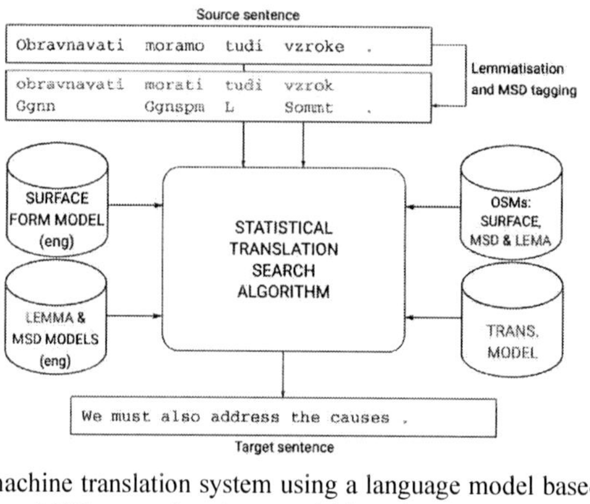

Figure 2. Statistical machine translation system using a language model based on surface forms, a language model based on MSD tags, a language model based on lemmas, and three OSMs.

Hybrid Machine Translation

While statistical methods still dominate research work in MT, most commercial MT systems were, from the beginning, only rule-based. Recently, boundaries between the two approaches have narrowed, and hybrid approaches emerged, which try to gain benefit from both of them. We distinguish two groups of hybrid MT, those guided by rule-based MT and those guided by statistical approaches. Hybrid systems, guided by rule-based MT, use statistical MT to identify the set of appropriate translation candidates and/or to combine partial translations into the final sentence in the target language. Hybrid systems, guided by statistical MT, use rules at pre-/post-processing stages.

Neural Machine Translation

Neural MT emerged as a successor of statistical MT. It has made rapid progress in recent years, and it is paving its way into the translation industry as well. Neural MT is a deep learning-based approach to MT that uses a large neural network based on vector representations of words. If compared with statistical MT, there is no separate language model, translation model, or reordering model, but just a single sequence model, which predicts one word at a time. The prediction is conditioned on the source sentence and the already produced sequence in the target language. The prediction power of neural MT is more promising than that of statistical MT, as neural networks share statistical evidence between similar words. In Figure 3 one of the proposed topology for neural machine translation is given with the same example sentence as in Figure 2 . The input words are passed through the layers of the encoder (blue circles) to its last layer, the context vector, updating it for every input word. The context layer is then passed through the decoder layers (red circles) to output words, and it is again updated for each output word.

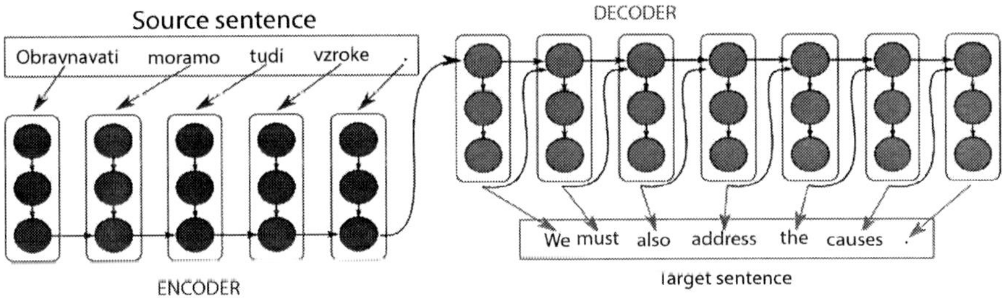

Figure 3. Neural machine translation system using the encoder-decoder topology.

The encoder-decoder recurrent neural network architecture with attention is currently the state of the art for machine translation.

Although effective, the neural MT systems still suffer some issues, such as scaling to larger vocabularies of words and the slow speed of training the models. In addition, large corpus is needed to train neural MT systems with performance comparable to statistical machine translation. Researchers continue to work on solving open problems.

PROBLEMS IN MACHINE TRANSLATION

The fast progress of MT has boosted translation quality significantly, but, unfortunately, machine translation approaches are not equally successful for all language pairs. Morphologically rich languages are problematic in MT, especially if the translation is from a morphologically less complex to a morphologically more complex language. Morphological distinctions not present in the source language need to be generated in the target language. Much work on morphology-aware approaches relies heavily on language-specific tools, which are not always available. Many morphologically rich languages fall in the category of low-resource languages.

One group of morphologically rich languages is a group of highly inflected languages. They are difficult not only for MT but also for other language technology applications [4, 5]. The main problem in highly inflected languages is that the large number of inflected word forms lead to data sparsity (see example in Table 1), which results in unreliable estimates in statistical MT [6]. Most words in a given corpus occur at most a handful of times. Therefore, the translation rule coverage is partial, and the estimation of translation probabilities is poor. Some approaches try to reduce the problem of data sparsity by using modelling units other than words; for example, stems and endings, lemmas and morphosyntactic tags, etc. Relaxed word order in inflectional languages poses another problem (see example in Table 2). Usually, very little information about the target word order is obtainable from the source sentence. Pre-ordering approaches learn to preprocess the source sentence during training in such a way that the words on the source side appear closer to their final positions on the target side. A frequent problem of inflectional languages is also an inaccurate translation of pronouns. There are also many cases in inflectional languages where the subject is dropped completely. Problematic also is differences in the expression of negation. Slavic languages fall into the category of highly inflected languages, and they cause many problems in machine translation [7, 8].

Table 1. Inflected word forms of the word "student" (masculine) in Slovene

	Singular	**Dual**	**Plural**
Nominative	študent	študenta	študenti
Genitive	študenta	študentov	študentov
Dative	študentu	študentoma	študentom
Accusative	študenta	študenta	študente
Locative	študentu	študentih	študentih
Instrumental	študentom	študentoma	študenti

In the example, the word has nine different endings.

Table 2. Word permutations of the English sentence "I have been studying English for two years" in Slovene

1.	Angleščino študiram dve leti.
2.	Dve leti študiram angleščino.
3.	Študiram angleščino, dve leti.

Third example is used in colloquial speech.

Another group of morphologically rich languages is a group of agglutinative languages, which are even more difficult to use in machine translation. In an agglutinative language, words may consist of more than one, and possibly many, morphemes. Each morpheme in a sequence indicates a particular grammatical meaning. Morphemes are used commonly as basic units in MT for those groups of languages. All these phenomena cause errors in translations produced by MT systems and make the use of MT questionable. It is necessary to evaluate MT quality before use in practice.

MACHINE TRANSLATION EVALUATION

As MT emerges as an important mode of translation, its quality is becoming more and more important. Judging translation quality is called machine translation evaluation. It is defined commonly by technical terms. It means, with the exception of human (i.e. manual) evaluation, that it is defined as an algorithm that can be coded into a programme and run by a computer that calculates the evaluation score, which tells the user how good a translation is. Translation evaluation methods count word- and/or sentence-based errors that can be detected automatically, while general text-level aspects are not taken into account. This weakness of automatic MT evaluation is one of the main criticisms in the translation community. Despite that, in the last decade, we have been witnessing great progress in automatic MT evaluation.

MT quality can be measured in many different ways, depending on the goal of the evaluation and the means available. Traditionally, there are two paradigms of machine translation evaluation: Glass-box evaluation and black-box evaluation. Glass-box evaluation measures the quality of a system based on internal system properties. Black-box evaluation examines only the system output, without connecting it to the internal mechanisms of the translation system. The focus in this section will be on black-box evaluation. It is concerned only with the objective behaviour of the system upon a predetermined evaluation set. An evaluation set is a set of sentences in the source language and their translations into the target language, obtained by the translation system.

These sentence pairs are then exposed to the evaluation. An evaluation set needs to be selected carefully to cover all data features important for future use of the translation system. The same translation quality can then be expected on the other data that is of the same type as the evaluation set; if not, translations of quite different quality could be obtained. The reason is in the fact that MT systems are trained on translation examples. If these examples are of a different type to the text that is afterwards translated by the system, the system has only weak knowledge about its translation and, consequently, produces poor translations. Different types of data mean variations in structure, genre, and style. Evaluation, on the other hand, can focus on testing the systems's robustness. In this case, the evaluation set is composed of subsets of different data types. One should be aware that obtaining a robust MT system means at least training it with translation examples of different data types.

There is also a difference between judging and measuring the quality of MT output as a final product and judging and measuring the usability of MT output for subsequent corrections by humans, called post-editing (PE). As regards the latter, it is interesting to know how much editing effort is needed to make the MT output match a reference translation or to become an acceptable translation. What is acceptable translation is left to be decided by the translation expert. In the MT community, there are no criteria for it.

For a long time, methods for evaluating human and MT quality have been disconnected. The comparison between them was impossible. In recent years, a framework called multidimensional quality metrics (MQM) [9] was developed for evaluating the quality of both human and machine translations. It includes over 100 issue types that cover all of the major translation quality evaluation metrics. For the specific translation quality judgement task, relevant issues may be chosen from MQM. The focus of this section is only on the evaluation of MT quality, whereas human translation is taken as the gold standard.

Manual Evaluation

The most common option for judging and measuring machine translation quality is human evaluation. The quality of MT output is judged by experts in translation and linguistics from two different perspectives. The first perspective is the degree of adherence to the target text and target language norms, referring, for example, to features such as grammaticality and clarity. This quality evaluation perspective is known as fluency. When judging fluency, the source text is not relevant. The evaluators have access to only the translation being judged and not the source data. Fluency requires an expert fluent only in the target language. On the other hand, source text adherence is judged to the source text norms and meaning, in terms of how well the target text represents the informational content of the source text. It is known as accuracy. The evaluators have access to the source text and translations being judged. Frequently, the context of a sentence is also taken into account. The evaluators must be bilingual in both the source and target languages. The adequacy and fluency are usually judged on a 5-point scale, as given in Table 3 .

Table 3. Numeric scale for judging adequacy and fluency

Adequacy		**Fluency**	
5	All meaning	5	Flawless language
4	Most meaning	4	Good language
3	Much meaning	3	Non-native language
2	Little meaning	2	Disfluent language
1	None	1	Incomprehensible

Human evaluation is time-consuming and expensive. It is also inherently subjective. To alleviate the problem of subjectivity, more experts are usually asked to evaluate the translations in the same evaluation set, and their evaluations are, finally, justified statistically.

Automatic Evaluation

MT systems are rarely static, and they tend to be improved over time as resources grow and bugs are fixed. The evaluation needs to be repeated many times. Automatic evaluation metrics are cost-free alternatives to human evaluation. They are used commonly during the development of MT systems to estimate improvement. They are also applicable to compare different MT systems. While using automatic metrics to judge the translation quality, it is important to understand what their scores mean. They rely on the idea that MT quality in itself should approach human quality. Automatic metrics depend on the availability of human reference translation. They evaluate the output of MT systems by comparing it to the reference translation. As there is a great variability even in human translation, it is important to have more human reference translations for each machine-translated sentence to be evaluated. Evaluation metrics then provide evaluation scores based on the most similar reference translation.

Standard and recently proposed automatic metrics for MT evaluation will be discussed in the continuation of this section. Statistical correlation coefficients are used to see how close automatic evaluation is to manual judgements. Three correlation coefficients will be described later in the section. Machine translation, coupled with subsequent post-editing, has become a widely accepted method in the translation industry. This type of translation workflow will be discussed at the end of this section.

BASIC METRICS FOR TRANSLATION EVALUATION IN MT

An obvious method for evaluation is to look at the translation and judge by hand, whether it is correct or not. To get reliable judgements, the evaluators should be appropriately qualified. From a practical point of view, manual evaluation, performed by translation experts, is expensive and takes time. What is needed are automatic metrics that are quick and cheap to use and approximate human judgements accurately. De facto metrics, used in the MT community, are BLEU, NIST, METEOR, and TER. All these metrics need reference translations because they compare the MT output with reference translations and provide comparison scores. If reference translations are available, these metrics can be used to evaluate the output of any number of systems quickly, without the need for human intervention. Let us take an example where the reference translation is "Dve leti že študiram angleščino" and the MT output to be evaluated is "Angleščino študiram dve leti". If we compute the precision, we get:

$$precision = \frac{correct}{length_o} = \frac{4}{4} = 100\%. \quad (3)$$

Correct counts the number of correctly translated words, and $length_o$ is the length of machine translation output. For the same example, the recall is:

$$recall = \frac{correct}{length_r} = \frac{4}{5} = 80\%. \quad (4)$$

$length_r$ is the length of reference translation. F-measure results in:

$$F_1 = \frac{precision \cdot recall}{\frac{precision + recall}{2}} = 89\%. \quad (5)$$

Based on given measures, the quality of translation is good, as reordering is not penalised. It is not always a good decision. For example, the MT output "Dve angleščino študiram leti" will get the same evaluation result, even though the translation is disfluent.

BLEU [10] measures the overlap of unigrams (single words) and high-order *n*-grams between MT output and reference translations. It is defined as follows:

$$BLEU = \min\left(1, \frac{length_o}{length_r}\right)\left(\prod_{i=1}^{4} precision_i\right)^{\frac{1}{4}}. \quad (6)$$

The main component of BLEU is *n*-gram precision, i.e. $precision_i$. It is calculated as the ratio between matched *n*-grams and the total number of *n*-grams in the evaluated translation. Precision is calculated separately for each *n*-gram order, and the precisions are combined via a geometric averaging. The highest *n*-gram order is defined commonly to be four (four words in a sequence). Higher-order *n*-grams are used as an indirect measure of a translations level of grammatical well-formedness. The BLEU metric computes the modified precision score, weighted by the brevity penalty, which punishes sentences that are shorter than the reference. The final scores range from 0 to 1. Table 4 contains the calculation of BLEU score for our example.

BLEU is typically computed over the entire corpus, not single sentences. It is important to point out that very few translations will attain a score of 1 unless they are identical to a reference translation. For this reason, even a human translator will not necessarily score 1, as there is great variability of possible correct translations. In this sense, it is also important to note that having more reference translations per sentence is highly welcome. It will increase the BLEU score. NIST [11] is a close derivate of BLEU.

Table 4. BLEU score computation for the MT output "Angleščino študiram dve leti", if the reference is "Dve leti že študiram angleščino"

Metric	Score
1-gram precision	$\frac{4}{4}$
2-gram precision	$\frac{1}{3}$
3-gram precision	$\frac{0}{2}$
4-gram precision	$\frac{0}{1}$
Brevity penalty	$\frac{4}{5}$
BLEU	0%

Both metrics, BLEU and NIST, focus only on *n*-gram precision and disregard recall. Recall is the ratio between matched *n*-grams and the total number of *n*-grams in the reference translation. METEOR metric [12] combines precision and recall. The authors of METEOR argue that the brevity penalty in BLEU does not compensate adequately for the lack of recall. METEOR computes a score only for unigram matching. Matching is done in three stages. The first stage is exact matching. Strings are aligned, which are identical in the reference and the translation. Words that are not matched are stemmed in the second stage. Stemming is the process of reducing inflected words to their word stem by cutting off the ends of words. Words with the same morphological root are aligned after stemming. In the last stage, unaligned words which are found to be synonyms are aligned, according to WordNet. WordNet [13] is a large lexical database of synonyms (called synsets). In WordNet, synsets are interlinked by means of conceptual-semantic and lexical relations. METEOR does not use higher-order *n*-grams, as *n*-gram counts do not require an explicit word-to-word matching. In METEOR, an explicit measure of the level of grammaticality is used. It captures directly how good the structure of the matched words in the machine translation is in relation to the reference.

Word error rate (WER) metric was first used to evaluate automatic speech recognition. It counts the minimum number of edits needed to change the evaluated translation so that it matches the references exactly, normalised by the average length of the references. The minimum number of edits is also called Levenshtein distance. Possible edits are insertion (*I*), deletion (*D*), and substitution (*S*) of single words. Matched words are denoted with M. Different edits can have different weights. For example, substitution is usually weighted at unity, but deletion and insertion are both weighted at 0.5:

$$WER = \frac{S + 0.5 \cdot D + 0.5 \cdot I}{length_r}. \quad (6)$$

$$TER = \frac{S + D + I + Shift}{length_r}. \quad (7)$$

Table 5 contains the calculation of WER for our example.

Translation edit rate (TER) metric [14] is a derivate from the WER. It uses an additional edit step, namely, shifts of word sequences (*Shift*). A shift moves a contiguous sequence of words within the evaluated translation to another location within the translation. All edits have equal cost. If more than one reference is available, and since the minimum number of edits needed to modify the translation is called for, only the number of edits to the closest reference is measured. TER is normalised by the average length of the reference. Position-independent error rate (PER) is another derivate from WER, which treats the reference and translation output as bags of words. Words from the translation are aligned to words in the reference, ignoring the position.

Table 5. WER computation for the MT output "Angleščino študiram dve leti", if the reference is "Dve leti že študiram angleščino"

Reference:			dve	leti	že	študiram	angleščino
Output:	angleščino	študiram	dve	leti			
Edit:	I	I	M	M	D	D	D
$WER = \frac{0.5 \cdot 2 + 0.5 \cdot 3}{5} = 50\%$							

ADVANCED METRICS FOR TRANSLATION EVALUATION IN MT

Although BLEU, NIST, METEOR, and TER metrics are used most frequently in the evaluation of MT quality, new metrics emerge almost every year. There is a metrics-shared task, held annually at the WMT Conference where new evaluation metrics are proposed [15, 16, 17]. Those which exhibit high correlation with human judgement will be presented from the pool of recently defined metrics.

CDER [18] is a more advanced metric that is concerned with edits and Levenshtein distance. It calculates the distance between two strings e_i^I and $e_i^{\sim L}$ using the auxiliary quantity D(i,l), defined as:

$$D(i,l) := d_{CD}\left(e_1^i, e_1^{\sim l}\right). \tag{9}$$

$$D(0,0) = 0, \tag{10}$$

$$D(i,l) = min \begin{Bmatrix} D(i-1,l-1) + c_{SUB}(e_i,\tilde{e}_l), \\ D(i-1,l) + 1, \\ D(i,l-1) + 1, \\ \min_{i'} D(i',l) + 1. \end{Bmatrix} \tag{11}$$

In addition to classical edit operations (i.e. insertion, deletion, and substitution), it models block reordering explicitly as an additional edit operation. As a further improvement, it introduces word dependent substitution costs $c_{SUB}(e_i, \tilde{e}_l)$. The observation that the substitution of a word with a similar one is likely to affect translation quality less than the substitution with a completely different word is accounted for in a metric score.

Tolerant BLEU [19] and LeBLEU [20] are derivates of BLEU with a relaxation of the strict word *n*-gram matching that is used in standard BLEU. Tolerant BLEU applies a specific distance measure that requires an exact match only in the middle of words, not in words as a whole. LeBLEU uses a distance measure based on characters. It also facilitates a fuzzy matching of longer chunks of text that allows, for example, to match two independent words with a compound.

CharacTER [21] is a derivate of TER:

$$CharacTER = \frac{S_{char} + D_{char} + I_{char} + Shift\ Cost}{length_{ochar}}. \quad (12)$$

It calculates the edit rate on character level, whereas shift edits are still performed on word level. First, a technique for word-level shifts is performed, words are then split into characters, and, finally, the edit distance is calculated based on characters, and Shift Cost is calculated. In addition, the lengths of translations in characters ($length_{ochar}$) instead of references are used for normalising the edit distance, which effectively counters the issue that shorter translations normally achieve lower TER. If we have two translations of different lengths, but with the same edit distance, they will obtain the same TER, as the length of the reference remains unchanged. In the same case, the longer translation will obtain lower TER if the edit distance is normalised by the length of translation.

METEOR universal [22] is a derivate of METEOR. It adds the fourth stage to matching. It is paraphrase matching. For each target phrase e_1, all source phrases f that e1 translates are found. Each alternate phrase $(e_2 \neq e_1)$ that translates f is considered a paraphrase with probability $P(f|e_1) \cdot P(e_2|f)$. The cumulative probability of e2 being a paraphrase of e1 is the sum over all possible pivot phrases f:

$$P(e_2|e_1) = \sum P(f|e_1) \cdot P(e_2|f). \quad (13)$$

Phrases are matched if they are listed as paraphrases in a language appropriate paraphrase table. Paraphrases are extracted automatically from the parallel corpora used to train statistical MT systems.

The BEER [23] metric provides a linear combination of different features:

$$BEER(h, r) = \sum_i w_i \times \phi_i(h, r) \quad (14)$$

where h is the system output and r is the reference. Each feature $\phi_i(h,r)$ has a weight w_i assigned to it. The first group of features consists of adequacy features. These features use precision, recall, and F1-score for different counts. F1-score is the harmonic mean of precision and recall multiplied by the constant of 2. The constant of 2 scales the F1-score to 1 when both recall and precision are 1. In BEER, function words and content words (nonfunction words) are counted separately. By differentiating function and nonfunction words, a better estimate is obtained of which words are more important and are less. The most important adequacy feature is a count of matching character *n*-grams. Using it, the translations are considered partially correct even if they did not get the morphology completely right. Character *n*-grams of order 6 are used. The second group of features comprises ordering features. Word order is evaluated by presenting the reordering as a permutation and calculating the distance to the ideal monotone permutation. Permutation trees are used to estimate long-distance reordering.

ChrF [24] is another, even simpler, metric based on character *n*-grams. It computes an F-score, based on precision and recall, using character *n*-grams:

$$ChrF\beta = (1 + \beta^2)\frac{ChrP \cdot ChrR}{\beta^2 \cdot ChrP + ChrR} \quad (15)$$

ChrP and ChrR are character *n*-gram precision and recall, averaged over all *n*-grams. ChrP is the percentage of *n*-grams in the translation, which have a counterpart in the reference. ChrR is the percentage of character *n*-grams in the reference, which are also present in the translation. In the final score, the parameter is used, which gives more importance to recall than to precision. In [25], the optimal value for β is found to be 2, and the metric is called chrF2. In this metric, a recall has two times more importance than precision. WordF2 is a similar metric, where words are used instead of characters. Different weightings for *n*-grams were also investigated. Uniform weights are the most promising for machine translation evaluation.

DREEM [26] is a new metric based on distributed representations of words and sentences generated by deep neural networks. Neural networks are models that imitate human brains to recognise patterns in sequences. DREEM employs three different types of word and sentence representations: One-hot representations, distributed word representations learned from a neural network model, and distributed sentence representations computed with a recursive autoencoder. The final score is the cosine similarity of the representation of the translation and the reference, multiplied with a length penalty.

Ratatouille [27] is a metric combination of Bleu, Beer, Meteor, and few more metrics, out of which meteor-WSD is a novel contribution. METEOR-WSD is an extension of METEOR that includes synonym mappings.

In this section, state-of-the-art MT evaluation metrics were investigated briefly. Only the most important characteristics of them were exposed. For a more elaborate description of each metric, the reader is advised to use the provided references to literature.

It should be noted that despite the well-known problems with BLEU, and the availability of many other metrics, MT system developers have continued to use BLEU as the primary measure of translation quality.

Today, different MT systems are available for use in practice. Usually, the qualities of different MT systems are compared between themselves by computing the translation quality scores on a predetermined evaluation set. The question arises whether, if there is a difference in quality on the evaluation set, one can be ensured that different MT systems indeed own different system quality. A difference in quality on an evaluation set may be just the result of happenstance. Research work on the statistical significance test for MT evaluation was done by Koehn [28], and the bootstrap resampling method is proposed to compute the statistical significance intervals for evaluation metrics on evaluation data. Statistical significance usually refers to the notions of the p-value, the probability that the observed difference in quality will occur by chance given the null hypothesis.

CORRELATION BETWEEN AUTOMATIC AND HUMAN EVALUATION

Human judgements of translation quality are usually trusted as the gold standard, and the aim of an automatic evaluation metric is to produce quality estimates that are as close as possible to human judgements. As there are many different evaluation metrics, the user needs to decide which automatic evaluation metric he trusts the most. Correlation coefficients are used commonly to measure the closeness of automatic metric scores and manual judgements. Manual MT quality judgements on a number of test data are needed for comparison. Correlation coefficients are then computed on system level and/ or segment level.

System-level comparison is done to compare different MT systems in general. First, each system gets a cumulative rank that reflects how high the annotators ranked that system. The metric scores of systems are also converted into ranks, and then the Spearman's rank correlation coefficient ρ is computed as [16]:

$$\rho = 1 - \frac{6 \cdot \sum_{i=1}^{n} d_i^2}{n \cdot (n^2 - 1)}. \tag{16}$$

d_i is the difference between the annotator's rank and metric's rank for system i . The number of systems is denoted with *n*. The possible values of ρ range between 1 (where all systems are ranked in identical order) and − 1 (where the systems are ranked in the reverse order). Metrics with values of Spearman's ρ closer to 1 are better. The Spearman's correlation coefficient ρ is sometimes too harsh [17]: If a metric disagrees with humans in ranking two systems of a very similar quality, the ρ coefficient penalises this equally as if the systems were very distant in their quality. Pearson's correlation coefficient *r* is sometimes preferred [17]. It measures the strength of the linear relationship between a metric's scores and human scores:

$$r = \frac{\sum_{i=1}^{n} (H_i - \overline{H}) \cdot (M_i - \overline{M})}{\sqrt{\sum_{i=1}^{n} (H_i - \overline{H})^2} \sqrt{\sum_{i=1}^{n} (M_i - \overline{M})^2}}. \tag{17}$$

H is the vector of annotator's scores of all systems, and M is the vector of the corresponding scores as predicted by the given metric. $\overline{H}$ and $\overline{M}$ are their means, respectively. Figure 4 shows Pearson's correlations of selected system-level metrics and MT systems built for different language pairs [15]. We can see that in majority of cases metrics correlate well with human judgements.

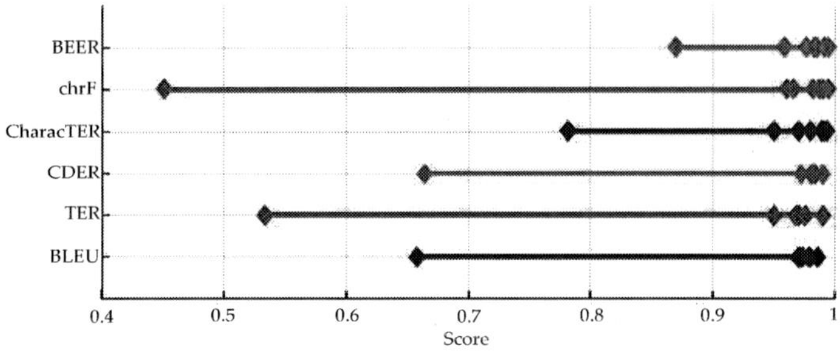

Figure 4. Pearson's correlation coefficient r for selected evaluation metrics used for different MT systems.

The quality of a metric's segment level scores is usually measured by means of Kendall's τ rank correlation coefficient [17]. Let r(·) denotes annotator's rank and m(·) metric's rank. To compute Kendall's τ , the annotators rank all the translations of each segment from the best to the worst. Pairs (a,b) are then built where one system's translation r(a) of a particular segment is judged to be (strictly) better than the other system's translation r(b) :

$$Pairs := \{(a,b) \mid r(a) < r(b)\}. \tag{18}$$

Afterwards, all concordant and discordant pairs are counted:

$$Con := \{(a,b) \in Pairs \mid m(a) > m(b)\},$$

$$Dis := \{(a,b) \in Pairs \mid m(a) < m(b)\}. \tag{19}$$

In a concordant pair, a human annotator and an automatic metric agree in ranking, and in a discordant pair, they disagree. Finally, Kendall's τ is computed as:

$$\tau = \frac{|Con| - |Dis|}{|Con| + |Dis|}. \tag{20}$$

τ value is between −1 (a metric always predicted a different order than humans did) and 1 (a metric always predicted the same order as humans). Metrics with higher τ are better.

In this section, no analysis of correlations for automatic metrics is presented, as it depends on many parameters. In general, all evaluation metrics presented in this chapter correlate well with human judgements. It is only worth mentioning that, for inflected languages, metrics that work on character level correlate better with human judgements than metrics that work only on word level.

POST-EDITING MACHINE TRANSLATION

In recent years, MT has become accepted more widely in the translation industry [29]. The most common workflow involves the use of machine-translated text as a raw translation that is corrected or post-edited by a translator. Post-editing (PE) tools and practices for such workflows are being developed in large multilingual organisations, such as the European Commission [30]. The researchers in [31] report that 30% of the companies in the translation industry currently use MT. The majority (70%) of the MT users combine MT with PE at least some of the time.

Post-editing MT is attractive because it has been shown to be faster than human translation. It is faster than translation from scratch and even faster than translation assisted by a translation memory [32]. Speed is not the only factor that should be taken into account when assessing the post-editing process. More recent studies have looked at ways of determining post-editing effort. In [33], three levels of post-editing effort are defined: Temporal effort, cognitive effort, and technical effort. The temporal effort is the time needed to post-edit a given text, cognitive effort is the activation of cognitive processes during post-editing, and the technical effort means the operations such as insertions and deletions that are performed during post-editing. All three levels of post-editing effort are influenced greatly by the translation quality. The use of PE and MT also raises the question about the quality of final translations. Has the quality improved, or is it worse?

As PE effort is related strongly to MT quality, derivatives of standard quality metrics are developed, which are concerned more with PE effort. Human-mediated translation error rate (HTER) [14] is a human-in-the-loop variant of TER. Instead of a reference, post-edited translation is used in the comparison. HTER centres on what edits are to be made to convert a translation into its post-edited version. It is computed as the ratio between the number of edit steps and the number of words in the post-edited version. HTER can be used as a measure of technical PE effort: The fewer changes necessary to convert the translation into its post-edited version, the less the effort required from the translator.

HTER is concerned more with the final translation and not the process. In [34] a metric called actual edit rate (AER) is proposed, which measures the translator's actual edit operations, which may involve more complex tasks, for example, applying corrections to previously post-edited parts of the text.

A study on PE of MT confirmed the relation between HTER and MT qualities [34]. An increase in HTER was evident as the quality of the MT system decreased. In contrast, they did not establish any significant association between AER and MT qualities. Keyboard activity may not be as sensitive to MT quality as PE time. They also found a linear relationship between MT quality and post-editing speed. MT quality was measured by the BLEU score of the system. The increase of BLEU score by one point resulted in a decrease of post-editing speed of about 0.16 seconds/word post-editing time. Their study also shows the correlation between the quality of machine translation output and the quality after post-editing. They confirmed that worse translation almost always leads to worse result after post-editing. As the use of MT and PE workflows has increased, there is a growing demand for expertise in PE skills. The research on and teaching of skills specific to post-editing has become necessary. The authors in [31] emphasise the impact of "familiarity with translation technology" on the employability of future translators.

CONCLUSION

Machine translation is being used by millions of people on a daily basis. This chapter discusses different MT approaches that were developed over time. Currently, the most promising approach is neural machine translation. Although effective, it also suffers some issues, such as scaling to larger vocabularies of words and the slow speed of training the models. Researchers continue to work on solving the problems and making translation a better service accessible to everyone. The second part of the chapter describes how machine translation output is evaluated. The main characteristics of human and automatic MT evaluation were outlined. Human evaluation of MT output remains crucial to look for ideas to improve MT systems still further. On the other hand, automatic MT evaluation is cheap and fast. In the chapter, traditional and advanced metrics for automatic MT evaluation were presented. Despite the well-known problems with BLEU, and the availability of many other metrics, MT system developers have continued to use BLEU as the primary measure of translation quality. MT quality is continually improving. Despite that, there are still a number of flaws in machine translation output. To make the translation correct, post-editing machine translation output is proposed to be integrated into the translation processes. It is discussed at the end of the chapter.

Future research in MT will be devoted to neural machine translation. It is still not very well understood. Its inner workings are commonly seen as a black-box, which works as the neurons of the human brain. As the computing power NMT requires becomes more widely available, many different configurations can be examined to further improve the accuracy of machine translation. Future effort in machine translation evaluation will be directed toward character-based metrics which show the highest correlation with human judgement at the system and segment levels. Human translators are worried to be replaced by machines. Machine translation, no matter how sophisticated, cannot match the accuracy of people. Human translators are also an important segment in MT evolution not only as post-editors but also as teachers for MT systems to become better and better.

ACKNOWLEDGMENTS

The authors acknowledge the financial support from the Slovenian Research Agency (research core funding No. P2-0069).

REFERENCES

1. Doherty S, Gaspari F, Groves D, van Genabith J. Mapping the industry. I: Findings on translation technologies and quality assessment. In: GALA. 2013
2. Koehn P, Och FJ, Marcu D. Statistical phrase-based translation. In: Proceedings of the 2003 Conference of the North American Chapter of the Association for Computational Linguistics

on Human Language Technology, Vol. 1. Association for Computational Linguistics; 2003. pp. 48-54

3. Durrani N, Schmid H, Fraser A. A joint sequence translation model with integrated reordering. In: Proceedings of the 49th Annual Meeting of the Association for Computational Linguistics: Human Language Technologies. Vol. 1. Association for Computational Linguistics; 2011. pp. 1045-1054
4. Donaj G, Kačič Z. Language Modeling for Automatic Speech Recognition of Inflective Languages: An Applications-Oriented Approach Using Lexical Data. Springer; 2016
5. Donaj G, Kačič Z. Contextdependent factored language models. EURASIP Journal on Audio, Speech, and Music Processing. 2017;2017(1):6
6. Maučec MS, Donaj G. Morphosyntactic tags in statistical machine translation of highly inflectional language. In: Proceedings of the Artificial Intelligence and Natural Language Conference (AINL FRUCT); Saint-Petersburg, Russia. 2016. pp. 99-102
7. Maučec MS, Brest J. Slavic languages in phrase-based statistical machine translation: A survey. Artificial Intelligence Review. 2019;51(1):77-117
8. Maučec MS, Donaj G. Morphology in statistical machine translation from english to highly inflectional language. Information Technology and Control. 2018;47(1):63-74
9. Lommel AR, Burchardt A, Uszkoreit H. Multidimensional quality metrics: A flexible system for assessing translation quality. In: Proceedings of ASLIB: Translating and the Computer. Vol. 35. 2013
10. Papineni K, Roukos S, Ward T, Zhu W-J. Bleu: A method for automatic evaluation of machine translation. In: Proceedings of the 40th Annual Meeting on Association for Computational Linguistics. Association for Computational Linguistics; 2002. pp. 311-318
11. Doddington G. Automatic evaluation of machine translation quality using n-gram co-occurrence statistics. In: Proceedings of the Second International Conference on Human Language Technology Research. Morgan Kaufmann Publishers Inc; 2002. pp. 138-145
12. Lavie A, Agarwal A. Meteor: An automatic metric for MT evaluation with high levels of correlation with human judgments. In: Proceedings of the Second Workshop on Statistical Machine Translation. Association for Computational Linguistics; 2007. pp. 228-231
13. Fellbaum C. WordNet. In: Poli R, Healy M, Kameas A, editors. Theory and Applications of Ontology: Computer Applications. Springer; 2010. pp. 231-243
14. Snover M, Dorr B, Schwartz R, Micciulla L, Makhoul J. A study of translation edit rate with targeted human annotation. In: Proceedings of Association for Machine Translation in the Americas. Vol. 200. 2006
15. Ma Q, Bojar O, Graham Y. Results of the wmt18 metrics shared task: Both characters and embeddings achieve good performance. In: Proceedings of the Third Conference on Machine Translation: Shared Task Papers. 2018. pp. 671-688
16. Macháček M, Bojar O. Results of the WMT13 metrics shared task. In: Proceedings of the Eighth Workshop on Statistical Machine Translation. 2013. pp. 45-51
17. Macháček M, Bojar O. Results of the wmt14 metrics shared task. Proceedings of the Ninth Workshop on Statistical Machine Translation. 2014:293-301
18. Leusch G, Ueffing N, Ney H. Cder: Efficient MT evaluation using block movements. In: 11th Conference of the European Chapter of the Association for Computational Linguistics. 2006
19. Libovický J, Pecina P. Tolerant bleu: A submission to the wmt14 metrics task. In: Proceedings of the Ninth Workshop on Statistical Machine Translation. 2014. pp. 409-413
20. Virpioja S, Grönroos S-A. Lebleu: N-gram-based translation evaluation score for morphologically complex languages. In: Proceedings of the Tenth Workshop on Statistical Machine Translation. 2015. pp. 411-416

21. Wang W, Peter J-T, Rosendahl H, Ney H. Character: Translation edit rate on character level. In: Proceedings of the First Conference on Machine Translation: Volume 2, Shared Task Papers, Volume 2. 2016. pp. 505-510

22. Denkowski M, Lavie A. Meteor universal: Language specific translation evaluation for any target language. In: Proceedings of the Ninth Workshop on Statistical Machine Translation. 2014. pp. 376-380

23. Stanojevic M, Sima'an K. Beer: Better evaluation as ranking. In: Proceedings of the Ninth Workshop on Statistical Machine Translation. 2014. pp. 414-419

24. Popović M. Chrf: Character n-gram f-score for automatic MT evaluation. Proceedings of the Tenth Workshop on Statistical Machine Translation. 2015: 392-395

25. Popović M. Chrf deconstructed: Beta parameters and n-gram weights. In: Proceedings of the First Conference on Machine Translation: Volume 2, Shared Task Papers, Volume 2. 2016. pp. 499-504

26. Chen B, Guo H, Kuhn R. Multi-level evaluation for machine translation. In: Proceedings of the Tenth Workshop on Statistical Machine Translation. 2015. pp. 361-365

27. Marie B, Apidianaki M. Alignmentbased sense selection in meteor and the ratatouille recipe. Proceedings of the Tenth Workshop on Statistical Machine Translation. 2015:385-391

28. Koehn P. Statistical significance tests for machine translation evaluation. In: Proceedings of the 2004 Conference on Empirical Methods in Natural Language Processing. 2004

29. Way A. Quality expectations of machine translation. In: Translation Quality Assessment. Springer; 2018. pp. 159-178

30. Bonet J. No rage against the machine. Languages and Translation. 2013;6(2)

31. Gaspari F, Almaghout H, Doherty S. A survey of machine translation competences: Insights for translation technology educators and practitioners. Perspectives. 2015;23(3):333-358

32. Plitt M, Masselot F. A productivity test of statistical machine translation post-editing in a typical localisation context. The Prague Bulletin of Mathematical Linguistics. 2010;93:7-16

33. Krings HP, Shreve GM. Repairing Texts: Empirical Investigations of Machine Translation Post-Editing Processes. Vol. 5. Kent State University Press; 2001

34. Sanchez-Torron M, Koehn P. Machine translation quality and posteditor productivity. In: AMTA 2016 Vol. 2016. p. 16

7

A Multi-Objective Optimization Method for Flexible Job Shop Scheduling Considering Cutting-Tool Degradation with Energy-Saving Measures

Ying Tian[1,2], Zhanxu Gao[1,2], Lei Zhang[3,4], Yujing Chen[1,2] and Taiyong Wang[1,2]

[1]Key Laboratory of Mechanism Theory and Equipment Design of Ministry of Education, Tianjin University, Tianjin 300072, China

[2]School of Mechanical Engineering, Tianjin University, Tianjin 300072, China

[3]School of Mechanical Engineering, Tianjin University of Commerce, Tianjin 300134, China

[4]Tianjin Tianshen Intelligent Equipment Co., Ltd., Tianjin 300300, China

ABSTRACT

Traditional energy-saving optimization of shop scheduling often separates the coupling relationship between a single machine and the shop system, which not only limits the potential of energy-saving but also leads to a large deviation between the optimized result and the actual application. In practice, cutting-tool degradation during operation is inevitable, which will not only lead to the increase in actual machining power but also the resulting tool change operation will disrupt the rhythm of production scheduling. Therefore, to make the energy consumption calculation in scheduling optimization more consistent with the actual machining conditions and reduce the impact of tool degradation on the manufacturing shop, this paper constructs an integrated optimization model including a flexible job shop scheduling problem (FJSP), machining power prediction, tool life prediction and energy-saving strategy. First, an exponential function is formulated using actual cutting experiment data under certain machining conditions to express cutting-tool degradation. Utilizing this function, a reasonable cutting-tool change schedule is obtained. A hybrid energy-saving strategy that combines a cutting-tool change with machine tool turn-on/off schedules to reduce the difference between the simulated and actual machining power while optimizing the energy savings is then proposed. Second, a multi-objective optimization model was established to reduce the makespan, total machine tool load, number of times machine tools are turned on/off and cutting tools are changed, and the total energy consumption of the workshop and the fast and elitist multi-objective genetic algorithm (NSGA-II) is used to solve the model. Finally, combined with the workshop production cost evaluation indicator, a practical FJSP example is presented to demonstrate the proposed optimization model. The prediction accuracy of the machining power is more than 93%. The hybrid energy-saving strategy can further reduce the energy consumption of the workshop by 4.44% and the production cost by 2.44% on the basis of saving 93.5% of non-processing energy consumption by the machine on/off energy-saving strategy.

Keywords: *Cutting-Tool Degradation, Machine Tool Turning-On/Off Schedule, Hybrid Energy-Saving Strategy, Multi-Objective Optimization, Flexible Job Shop Scheduling.*

INTRODUCTION

In the current industrial environment, the manufacturing industry, as an important part, consumes a lot of energy and resources in the process of product manufacturing [1]. The report on power consumption released by the China Electricity Council in 2022 showed that China's industrial electricity consumption accounted for 64.5% of the total social electricity consumption in the first 10 months of 2022, while manufacturing electricity consumption accounted for 76% of industrial electricity consumption. In addition, research shows that 99% of environment-related problems in mechanical processes are due to electrical energy consumption [2]. Therefore, the establishment of an energy-saving machining system is an urgent requirement to reduce environmental impacts and every manufacturing enterprise needs to focus on it.

Energy-saving strategies using new materials and technologies may require enterprises to transform and invest a lot in existing manufacturing systems, therefore enterprises are usually inclined to carry out energy-saving scheduling and management [3]. Through scientific matching of production tasks and machine tools, more accurate calculation of tasks sequencing, reduce idle time of machine tools, and reasonable selection of machine tools on/off time can improve energy efficiency [4]. Additionally, Guzman et al. indicated that a gap still exists in developing mathematical models to deal with scheduling problems. Novel modeling approaches should be developed to address and associate the parameters related to production and sustainability [5], among which Feng et al. integrated multiple optimization algorithms and apply edge artificial intelligence (AI) to smart green scheduling of sustainable flexible shop floors [6]. Guzman et al. provided a mixed integer linear programming (MILP) model to address the multi-machine CLSD-BPIM (a capacitated lot-sizing problem with sequence-dependent setups and parallel machines in a bi-part injection molding) [7]. Mula et al. proposed a matheuristic algorithm to optimize the job-shop problem, which combines a genetic algorithm with a disjunctive mathematical model to cut computational times, and the Coin-OR Branch and Cut open-source solver is employed [8]. Rakovitis et al. developed a novel mathematical formulation for the energy-efficient flexible job-shop scheduling problem using the improved unit-specific event-based time representation and proposed a grouping-based decomposition approach to efficiently solve large-scale problems [9]. Knowing that approximately 80% of the energy consumption of machine tools is attributed to non-processing operations, whereas the actual energy consumed by processing operations accounts for less than 20% [10]. If only relying on advanced algorithms to achieve further energy saving in the workshop, the effect is limited. Wu and Sun realized energy saving by changing the turning on/off time of machine tools and choosing different machining speeds [11]. Gong et al. effectively reduced the number of machine restarts and total energy consumption by changing the start time of operations on different machines [12]. Cheng et al. proposed machine tool on/off criterion criteria, speed-scaling policy and transportation optimization strategy, and applied them to manufacturing unit scheduling problems to achieve overall energy saving [13]. An et al. proposed a worn cutting-tool maintenance strategy that reduced the impact of cutting-tool degradation and the total energy consumption of cutting-tool maintenance in manufacturing workshops [14]. Setiawan et al. studied a shop rescheduling problem caused by the failure or reduced service life of cutting tools [15].

As can be seen from the aforementioned literature, on the one hand, most energy-saving scheduling problems start from the perspective of improving the performance of the algorithm, which makes the optimization calculation of shop energy consumption more accurate. However, on the other hand, from the perspective of workshop system management to achieve energy saving, in order to further realize the energy saving of the manufacturing system, it is important to consider the contribution of the coupling relationship between the energy consumption of individual equipment and the energy consumption of the system to the actual production and optimization objectives; however, this was almost ignored in previous studies. As the basic energy consumption equipment in the manufacturing process [16], the energy consumption caused by machine tools cannot be ignored. However, accurate estimation of energy consumption is the basis for improving energy efficiency. In recent years, different modeling methods for machine tool energy consumption have been proposed, such as those by He et al. and He et al., who combined the tool machining path with the energy consumption model to improve machining efficiency [17,18]. Shailendra et al. established an empirical model between cutting parameters and energy consumption of end turning by experiments [19]. Haruhiko et al. proposed an empirical model for predicting machine tool power consumption based on the power function between specific energy consumption and material removal rate [20].

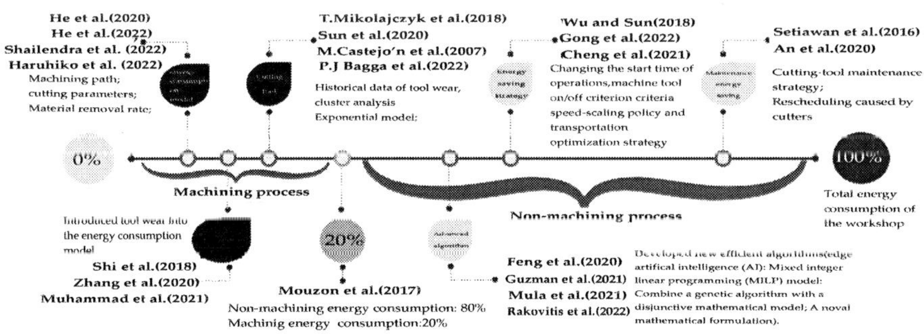

Figure 1. Analysis of energy-saving scheduling research status.

In addition, as the direct implementer of machine tool cutting, tool changing and maintenance will directly affect the production schedule, in order to avoid the tool suddenly reaching the end of life, resulting in the conflict of resources, energy consumption increase and the extension of the makespan and other problems. T. Mikołajczyk et al. and Sun et al. established the prediction model of tool residual life based on the historical data of tool wear [21,22]. M. Castejo'n et al. and P.J. Bagga et al. constructed a tool wear image dataset to predict tool life using cluster analysis and an exponential model [23,24]. Shi et al., Zhang et al. and Muhammad et al. introduced tool wear into the energy consumption model to achieve accurate energy consumption modeling, which laid a foundation for the integration of tool life prediction and energy consumption model [25,26,27]. Figure 1 summarizes the above literature. In summary, few researchers combine shop scheduling under low-carbon production with single-machine tool energy consumption and tool life prediction. This paper analyzes the coupling relationship between shop scheduling, single-machine tool energy consumption and tool life prediction, and organically integrates the three to achieve deeper shop consumption reduction. Firstly, the machining power model and the tool life model of the machine tool were established through the tool wear-cutting experiment. Then, the two models were integrated into the shop scheduling system to obtain the machining power of each production procedure and the tool change time of each machine tool in the shop scheduling process, so as to realize the precise modeling of energy consumption at the system level. In addition, on the basis of the machine tool turn-on/off strategy of the workshop, considering the relationship between the tool change time and the turn-on/off time of the machine tool, the tool change time is adjusted to further reduce the machining power and the makespan of the workshop, so as to reduce the production energy consumption of the workshop, as shown in Figure 2.

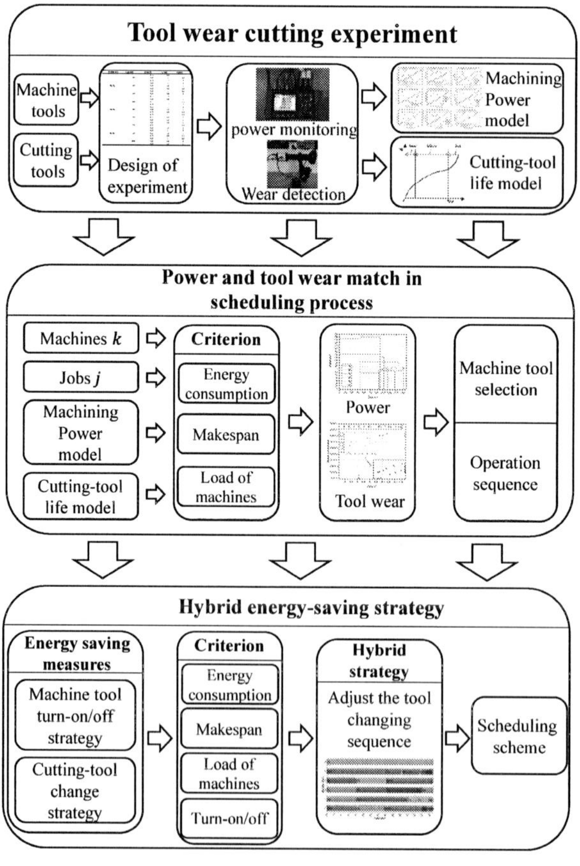

Figure 2. Energy-saving scheduling research route.

PROBLEM DESCRIPTION

The relevant symbols are provided in this section. Then, the FJSP that considers cutting-tool degradation with energy-saving measures (FJSP–CTD–ESM) is described. First, the FJSP is described. Then, the calculation method of the cutting-tool life, dynamic machining power, and the hybrid energy-saving strategy of cutting-tool change and machine tool turn-on/off is proposed, which combines the cutting-tool degradation and machine tool turn-on/off effects.

FJSP Description

In the FJSP, there are n kinds of jobs $J=\{J_i\}_{i=1,2,\dots,n}$ and k machine tools $M=\{M_m\}_{m=1,2,\dots,k}$, and each job J_i has S_i preset sequence of operations $O=\{o_{i,j}\}_{j=1,2,\dots,Si}$ (Li et al., 2012). At least one operation $o_{i,j}$ in O can be processed by different machine tools, with a corresponding difference in the processing time and efficiency for the same operation.

Table 1. The symbols used in this paper

Symbol	Descriptions
i,h	The index for jobs, $i,h = 1, 2,\dots, n$
j,g	The index for operations, $j,g = 1, 2, \dots, max\{S_i, S_g\}$
m	The index for machine tools, $m = 1, 2, \dots, k$
r	The index for the machine tool's processing task, $r = 1, 2, \dots, l_m$
l_m	The number of processing tasks for the machine tool M_m
S_i	The number of operations for job J_i
n	The number of jobs
k	The number of machine tools
J_i	The $i-th$ job
$o_{i,j}$	The $j-th$ operation of the job J_i
M_m	The $m-th$ machine tool
P_m	The total power of the machine tool M_m
P_{ijm}	The power of operation $o_{i,j}$ which is on the machine tool M_m
P_{dm}	The dynamic power of the machine tool M_m
P_{sm}	The static power of the machine tool M_m
P_{ctm}	The cutting-tool changing power of the machine tool M_m
P_{Add}	The additional power of the workshop
$a_1 - a_8$	The exponential parameters between each cutting parameter and the dynamic power
K_1, K_2	The coefficients of the dynamic power model
$b_1 - b_4$	The exponential parameters between each cutting parameter and the cutting-tool life
K_3	The coefficients of the tool life model
n_v	The spindle speed
f	The feed speed
a_p	The cutting depth
a_e	The cutting width
t_m	The used time of the cutting tool of the machine tool M_m
T_m	The cutting-tool life of the machine tool M_m
t_{ctm}	The cutting-tool changing time of the machine tool M_m
PT	The processing time of an operation
PT_{ij}	The processing time of the operation $o_{i,j}$
PT_{ijm}	The processing time of the operation which is on the machine tool M_m
ST_{ij}	The start time of the operation $o_{i,j}$
ST_{mr}	The start time of the $r-th$ processing task of the machine tool M_m
CT_{ij}	The end time of the operation $o_{i,j}$
CT_{mr}	The end time of the $r-th$ processing task of the machine tool M_m
T_{Rm}	The no-load balance time of the machine tool
H_m	The on/off security threshold time of the machine tool M_m
RT_{mean}	The actual average turning-on/off machine tool time
W_m	The degree of tool wear

Symbol	Descriptions
E_{total}	The total energy consumption of the workshop
E_c	The processing energy consumption of machine tools
E_{Re}	The energy consumption of turning on/off machine tools
E_{Rem}	The energy consumed by a single on/off of the machine tool
E_{ct}	The total energy consumption of changing the cutting tool
E_s	The standby energy consumption of machine tools
E_{Add}	The additional energy consumption of the workshop
RTE_{mean}	The actual average energy consumption of turning on/off the machine tool
C_{max}	The makespan
G	The total number of turning-on/off machine tools and changing cutting tools
WL	The total load of machine tools
CF_m	The coefficient of cutting tool capacity of the machine tool M_m
DW	The degree of reduction in processing capacity of the cutting tool
$COST$	The production cost
SF_m	The additional coefficient of turning on/off the machine tool M_m
ω_e	Unit energy cost
ω_m	The unit operating cost of the machine tool
ω_t	Machine tool turn on/off loss cost
ω_l	Cost per unit of labor time
x	The number of tasks that cutting-tool changing operation can be advanced
$\gamma_{ijmr}/\gamma_{hgmr}$	$\gamma_{ijmr}/\gamma_{hgmr}=1$, if the operation $o_{i,j}$ is the $r-th$ processing task of M_m, γ_{ijmr}=1; otherwise $\gamma_{ijmr}/\gamma_{hgmr}=0$
η_{mr}	$\eta_{mr}=1$, if the machine tool M_m is turned on/off before its $r-th$ processing task; otherwise, $\eta_{mr}=0$
λ_{mr}	$\lambda_{mr}=1$, if the machine tool M_m changes the cutting tool before its $r-th$ processing task; otherwise, $\lambda_{mr}=0$
δ_m	$\delta_m=1$, if the machine tool M_m turns on/off twice or more; otherwise, $\delta_m=0$

The following conditions should be met in the FJSP:

(1) A machine tool cannot be assigned to two or more operations simultaneously.

(2) Each job has the same processing priority: initially, all jobs can be processed.

(3) There is no constraint relationship between different jobs.

(4) The optional machine tools for the job have no priority relationship.

(5) All job processing tasks are non-preemptive.

(6) The processing power of the machine tool and degree of cutting-tool wear obey the law of tool degradation.

(7) Once a process begins, it cannot be interrupted before completion. Changing the cutting tool and turning the machine tool on/off cannot be inserted into the machining process.

(8) The conversion time between different jobs with the same machine tool as well as the transportation time between different stages of the same job are ignored.

The symbols used in this paper are defined in Table 1.

Cutting-Tool Degradation Model

In the FJSP, the degradation of the cutting tool reduces its machining capacity, leading to an increase in the machining power and the interruption of the process caused by the blunt cutting tool. If the cutting-tool wear is considered in advance during the scheduling process, the change in machining power caused by cutting-tool wear can be accurately predicted. This not only improves processing efficiency and reduces energy consumption but also prevents the cutting tool from becoming blunt. This section introduces the machining power model and cutting-tool life model derived from the tool degradation model.

(1) Machining power model

From the point of view of the working state of the machine tool, the machine tool power P_m in the workshop production process can be divided into two parts, as shown in Equation (1). The first part is the dynamic machining power of the machine tool P_{dm}, which includes the spindle power of the machine tool in the workpiece-cutting process. The second part is the static power P_{sm} of the machine tool, including the no-load power of the motor and the power of the numerical control, lighting, and cooling systems.

$$P_m = P_{dm} + P_{sm}, \quad (1)$$

P_{sm} exhibits little change in the machining process; hence, it is regarded as a constant value.

The dynamic power model [28,29] proposed by Tian et al. and Tian et al. is divided into two parts: the initial dynamic power without tool wear, and the additional dynamic power caused by tool wear, as shown in Equation (2):

$$P_{dm} = K_1 n_v{}^{a_1} f^{a_2} a_p{}^{a_3} a_e{}^{a_4} + K_2 t_m n^{a_5} f^{a_6} a_p{}^{a_7} a_e{}^{a_8} \quad (2)$$

(2) Cutting-tool life model

To determine the relationship between the cutting-tool life and different cutting parameters, a type of cutting-tool failure should be selected as the criterion. According to ISO 8688-2:1989 *Tool life testing in milling-part 2: end milling* (1989), the wear of an end milling cutter can be divided into rake-face wear and flank-face wear [30]. Because the flank-face wear is easy to measure, the blunt standard of the tool wear is often set according to the maximum allowable value of the flank-face wear (usually expressed as VB). In this study, the end of the end milling cutting tool's life was defined as having a maximum VB of 0.3 mm in one of all teeth ($VB_{max} = 0.3$). The cutting-tool life model of Tian et al. and Sun et al. is shown in Equation (3) [22,29]:

$$T_m = K_3 \cdot n_v{}^{b_1} f^{b_2} a_e{}^{b_3} a_e{}^{b_4} \quad (3)$$

As we all know, tool wear is produced in complex mechanical and thermal environments, and there will be different dullness criteria for different processing objects or different quality requirements. In this paper, according to the dullness criterion mentioned in the ISO standard, in other application scenarios with higher cutting quality requirements, this part of modeling needs to establish a dullness criterion that meets the quality requirements and build models under these standards. This article only provides such a solution.

The Hybrid Energy-Saving Strategy

The cutting-tool life is not only related to the material and specifications of the cutting tool but also to the cutting parameters. Therefore, the cutting tool remaining useful life (RUL) cannot be calculated directly from the processing time of different operations. This results in a unique tool-changing schedule that affects the makespan and machine tool turn-on/off schedule.

Three measures are proposed to solve this problem.

(1) The cutting-tool change strategy

In this study, the cutting tool is changed before it is damaged to ensure that it meets processing quality requirements, reduces the risk of accidents, and improves the reliability of the processing system. Therefore, if the remaining service life of the cutting tool is insufficient to support the next processing task in the schedule, the cutting tool is considered unavailable and changed before the start of the next processing task, as expressed by Equation (4).

$$T_m - t_m < PT \tag{4}$$

Owing to the different cutting-tool lives under different cutting parameters, the cutting-tool service time cannot be added directly. A normalized approach is adopted to deal with this problem, that is, the increase in cutting-tool wear caused by the processing task is obtained using the processing task time//cutting-tool life under the cutting parameters of the task. Then, the total cutting-tool wear W_m is used to determine whether the cutting tool has reached the end point of its service life, as expressed by Equation (5).

$$W_m + PT/\ T_m < 1 \tag{5}$$

Equation (5) defines that cutting-tool wear must be less than 1.

(2) The machine tool turn-on/off strategy

During the production process, if a machine tool remains idle for some time, it is sensible to turn it off to avoid wasting energy and reduce carbon emissions. Turning machine tools on/off leads to additional energy consumption and could also damage their performance and service life. Therefore, the no-load balance time T_{Rm} should be set to control when to turn the machine tool on/off, as expressed by Equation (6). Meanwhile, to reduce the damage caused by turning the machine tool on/off, the interval between on/off times is controlled by setting the on/off security threshold time H_m, as expressed by Equation (7) [11].

$$ST_{mr} - CT_{m(r-1)} \geq T_{Rm}\eta_{mr} \tag{6}$$

$$\left|\eta_{mr}CT_{m(r-1)} - \eta_{mr'}ST_{mr'}\right| \geq H_m\delta_m,\ \ r > r' \tag{7}$$

Equation (6) shows that if the time interval between two subsequent processing tasks is greater than the no-load balancing time, the machine tool should be turned off. Equation (7) shows that if the machine tool is turned on/off twice or more, the interval between the time the machine tool is turned on and the next turn-off must exceed the on/off security threshold time of the machine tool.

(3) Hybrid energy-saving strategy of cutting-tool change and machine tool turn-on/off

If the cutting-tool change operation is separated from the machine tool turn-on/off operation, the single cutting-tool change operation not only increases the makespan but also the standby energy consumption of the machine tool. Sacrificing a small amount of cutting-tool processing capacity by advancing the timing of the cutting-tool change will shorten the makespan and reduce energy consumption. Here, we set a reasonable coefficient C_{Fm} of the cutting-tool capacity to control when to change the cutting tool. Equation (8) ensures that the reduced processing capacity of the machine tool M_m is within an acceptable range. The cutting-tool change operation can be carried out before x tasks to realize energy savings.

$$CF_m \geq 1 - W_m + \sum_{r=0}^{x} (\lambda_{mr} PT_{mr} / T_m) \tag{8}$$

FORMULATION OF FJSP–CTD–ESM

In this section, the energy footprint model is defined. Then, the optimization model of the FJSP–CTD–ESM is established.

Energy Footprint Model

The total energy consumption E_{total} of the workshop consists of five parts, as shown in Equation (9). Figure 3 shows the energy consumption of the machine tool at different stages [1].

$$E_{total} = E_C + E_{Re} + E_{ct} + E_S + E_{Add} \tag{9}$$

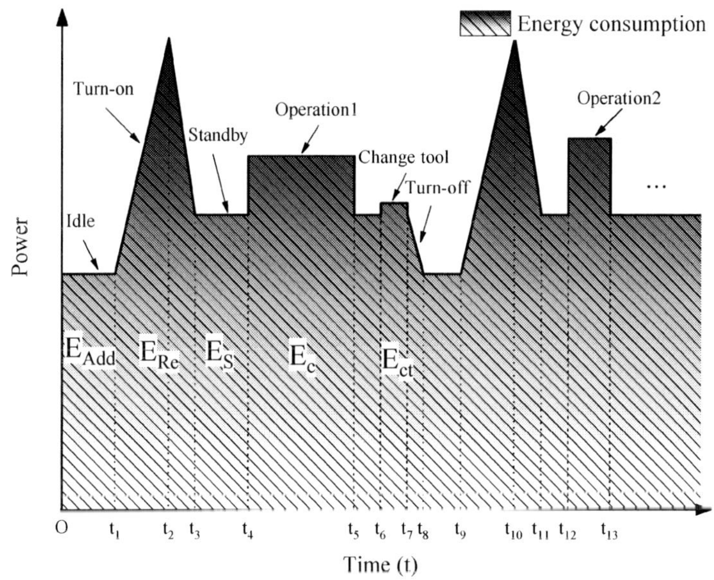

Figure 3. Schematic diagram of energy consumption distributions for different running states.

The energy consumption of each part is analyzed in detail below.

(1) Processing energy consumption E_c of machine tools

The processing energy consumption E_c of process $o_{i,j}$ is closely related to the cutting time PT_{ijm} and the machine tool power P_{ijm}, which varies with the machine tool type, cutting parameters, and cutting-tool wear. The energy consumption of cutting is calculated as Equation (10).

$$E_c = \sum_{m=1}^{k} \sum_{i=1}^{n} \sum_{j=1}^{S_i} \sum_{r=1}^{l_m} \gamma_{ijmr} P_{ijm} PT_{ijm} \tag{10}$$

(2) Energy consumption E_{Re} of turning machine tools on/off

The energy consumption when turning the machine tool on/off E_{Re} is influenced by the type and performance of the machine tool; it has no relation with the processing operation. Thus, the energy consumption of turning the machine tool on/off E_{Rem} once was set as a constant value. The energy consumption of machine tool turn-on/off is calculated as Equation (11).

$$E_{Re} = \sum_{m=1}^{k} \sum_{r=1}^{l_m} \eta_{mr} E_{Rem} \tag{11}$$

(3) Total energy consumption E_{ct} of changing the cutting tool

As the processing time increases, it is necessary to change the cutting tool before it becomes blunt. The energy consumption of cutting-tool change is calculated as Equation (12).

$$E_{ct} = \sum_{m=1}^{k} \sum_{r=1}^{l_m} \lambda_{mr} P_{ctm} t_{ctm} \tag{12}$$

(4) Standby energy consumption E_s

When the machine tool is idle and kept on between two processes, it consumes energy while on standby, which is expressed as:

$$E_s = \sum_{m=1}^{k} \sum_{r=1}^{l_m} P_{sm}(1 - \eta_{mr})\left(ST_{mr} - CT_{m(r-1)}\right) \tag{13}$$

(5) Additional energy consumption E_{Add} of the workshop

The energy consumption of the workshop results not only from machine tool-related processes but also from lighting, computer utilization, and other sources. In this study, the additional energy consumption is not examined in detail; hence, it is set to a constant and calculated as Equation (14).

$$E_{Add} = P_{Add} * C_{max} \tag{14}$$

where P_{Add}=9.65 Kw.

Formulation of the FJSP–CTD–ESM Optimization Model

In actual production, the total energy consumption is not the only indicator; the makespan, total load of the machine tool, and the total number of times the machine tool is turned on/off and cutting tools are changed also need to be considered. Therefore, the multi-objective optimization model proposed in this paper has four objectives: the makespan f_1 (min), the total energy consumption of f_2 (Kw·min), the total load of machine tools f_3 (min), and the total number of times the machine tools are turned on/off and cutting tools are changed f_4 (time), expressed as Equations (15)–(35).

$$min\ F = [f_1, f_2, f_3, f_4] \tag{15}$$

where

$$f_1 = C_{max} = \max_{m,r} CT_{mr} \tag{16}$$

$$f_2 = E_{total} = E_c + E_{Re} + E_{ct} + E_s + E_{Add}$$
$$= \left\{ \begin{array}{c} \sum_{m=1}^{k} \sum_{i=1}^{n} \sum_{j=1}^{S_i} \sum_{r=1}^{l_m} \gamma_{ijmr} P_{ijm} PT_{ijm} + \\ \sum_{m=1}^{k} \sum_{r=1}^{l_m} \eta_{mr} E_{Rem} + \\ \sum_{m=1}^{k} \sum_{r=1}^{l_m} \lambda_{mr} P_{ctm} t_{ctm} + \\ \sum_{m=1}^{k} \sum_{r=1}^{l_m} P_{sm} (1 - \eta_{mr}) \left(ST_{mr} - CT_{m(r-1)} \right) + P_{Add} * C_{max} \end{array} \right. \tag{17}$$

$$f_3 = WL = \sum_{m=1}^{k} \sum_{i=1}^{n} \sum_{j=1}^{S_i} \sum_{r=1}^{l_m} \gamma_{ijmr} PT_{ijm} \tag{18}$$

$$f_4 = G = \sum_{m=1}^{k} \sum_{r=1}^{l_m} (\eta_{mr} + \lambda_{mr}) \tag{19}$$

Subject to

$$CT_{ij} - PT_{ij} \geq CT_{i(j-1)} \tag{20}$$

$$\begin{cases} ST_{m(r+1)} - ST_{mr} > 0 \\ ST_{m(r+1)} - CT_{mr} \geq 0 \end{cases} \tag{21}$$

$$\sum_{m=1}^{k} \gamma_{ijmr} = 1 \tag{22}$$

$$ST_{mr} - CT_{m(r-1)} \geq T_{Rm} \eta_{mr} \tag{23}$$

$$\left| \eta_{mr} CT_{m(r-1)} - \eta_{mr'} ST_{mr'} \right| \geq H_m \delta_m, \quad r > r' \tag{24}$$

$$W_{mr} < 1 \tag{25}$$

$$ST_{mr} - CT_{m(r-1)} \geq t_{ctm} \lambda_{mr} \tag{26}$$

$$CF_m \geq 1 - W_m + \sum_{r=0}^{x} (\lambda_{mr} PT_{mr} / T_m) \tag{27}$$

$$\gamma_{ijmr} = \begin{cases} 1, & \text{if the operation } o_{i,j} \text{ is the r th processing task of the machine tool } M_m \\ 0, & \text{otherwise} \end{cases} \tag{28}$$

$$\eta_{mr} = \begin{cases} 1, & \text{if the machine tool } M_m \text{ is turned on/off before its r th processing task} \\ 0, & \text{otherwise} \end{cases} \tag{29}$$

$$\lambda_{mr} = \begin{cases} 1, & \text{if the machine tool } M_m \text{ changes the cutting tool before its r th processing task} \\ 0, & \text{otherwise} \end{cases} \tag{30}$$

$$\delta_m = \begin{cases} 1, & \text{if the machine tool } M_m \text{ is turned on/off twice or more} \\ 0, & \text{otherwise} \end{cases} \tag{31}$$

$$ST > 0 \tag{32}$$

$$CT > 0 \tag{33}$$

$$PT > 0 \tag{34}$$

$$i \in [1, n], j \in [1, s], m \in [1, k], r \in [1, l_m] \tag{35}$$

Constraint [20] indicates that an operation cannot begin unless the preceding operation was completed. Constraint [21] confirms that a machine tool cannot be assigned to two or more processes simultaneously. Constraint [22] ensures that the same process cannot be conducted by two or more machine tools. Constraint [23] states that the machine tool turn-on/off does not overlap with the processing task, and the on/off time must exceed the no-load balance time. If it is the first round of processing, $CT_{ijm0}=0$; otherwise, $CT_{ijm0}=CT_{ijmlm}$. Constraint [24] indicates that the interval between the time the machine tool is turned on and the next turn-off must exceed the machine tool on/off security threshold time M_m. Constraint [25] implies that the actual degree of tool wear W_{mr} must be less than 1. Constraint [26] requires that the cutting-tool change does not overlap with the processing task, and the time interval between the two processes is greater than the defined cutting-tool change time. Constraint [27] shows that the cutting-tool change of M_m is carried out in advance to achieve energy savings under the reduced processing capacity of the machine tool within an acceptable range. Constraints [28,29,30,31,32,33,34,35] are the constraints of decision variables.

PROPOSED NSGA-II

In this section, a general framework to solve the FJSP–CTD–ESM is proposed; the NSGA-II is briefly introduced, and the motivation behind the NSGA-II to optimize the FJSP–CTD–ESM is analyzed. Specific improvement measures of the NSGA-II algorithm are also described.

Framework

The optimization method of integrating the cutting-tool degradation, hybrid energy-saving strategy, and production scheduling determines the cutting-tool capability and the order and priority of production tasks by combining machine tools and scheduling. The scheduling scheme is implemented in two steps: First, the machining power model and cutting-tool life model based on tool degradation were added to the fast and elitist multi-objective genetic algorithm (NSGA-II) scheduling algorithm [31] to generate an initial scheduling scheme, which includes the cutting-tool change. Second, through the scheduling mechanism, the cutting-tool change and machine tool turn-on/off were arranged to generate the final scheduling scheme to achieve the goal of energy conservation.

Details and Improvements in NSGA-II

Scheduling Mechanisms

In the FJSP–CTD–ESM, processing energy consumption is mainly determined by machining power, which is also affected by cutting parameters and machine tool type. Non-machining energy consumption is mainly determined by the running state of machine tools. Because the cutting parameters were determined, the allocation of the appropriate machine tool to the operation and choosing the suitable machine tool turn-on/off and cutting-tool change times are the main considerations of the scheduling scheme. Two scheduling mechanisms are proposed:

(1) Cutting-tool degradation mechanism

During the processing operation, the cumulative processing time of the cutting tool is calculated in advance and the machining power P_m and degree of cutting-tool wear W_m of machine tool M_m are then calculated using the tool degradation model. When the degree of cutting-tool wear is expected to be greater than

1 (W_m>1) after the machine tool completes the next operation, the cutting tool will be changed before processing (λ_{mr}=1), and the machining power P_m is recalculated. The cutting-tool degradation mechanism is shown in Figure 4.

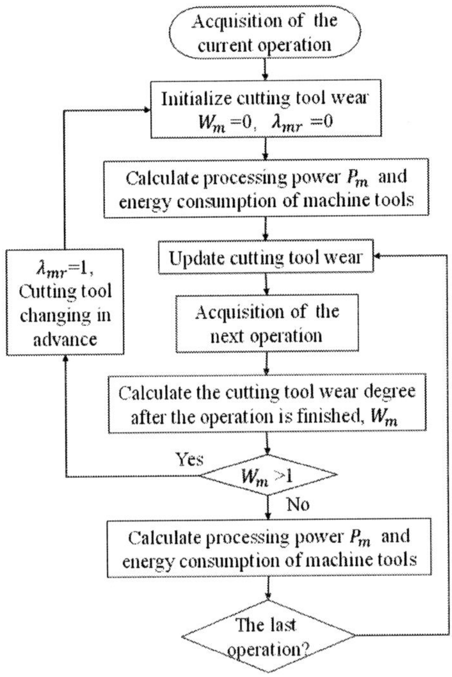

Figure 4. Cutting-tool degradation mechanism.

(2) Hybrid mechanism of cutting-tool change and machine tool turn-on/off

Based on the scheduling algorithm, the hybrid mechanism of cutting-tool change and machine tool turn-on/off is added to determine when to turn the machine tool on/off and change the cutting tool, as shown in Figure 5.

Step 1: According to the start and end time of the processing task, determine whether the non-processing time is greater than the no-load balancing time T_{Rm}. If so, go to Step 2; otherwise, end.

Step 2: Determine whether there is an on/off operation before this non-processing stage. If so, go to Step 3. Otherwise, turn off the machine tool in this non-processing stage and go to Step 5.

Step 3: Compare whether the time difference between the start of the non-processing stage and the last turn-on time of the machine tool is greater than the defined on/off security threshold time H_m. If the difference exceeds H_m, turn off the machine tool at the beginning of the non-processing stage and go to Step 5; otherwise, go to Step 4.

Step 4: Set the last turn-on time of the machine tool to t_1 and the start time of the non-processing stage to t_2. If $t_2-t_1-H_m>T_{Rm}$, turn off the machine tool at (t_1+H_m) and go to Step 5; otherwise, end.

Step 5: Check whether the machine tools have both cutting-tool change and turn-on/off operations. If so, go to Step 6; otherwise, end.

Step 6: Determine whether the degree of tool wear W_m at the nearest machine tool on/off position before the cutting-tool change operation is greater than the difference between 1 and the cutting-tool capacity coefficient. If so, combine the cutting-tool change and machine tool turn-on/off operations, and recalculate the optimization target value; otherwise, end.

```
Input: Initial Schedulingscheme, k, T_Rm, CF_m #See original NSGA-II Deb et al. (2002) and Section 4.2.2.
for i in range (k):
    Tst_i = TurnonTime(Schedulingscheme) #The turn on start time set of M_i.
    St_i = StandbyTime(Schedulingscheme) #The standby time set of M_i.
    Sst_i = StandbystartTime(Schedulingscheme) #The standby start time set of M_i.
    for j in range(len(St_i)):
        if St_i[j] > T_Rm:
            Less_list = [o for o, x in enumerate(Tst_i) if x < Sst_i[j]]
            if Lese_list != []:
                if Sst_i[j] - max(Less_list) >= H_m:
                    Schedulingscheme = ChangeScheme1(Schedulingscheme, Tst_i, St_i, Sst_i) #Modify the scheduling scheme to change the standby state to the turn off state and Section 4.2.2.
                elif St_i[j] - max(Less_list) - H_m + Sst_i[j] > T_Rm:
                    Schedulingscheme = ChangeScheme2(Schedulingscheme, Tst_i, St_i, Sst_i, H_m)#Modify the scheduling scheme to change the standby state to the turn off state from max(Less_list) + H_m and Section 4.2.2.
            else:
                    Schedulingscheme = ChangeScheme1(Schedulingscheme, Tst_i, St_i, Sst_i)
for i in range (k):
    CTt_i = ChangetoolTime(Schedulingscheme) #The change tool time set of M_i.
    CTst_i = ChangetoolTime(Schedulingscheme) #The change tool start time set of M_i.
    Tt_i = Turnon/offTime(Schedulingscheme) #The turn on/off time set of M_i.
    Tst_i = TurnonTime(Schedulingscheme) #The turn on start time set of M_i.
    if CTt_i != [] and Tt_i != []:
        for j in range(len(CTst_i)):
            W_m = ObtainWear(Tst_i[j], CTst_i[j]) #Obtain tool wear at the nearest turn-on/off position before the cutting tool change
            if (1-W_m) < CF_m and Tt_i >= CTt_i:
                Schedulingscheme = ChangeScheme3(Schedulingscheme, CTt_i, CTst_i, Tt_i, Tst_i) #Modify the scheduling scheme to combine the cutting tool changing with the turn-on/off and Section 4.2.2.
            elif (1-W_m) < CF_m and Tt_i < CTt_i:
                Schedulingscheme = ChangeScheme4(Schedulingscheme, CTt_i, CTst_i, Tt_i, Tst_i) #Modify the scheduling scheme to delete the turn-on/off and bring the cutting tool changing to this position in advance and Section 4.2.2
Output: Schedulingscheme
```

Figure 5. Hybrid mechanism algorithm form of cutting-tool change and machine tool turn-on/off.

Encoding and Decoding with Changing Cutting and Turn-on/off

In the FJSP, encoding and decoding are expressed in the form of chromosomes, which are divided into the process chromosome and the machine tool chromosome. We utilize the encoding and decoding methods proposed by Zhang et al. [32], as shown in Figure 6.

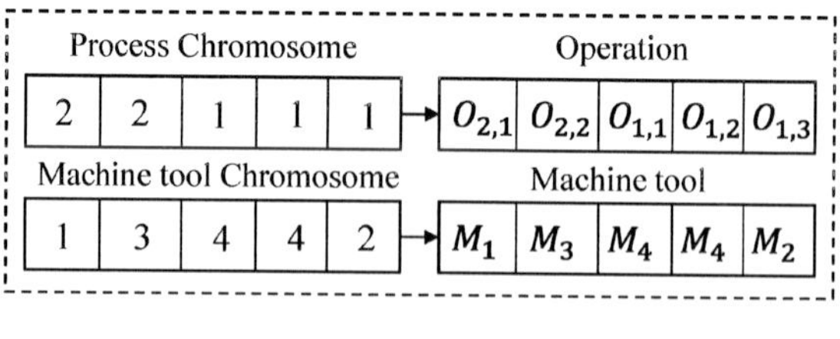

Figure 6. Chromosome encoding process.

In addition, changing the cutting tool and turning the machine tool on/off affects the scheduling scheme, including the following six scenarios. (1) Scenario 1: If the machine tool M_m needs to be turned off before $o_{i,j+1}$, the non-processing time and the last turn-on time of M_m should be considered. When the non-processing time is greater than the no-load balancing time T_{Rm}, and the difference between the start time CT_{mr} of the non-processing time and the last turn-on time $ST_{mr'}$ of M_m is greater than the defined on/off security threshold time H_m, the machine tool is directly turned off between CT_{mr} and $ST_{m(r+1)}$, as shown in Figure 7. (2) Scenario 2: If $CT_{mr}-ST_{mr'} < H_m$ and $ST_{m(r+1)}-ST_{mr'}-H_m > T_{Rm}$, turn off M_m between $(ST_{mr'}+ H_k)$ and $ST_{m(r+1)}$, as shown in Figure 8. (3) Scenario 3. If machine tool M_m needs a cutting-tool change before $o_{i,j+1}$, the non-processing time must be considered. If $(ST_{m(r+1)} - CT_{mr})$ is greater than the cutting-tool change time t_{ctm}, change the cutting tool in $CT_{mr'}$, as shown in Figure 9. (4) Scenario 4: If the machine tool M_m needs a cutting-tool change before $o_{i,j+1}$ and $ST_{m(r+1)} - CT_{mr} < t_{ctm}$, $ST_{m(r+1)}$ needs to move to the right to $ST'_{m(r+1)}$ to make $ST'_{m(r+1)}\text{-}CT_{mr} = t_{ctm}$, as shown in Figure 10. (5) Scenario 5: If the cutting-tool change and machine tool turn-on/off occurs in sequence, these should be combined, as shown in Figure 11. (6) Scenario 6: If the conditions of scheduling mechanism 2 are met, two cases will occur. Case 1: the cutting-tool change is incorporated into the machine tool turn-on/off. Case 2: Advance the cutting-tool change and eliminate the machine tool turn-on/off, as shown in Figure 12.

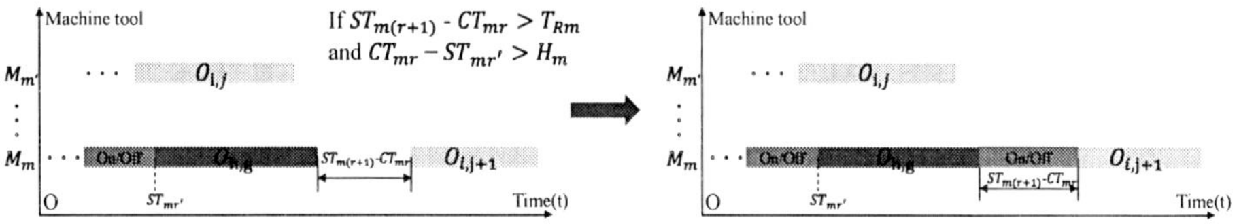

(a) (b)

Figure 7. Scenario 1: (a) Initial Gantt chart; (b) Adjusted Gantt chart.

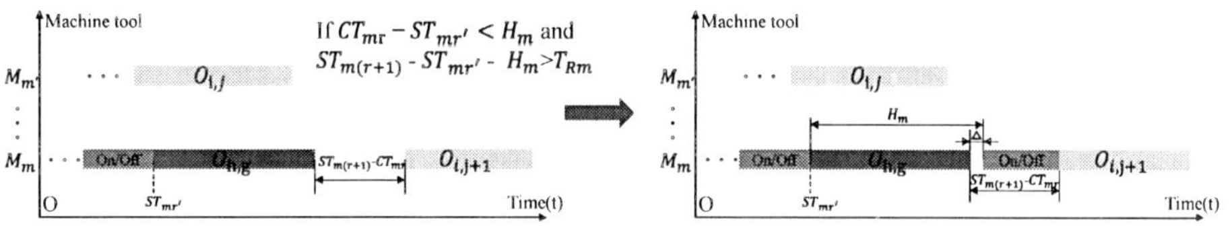

(a) (b)

Figure 8. Scenario 2: (a) Initial Gantt chart; (b) Adjusted Gantt chart.

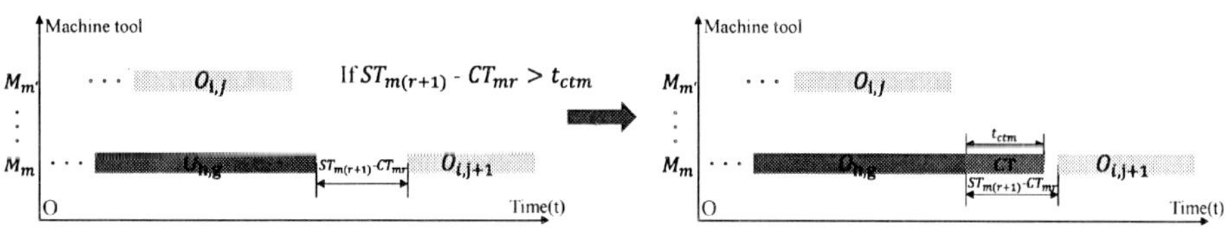

(a) (b)

Figure 9. Scenario 3: (a) Initial Gantt chart; (b) Adjusted Gantt chart.

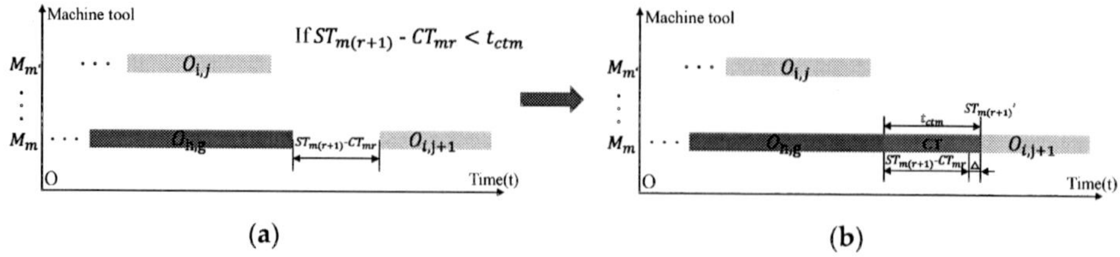

Figure 10. Scenario 4: (a) Initial Gantt chart; (b) Adjusted Gantt chart.

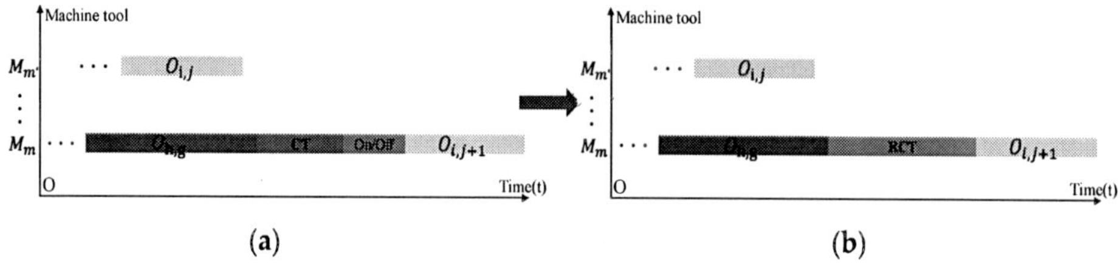

Figure 11. Scenario 5: (a) Initial Gantt chart; (b) Adjusted Gantt chart.

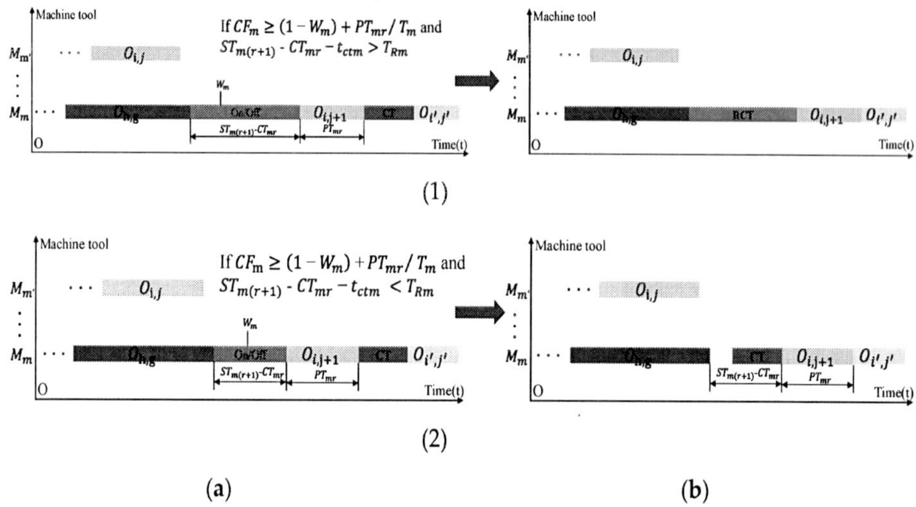

Figure 12. Scenario 6: (1) Sufficient machine-off time; (2) Insufficient machine-off time. (a) Initial Gantt chart; (b) Adjusted Gantt chart.

Crossover

A crossover is used to maintain population diversity and explore a new solution space. In the parent population, two types of crossover were performed according to chromosome types [32], with the crossover of the process chromosome occurring in odd positions, while that of the machine tool chromosome occurring in even positions, as shown in Figure 13.

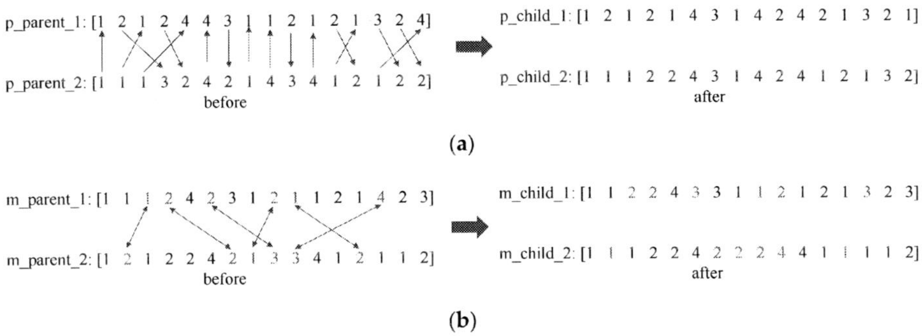

Figure 13. Crossover: (a) Crossover of the process chromosome; (b) Crossover of the machine tool chromosome.

Mutation

A mutation is the use of the solution space to generate different neighborhood solutions through different mutations to prevent the population from falling into a local optimum during the process of population evolution convergence and increase the diversity of the population. The mutation can be divided into the process chromosome mutation and the machine tool chromosome mutation [32]. In the process chromosome mutation, gene I at a random mutation site on a random parental chromosome is mutated into the random gene I'. At the same time, one of the genes I 'on the other sites of this chromosome is randomly selected to become gene I, and the corresponding machine tool chromosome is changed accordingly. In the machine tool chromosome mutation, the genes at two random mutation sites on a random parental chromosome are mutated into any gene within the allowed mutation range, as shown in Figure 14.

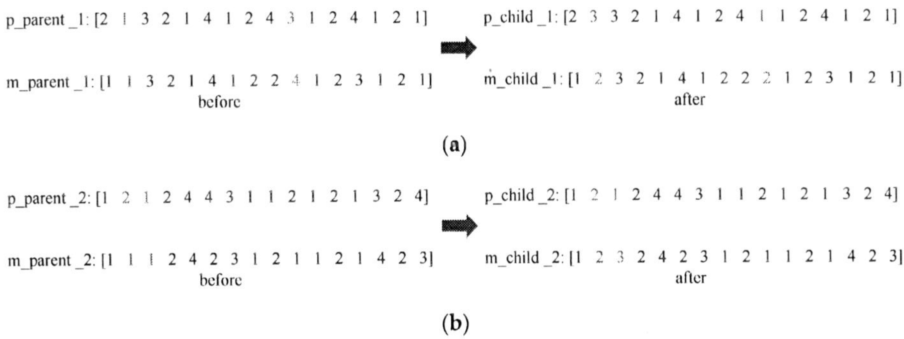

Figure 14. Mutation: (a) Crossover of the process chromosome; (b) Crossover of the machine tool chromosome.

CASE STUDY

In this section, the parameter determination method in FJSP–CTD–ESM is briefly described, and the comparison experiment based on the FJSP is designed. In addition, to provide enterprises with a better basis for selecting scheduling schemes, this paper integrates production functional resources with job-shop scheduling and provides production cost indicators to evaluate scheduling schemes. Thereafter, the rationality and effectiveness of the cutting-tool degradation model and hybrid energy-saving strategy of cutting-tool change and machine tool turn-on/off are illustrated by the example results.

Design of Experiments

Environment Setting

All the algorithms were run in Python 2.7 on a personal computer with an Intel (R) Core (TM) i7-9750H, 2.6 GHz CPU and 8 GB RAM.

Model Parameter Determination

To obtain stable machining power and tool wear data, the workpiece (i.e., 45# steel with dimensions 60 × 60 × 35 mm) was processed by milling. The cutting mode was straight-line face milling. The cutting path of the experimental workpiece is shown in Figure 15. The basic properties of the machine tool and tool used in the experiment are shown in Table 2. To establish the relationship between the machining power of machine tools and machining parameters, and that between the tool life and machining parameters, the machining power of machine tools and tool life under different cutting parameters were obtained by an orthogonal experiment. By referring to the Concise Manual of Cutting Parameters, it is found that in general, when the high-speed end milling cutter face-milling 45 steel, the recommended cutting speed is 21~40 m/min, and the recommended range of feed per tooth is 0.12~0.2 mm. Therefore, within the recommended range, we consider the workpiece conditions, machine conditions, test costs and other factors, and through a large number of tests select the cutting parameters, as shown in Table 3 for the experiment. All the power data of a single milling cutter in a stable cutting period were collected for each group of experiments. The experimental devices are shown in Figure 16.

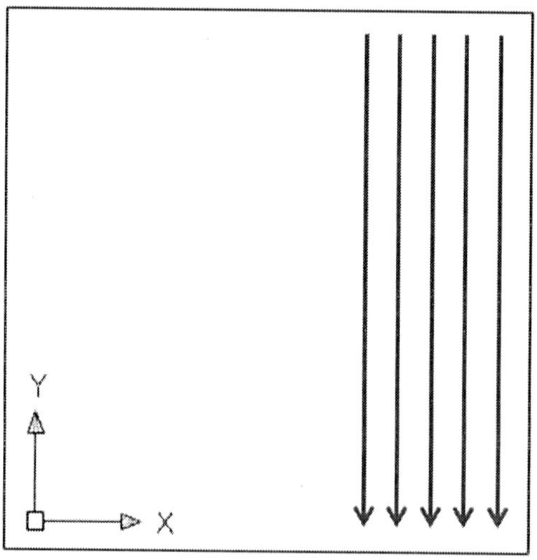

Figure 15. The tool cutting path.

Table 2. Basic parameters of experimental devices

Machine Tools	Machine Tools Type (Model)	Cutting-Tool Type	Diameter of Milling Cutter Edge (mm)	Milling Cutter Material	Number of Milling Cutter Edges	Length of Milling Cutter Edge (mm)	Length of Milling Cutter (mm)	Cutting Fluid	Anti-wear Coating
M_1,M_2	Three-axis CNC machining center(TSIM-VMA8050V4)	End Mill	φ10	M2AI high-speed steel	4	25	66	Water	No
M_3,M_4	Three-axis CNC machining center (TSIM-VMC1580)	End Mill	φ12	M2AI high-speed steel	4	35	85	Water	No
M_5,M_6	Five-axis CNC machining center (TSIM-VMA210V)	End Mill	Φ8	M2AI high-speed steel	4	22	66	Water	No

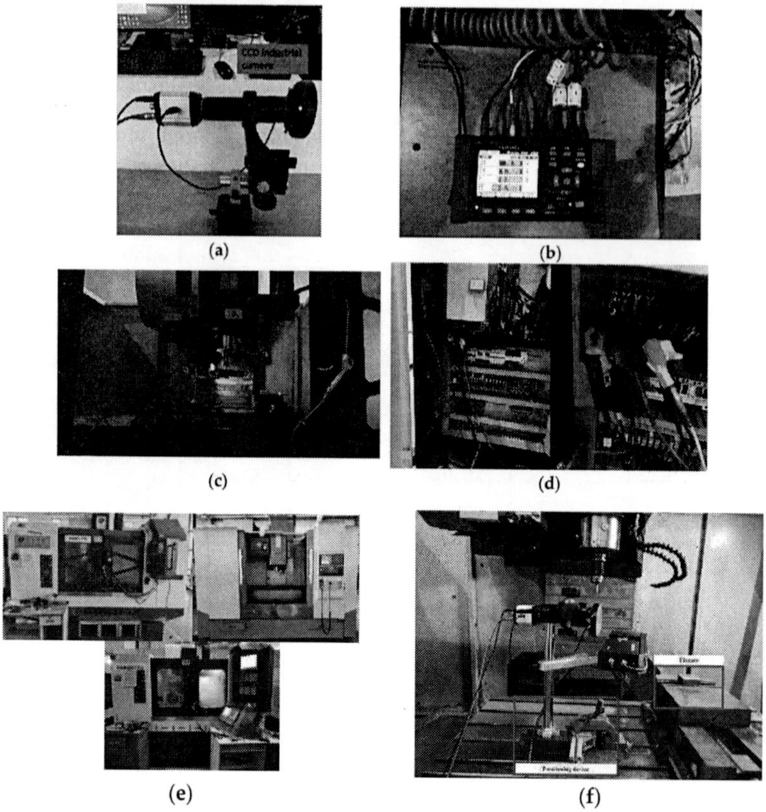

Figure 16. Experimental device: (a) Tool wear detection device; (b) Clamp on power logger (PW3360A982-04); (c) Tool wear detection process; (d) Power acquisition wiring diagram; (e) CNC machining center ($M_{1/2}$,$M_{3/4}$,$M_{5/6}$); (f) Positioning device and fixture.

Table 3. Experimental cutting parameters table

Machine Tools	n_v (r/min)	f (mm/r)	a_p (mm)	a_e (mm)
M_1,M_2	700	0.15	0.8	1
		0.16	1	1.5
		0.17	1.2	2
	800	0.15	1	2
		0.16	1.2	1
		0.17	0.8	1.5
	900	0.15	1	1.5
		0.16	0.8	2
		0.17	1.2	1

M_3,M_4	600	0.17	0.8	1
		0.18	1	1.5
		0.19	1.2	2
	700	0.17	1	2
		0.18	1.2	1
		0.19	0.8	1.5
	800	0.17	1	1.5
		0.18	0.8	2
		0.19	1.2	1
M_5,M_6	850	0.13	0.8	1
		0.14	1	1.5
		0.15	1.2	2
	950	0.13	1	2
		0.14	1.2	1
		0.15	0.8	1.5
	1050	0.13	1	1.5
		0.14	0.8	2
		0.15	1.2	1

During the milling process, cutting-tool wear was detected once per ten cuts according to the cutting route. When the end point of the cutting-tool wear was reached, machining was stopped and the tool was changed. Photos of the detected partial cutting-tool wear are shown in Figure 17.

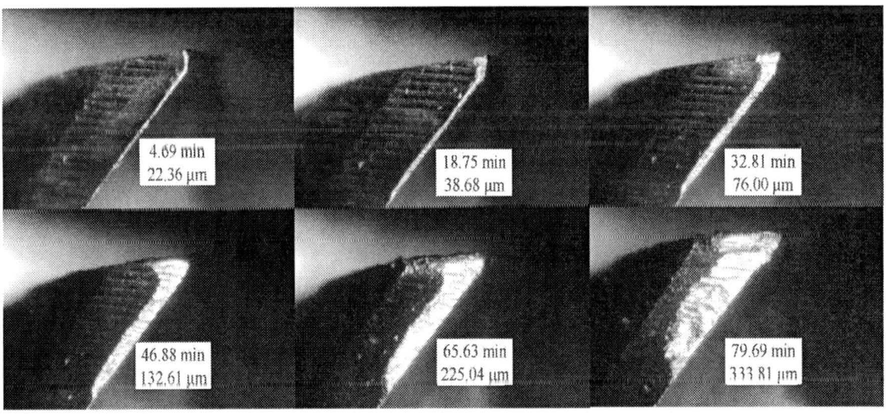

Figure 17. Partial tool wear detection photos.

The multivariate linear regression method [33] was used to determine the parameters in the cutting-tool degradation model, as shown in Figure 18. The machining power and cutting-tool life models are shown in Table 4.

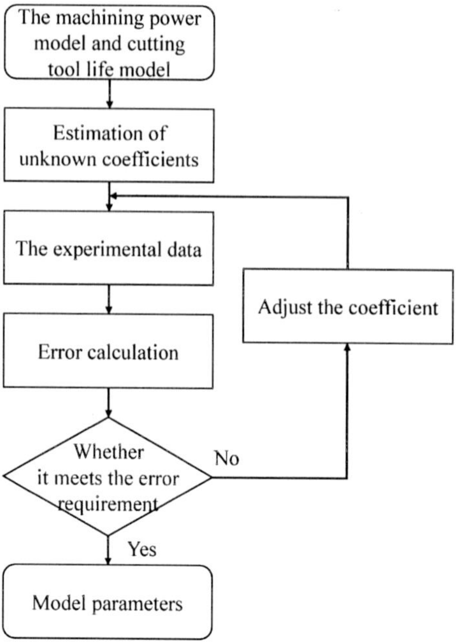

Figure 18. Multivariate linear regression method.

Table 4. Cutting-tool degradation model

Machine Tools	Model
M_1,M_2	$P_d = 0.9442{n_v}^{0.6385}f^{0.1416}{a_p}^{0.3255}{a_e}^{0.2693} + 4.24 \times 10^{-5}t_m{n_v}^{1.6716}f^{1.2510}{a_p}^{0.9296}{a_e}^{0.7356}$ $T = 10.0048{n_v}^{-0.3821}f^{-2.44733}{a_p}^{0.59782}{a_e}^{-0.26984}$
M_3,M_4	$P_d = 1.0400{n_v}^{0.6580}f^{-0.2245}{a_p}^{0.1842}{a_e}^{0.0789} + 2.24 \times 10^{-5}t_m n^{2.2058}f^{3.0474}{a_p}^{0.0977}{a_e}^{0.4933}$ $T = 23.3873{n_v}^{-0.1448}f^{-1.2645}{a_p}^{0.7309}{a_e}^{-0.0774}$
M_5,M_6	$P_d = 1.7413{n_v}^{0.5870}f^{0.1269}{a_p}^{0.1231}{a_e}^{0.0932} + 1.15 \times 10^{-5}t_m{n_v}^{0.3816}f^{-2.5387}{a_p}^{-0.5164}{a_e}^{0.2689}$ $T = 25.5911{n_v}^{0.1248}f^{-0.0842}{a_p}^{0.0048}{a_e}^{-0.0726}$

The no-load balance time T_{Rm} of the machine tool was determined by measurement experiments and the on/off security threshold time H_m was obtained from the equipment manual.

The no-load balance time T_{Rm} must meet the following condition:

$$\begin{cases} T_{Rm} \geq RT_{mean} \\ T_{Rm} = \frac{RTE_{mean}}{P_{sm}} * SF_m \end{cases} \quad (36)$$

where SF_m=1.2.

Job and Workshop Configuration Information

The flexible job shop has six machine tools and five types of workpieces. The machining process information on the machine tools and workpieces are listed in Table 5 and Table 6, respectively. The axonometric drawing of the five workpieces is shown in Figure 19.

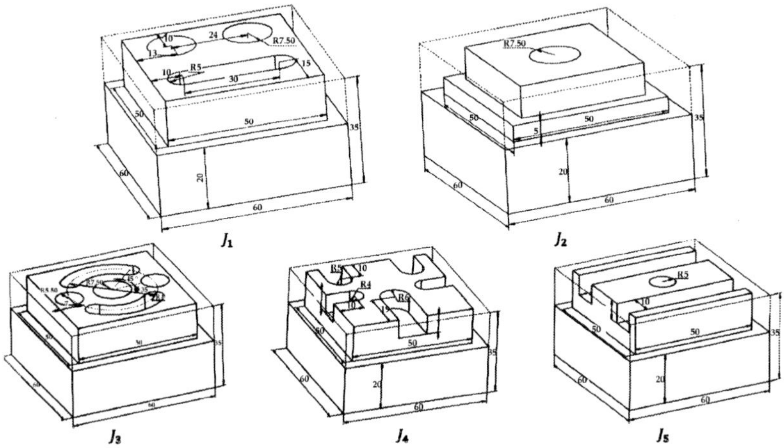

Figure 19. Three-dimensional model drawing of the five workpieces.

Table 5. Machine tool information

Machine Tools	The No-Load Balance Time (T_R^m/s)	The on/off Security Threshold Time (H_k/s)	Cutting-Tool Change Time (t_{ct}/s)/Power (P_{ct}/W)	Static Power (P_{sm}/W)
M_1,M_2	48	100	60/195	520
M_3,M_4	45	90	80/295	420
M_5,M_6	32	60	40/156	325

Table 6. Workpiece information

Job Number		Operations	Optional Machine Tools	Processing Time (min)	Cutting Parameters (n_v, f, a_p, a_e)
J_1	$O_{1,1}$	Milling 50 × 50 × 15 convex platform	M_1, M_2 M_3, M_4	16.34 8.16	900,0.17,3,2.5 800,0.19,3,5
	$O_{1,2}$	Milling 30 × 10 × 15 slot	M_1, M_2	2.68	700,0.16,1.5,2
	$O_{1,3}$	Enlarge holes 2 × ⌀12 × 15 → 2 × ⌀15 × 15	M_1, M_2 M_5, M_6	3 4	700,0.15,1.5,1.5 850,0.13,1.5,1.5
J_2	$O_{2,1}$	Milling 50 × 50 × 15 convex platform	M_1, M_2 M_3, M_4	16.34 8.16	900,0.17,3,2.5 800,0.19,3,5
	$O_{2,2}$	Milling 40 × 40 × 10 convex platform	M_1, M_2 M_5, M_6	12.45 14.8	900,0.15,2.5,2.5 1050,0.13,2,2.5
	$O_{2,3}$	Enlarge hole ⌀12 × 15 → ⌀15 × 15	M_5, M_6	2	850,0.13,1.5,1.5
J_3	$O_{3,1}$	Milling 50 × 50 × 15 convex platform	M_1, M_2 M_3, M_4	16.34 8.16	900,0.17,3,2.5 800,0.19,3,5
	$O_{3,2}$	Milling 2 × 27 × 8 × 8 slots	M_5, M_6	4	850,0.13,1,2
	$O_{3,3}$	Enlarge hole ⌀12 × 15 → ⌀15 × 15	M_1, M_2 M_5, M_6	1.5 2	700,0.15,1.5,1.5 850,0.13,1.5,1.5
	$O_{3,4}$	Enlarge holes 2 × ⌀10 × 15 → 2 × ⌀11 × 15	M_5, M_6	2.56	850,0.13,1,0.5
J_4	$O_{4,1}$	Milling 50 × 50 × 15 convex platform	M_1, M_2 M_3, M_4	16.34 8.16	900,0.17,3,2.5 800,0.19,3,5
	$O_{4,2}$	Milling 19 × 12 × 8 slot	M_3, M_4	1.49	600,0.17,1,2
	$O_{4,3}$	Milling 2×10×10 × 8 slots	M_1, M_2	1.53	700,0.15,1,2
	$O_{4,4}$	Milling 2 × 10 × ×8 × 8 slots	M_5, M_6	1.45	850,0.13,1,2
J_5	$O_{5,1}$	Milling 50 × 50 × 15 convex platform	M_1, M_2 M_3, M_4	16.34 8.16	900,0.17,3,2.5 800,0.19,3,5
	$O_{5,2}$	Milling 2 × 50 × 10 × 8 slots	M_1, M_2	7.62	700,0.15,1,2
	$O_{5,3}$	Enlarge hole ⌀9 × 15 → ⌀10 × 15	M_5, M_6	0.85	850,0.13,1,0.5

Establishment of Production Cost Indicator

Reducing cost plays an important role in the profitability, survival and development of an enterprise. How to get the maximum benefit with the minimum cost is an important topic that enterprises and even the whole society face and need to study and solve. To provide a better basis for selecting scheduling schemes, this paper establishes a mathematical model of production cost to evaluate scheduling schemes [34,35], as shown in Equation (36).

$$COST = \omega_e E_{total} + \omega_m WL + \omega_t G + \omega_l C_{max} \tag{37}$$

Table 7 shows the specific unit cost components in the production cost indicator, which includes unit energy cost, unit operating cost of machine tool, machine tool turn-on/off loss cost and cost per unit of labor time.

Table 7. Related unit costs

Unit Energy Cost (CNY/KW·h)	Unit Operating Cost of Machine Tool (CNY/h)	Machine Tool Turn on/off Loss Cost (CNY/time)	Cost Per Unit of Labor Time (CNY/h)
0.7250.725	9	1	30

Evaluation

Experiment Results

(1) Hybrid mechanism of cutting-tool change and machine tool turn-on/off

It can be seen that machining power is not only related to tool wear but also related to cutting parameters. Therefore, to reflect and highlight the relationship between machining power variations and tool wear, the relationship between machining power and tool wear and the accuracy of the power model was analyzed by using actual and simulation data under the premise of certain cutting parameters.

It can be seen from the model that the machining power is linearly related to the tool utilization time. By comparing the actual collected power data with the tool utilization time and power data predicted by regression, it was found that the errors were all within a controllable range. The maximum error of the M_1,M_2; M_3,M_4; and M_5,M_6 models are 6.44%, 3.36%, 4.67%, respectively, as shown in Figure 20.

(2) Scheduling algorithm results

To reflect the performance of the improved NSGA-II (INSGA-II), scheduling solutions were generated under the premise that the degrees of cutting-tool wear of machine tools M_1-M_6 are 60%, 70%, 50%, 50%, 70% and 60%, respectively. Table 8 summarizes the experimental results and shows the number of Pareto solutions, target values (Cmax, Etotal, WL, and G) and production cost indicator for each Pareto solution. The production cost is between CNY 36 and 40. The Pareto solution of the example is shown in Figure 21, where the X-, Y-, and Z-axis represents the W_L, C_{max}, and E_{total}, respectively; the color represents G.

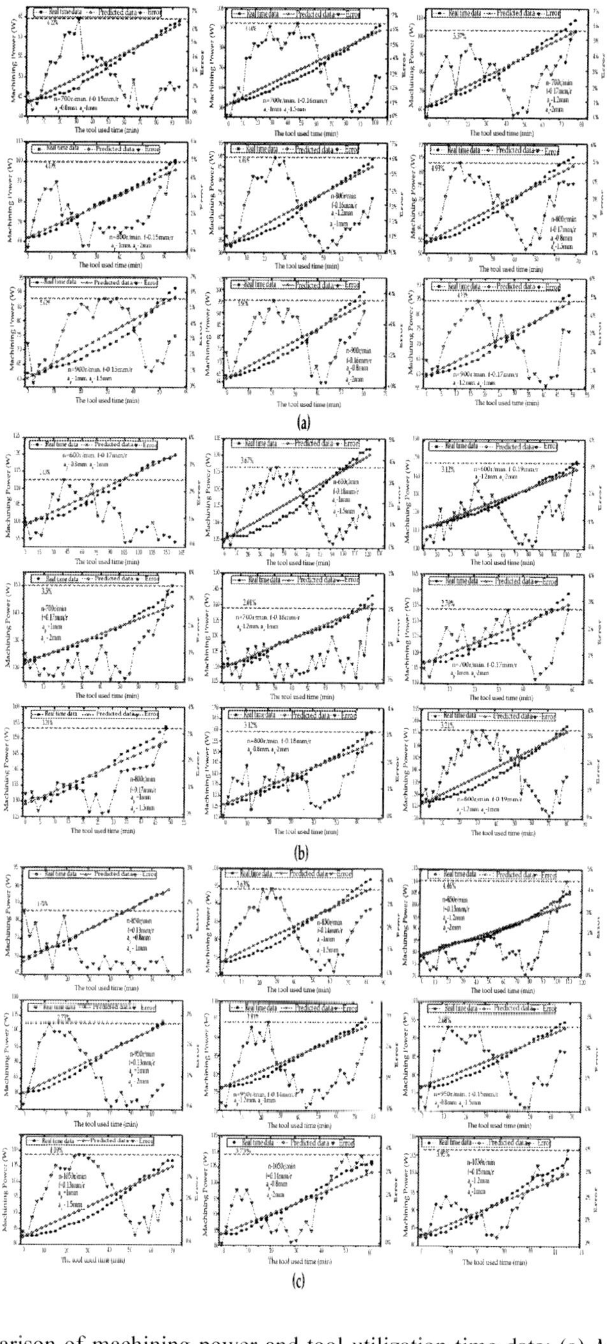

Figure 20. Comparison of machining power and tool utilization time data: (a) M_1,M_2; (b) M_3,M_4; (c) M_5,M_6.

As seen in Figure 21, the solution space is sufficient and the Pareto front is well distributed. The makespan is between 27 and 31 min, the total energy consumption of the workshop is between 319 and 350 Kw·min, the total machine tool load is 80–90 min, and the total number of times machine tools were turned on/off and cutting tools were changed is from five to nine times. The above data show that the INSGA-II algorithm can balance the four target values. The decision-maker can choose the optimal compromise using the multicriteria decision-making method.

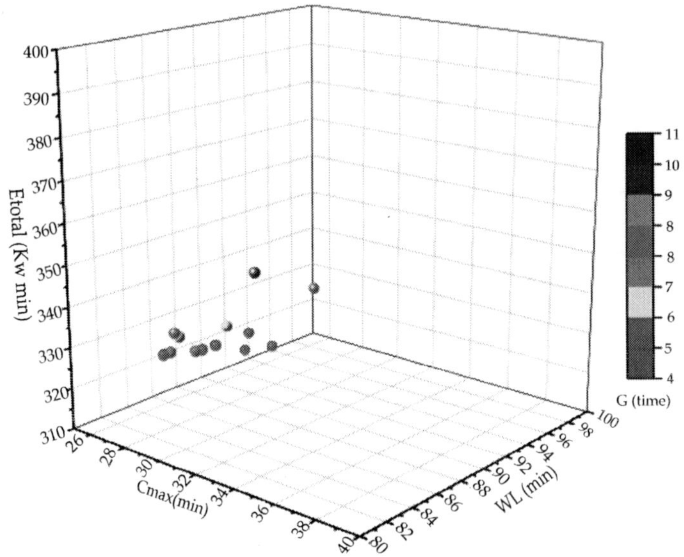

Figure 21. Pareto solutions.

Table 8. Cutting-tool degradation model

Pareto Numbers	Pareto Solutions (C_{max}(min),E_{total}(Kw·min), WL(min),G (time))	**Production Cost (CNY)**
15	(29.60,337.46,81.93,7), (28.95,329.10,84.78,8), (27.18,319.5,90.61,8), (28.95,331.36,81.93,8),(28.95,331.32,82.43,9), (27.18,317.67,92.96,8), (28.95,329.10,84.78,8), (28.95,329.34,84.28,9),(28.96,329.01,85.78,8), (28.95,331.36,81.93,8), (27.79,325.47,90.11,8), (28.96,334.26,93.96,7), (29.47,335.72,82.43,6), (31.18,349.53,85.78,5), (29.60,334.64,85.78,6)	37.17, 38.17, 38.04, 37.77, 38.84, 38.37, 38.17, 39.10, 38.32, 37.77, 38.34, 38.61, 36.16, 36.68, 36.71

Figure 22 is a Gantt chart of Pareto solutions for this example. The X-axis represents the time, the Y-axis represents the machine number, and each block represents an operation. O denotes the machine tool processing operation, e.g., the first block $O_{5,1}$ of M_3 indicates that the first process of J_3 was processed on M_3. CT denotes the cutting-tool change. Idle indicates that the machine tool is not in use, e.g., the gray block on M_6. On/Off indicates that the machine tool is turned off, e.g., the green block on M_1. R_C_T indicates that the machine tool is off; however, the cutting tool will be changed at the beginning or end of this period, e.g., the gray-green block on M_2. S indicates that the machine tool is on standby, e.g., the light blue block on M_5. The scheduling scheme can provide the appropriate cutting-tool change time and turn off the machine tools on standby when necessary to save energy.

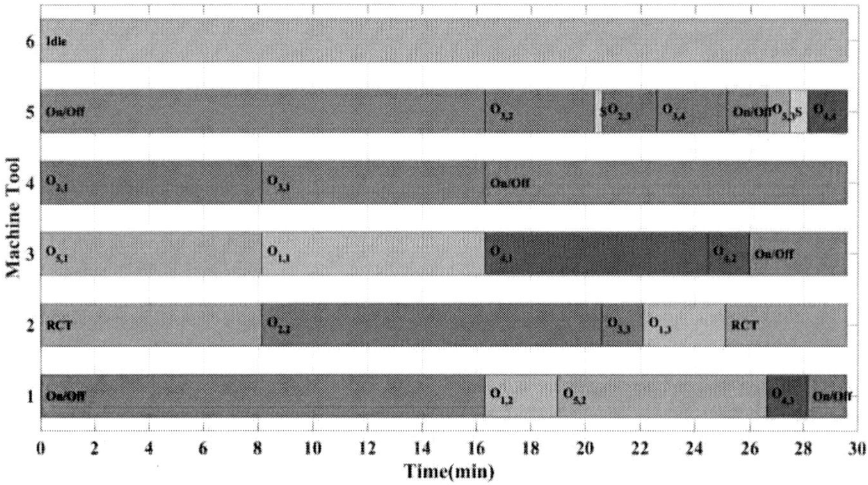

Figure 22. Gantt chart of an instance.

Assessing the Effects of the Cutting-Tool Degradation Model

In this section, based on the cutting-tool degradation model, multi-objective scheduling optimization is conducted starting with new cutting tools. Five schemes are selected from the Pareto optimal solutions for comparison, as follows: Scheme 1 includes the minimum sum of the four target values (C_{max}, E_{total}, W_L, and G) with the weight of [0.3, 0.1, 0.5, and 0.1], and its four target values and cost are CNY (26.64, 309.7, 92.96, and 7) and 37.01. Scheme 2 includes the minimum makespan, and its four target values and cost are CNY (26.64, 309.7, 92.96, and 7) and 37.01. Scheme 3 includes the minimum total energy consumption of the workshop, and its four target values and cost are CNY (26.64, 309.7, 92.96, and 7) and 37.01. Scheme 4 includes the minimum total load of machine tools, and its four target values and cost are CNY (28.95, 328.13, 81.93, and 7) and 36.73. Scheme 5 includes the least number of times that the machine tools are turned on/off and cutting tools are changed, and its four target values and cost are CNY (36.82, 408.87, 90.61, and 5) and 40.94. Figure 23 shows the Gantt chart of production scheduling of Scheme 1. Figure 24 and Figure 25 show the simulation power curve and degree of cutting tool wear curve of each machine tool, respectively, in the production process of Scheme 1. These reflect the change in the machining power of each machine tool with the processing operation, verify the influence of the cutting-tool degradation model on the total energy consumption of machine tools, and highlight the necessity of the tool degradation model.

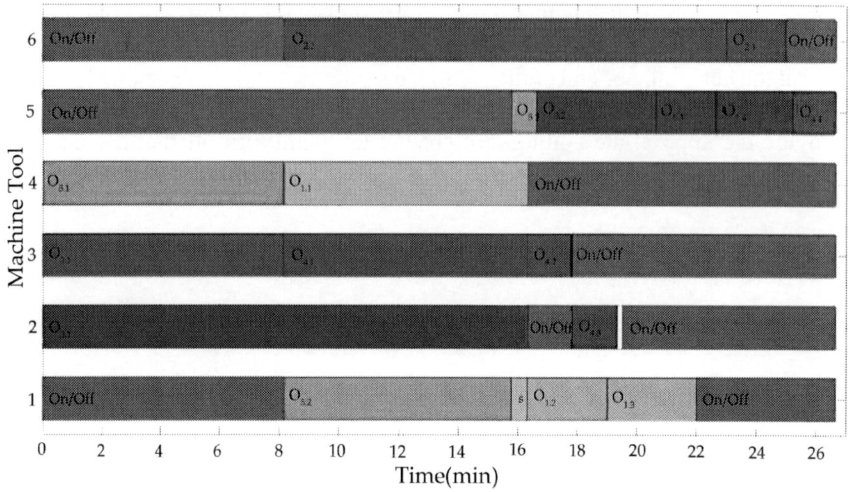

Figure 23. Gantt chart of scheme 1.

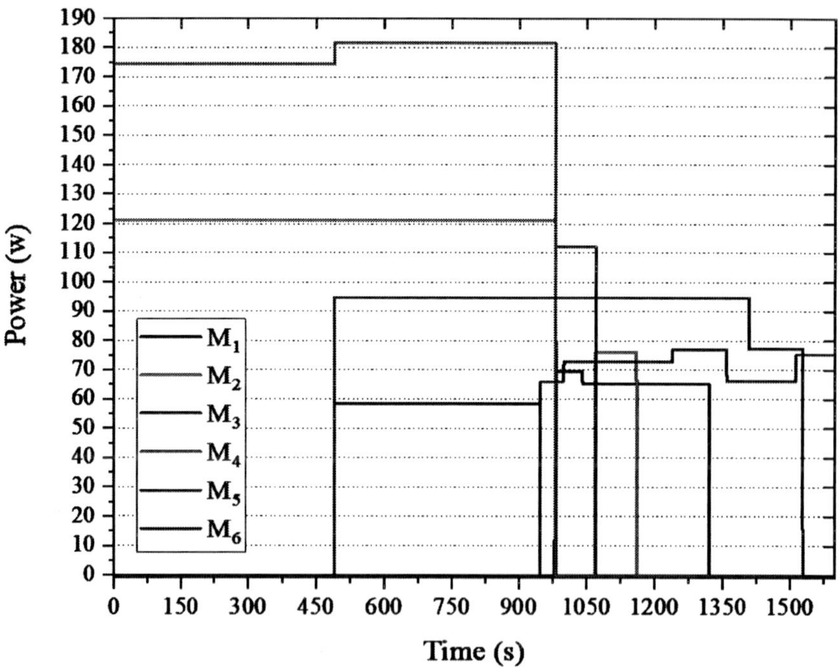

Figure 24. Simulation machining power curve.

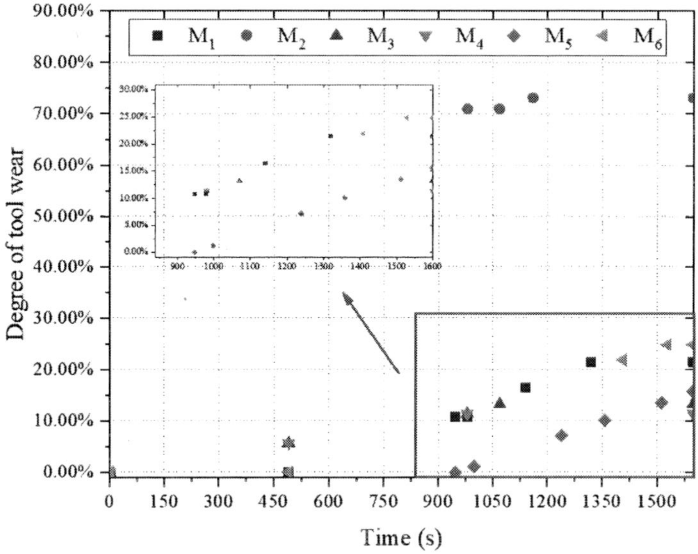

Figure 25. Scatter chart of tool wear.

From the cutting-tool degradation model, all machine tools can provide feedback on the real power condition of the machining process. Taking machine tool M_1 as an example, the curve of simulated and actual machining power can be obtained after actual machining, as shown in Figure 26.

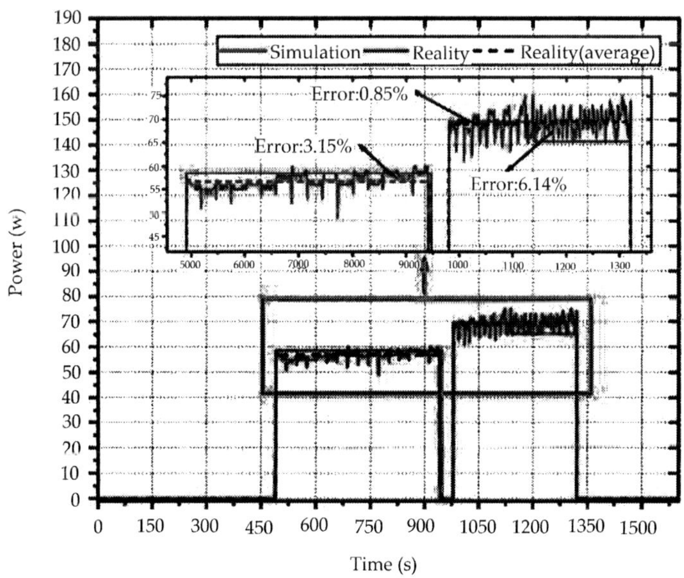

Figure 26. Comparison curve between simulated power and actual machining power.

The simulated and actual average machining power of the three processes are 58.46 W, 69.49 W, and 65.24 W; and 56.7 W, 68.9 W, and 69.5 W, respectively. The power errors of the three processes are 3.15%, 0.85%, and 6.14%, respectively. The main reason for the considerable fluctuation in the actual machining power is that the cutting direction is not constant during machining. Changes in the cutting direction lead to an instantaneous power decrease because no cutting occurs at that moment, and the spindle generates a large amount of instantaneous power when it just touches the workpiece. The reason for the large error in the simulation results of the third process is that during hole enlargement, the actual cutting width is larger than the given cutting width (1.5 mm) because the actual processing path is circumferential; this makes the actual machining power larger than the simulation power. However, overall, the errors are all within the acceptable range and the cutting-tool degradation model can be applied in scheduling planning. This is conducive to making the simulation closer to the actual production, making the scheduling scheme and scheduling results more practical, and it plays a key role in predicting the machining power of machine tools.

Assessing the Effects of the Energy-Saving Strategies

Comparing the results of the five scheduling schemes shows that adopting the machine tool turn-on/off measure reduced the average total machine standby time in the five schemes by over 99.2%: from 77.18 min to 35.40 s. The total energy consumption of turning machine tools on/off increased from 0 Kw·min to 1.744 Kw·min, whereas the standby energy consumption of the machine tools decreased from 31.891 Kw·min to 2.044 Kw·min. In addition, the cost of energy consumption decreased by about CNY 0.36. Although the machine tool turn-on/off strategy slightly increased the energy consumption when these are turned on/off, it significantly reduced the standby energy consumption, as shown in Figure 27. Therefore, it can be concluded that the machine tool turn-on/off energy-saving strategy is very effective.

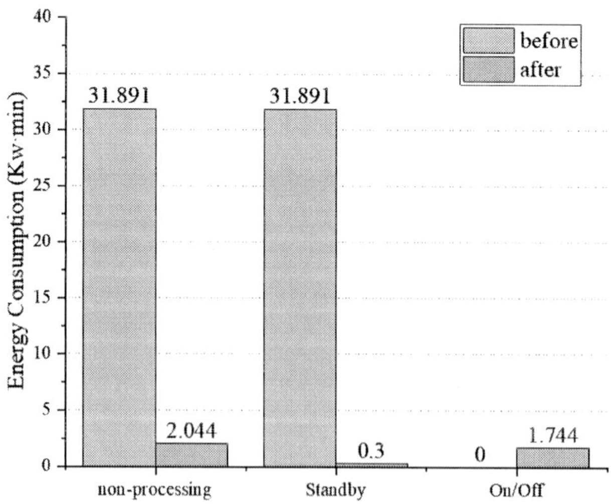

Figure 27. Influence of the machine tool on/off strategy on non-processing energy consumption.

To assess the effects of the hybrid energy-saving strategy, we compared the energy consumption and makespan distinction before and after its adoption. Figure 28 shows the scheduling scheme changes before and after the hybrid energy-saving measure was applied. The four target values and cost before and after optimization are CNY 30.47, 347.18, 89.93, 10 and 39.92 and CNY 28.95, 331.76, 89.93, 10 and 38.97, respectively. It can be seen from the Gantt chart that after adopting the energy-saving strategy, the cutting-tool change of M_3 was performed before $O_{5,1}$, resulting in a 3.95% reduction in the makespan from 30.14 min to 28.95 min, a 4.44% reduction in the total energy consumption of the workshop from 347.18 kW ·min to 331.76 kW ·min and a 2.44% reduction in the production cost from CNY 39.92 to 38.97, equivalent to CNY 47.3 saved every 24 h. However, the cutting-tool life of M_3 was calculated as 143.002 min using the cutting-tool life model, while the processing time of $O_{5,1}$ was 8.16 min, thus reducing the processing capacity of the cutting tool DW by 5.7%, as shown in Figure 29.

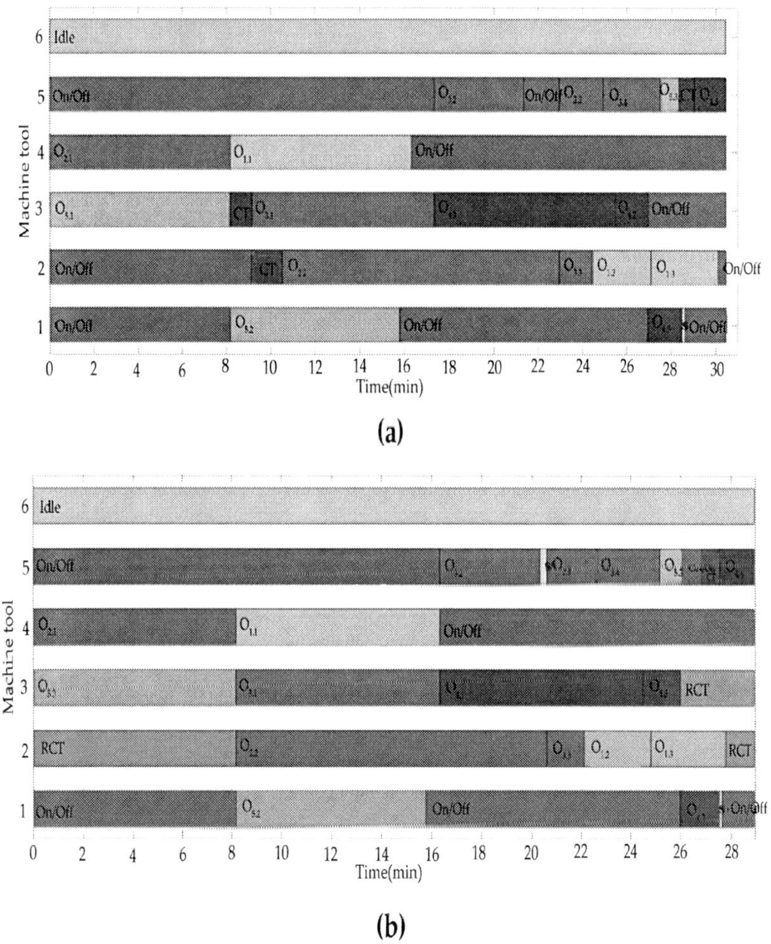

Figure 28. Comparison of scheduling schemes before and after the hybrid energy-saving strategy: (a) Before the hybrid energy-saving strategy; (b) After the hybrid energy-saving strategy.

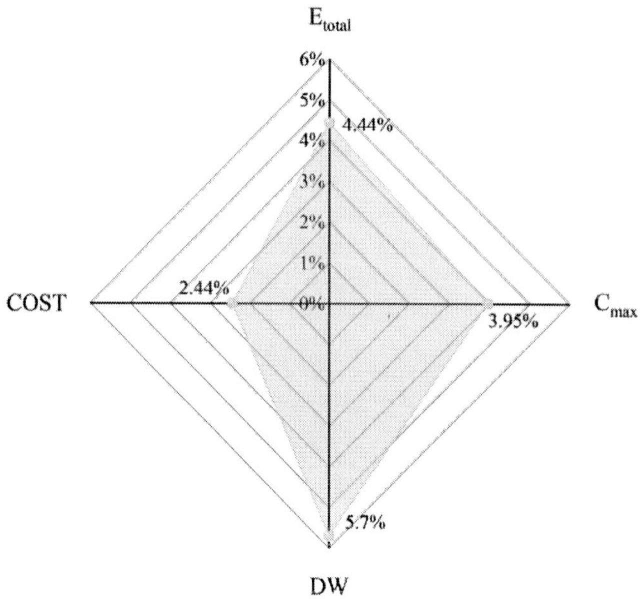

Figure 29. Total impact of the hybrid energy-saving strategy.

The energy-saving strategy mainly reduced the energy consumption of the workshop by changing the timing of the cutting-tool change while reducing the makespan; the total machine tool load and the total number of times the machine tools were turned on/off and cutting tools were changed were not affected.

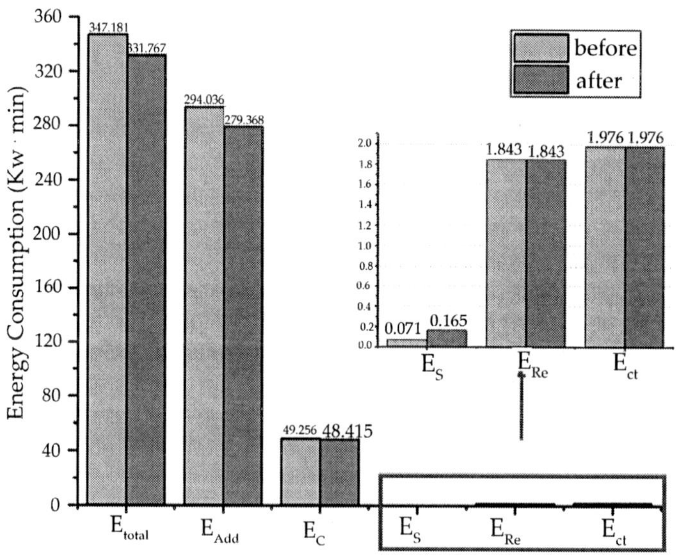

Figure 30. Effect of the hybrid energy-saving strategy on energy consumption.

The changes in the total energy consumption of the workshop were analyzed, as shown in Figure 30. In the solutions before and after optimization, the additional energy consumption of the workshop E_{Add} was the highest. This is because the energy consumption of a large number of additional equipment such as lighting, air pumps, and air conditioners in the actual workshop was far greater than that of the machine tools. Because this equipment is continuously operated, its energy consumption is positively correlated with time. As shown in Figure 31, the power consumption of M_3 changed when the cutting tool was changed in advance. The red and green parts represent the energy consumed before and after optimization, respectively. On the whole, the processing energy consumption E_c of the optimized solution decreased.

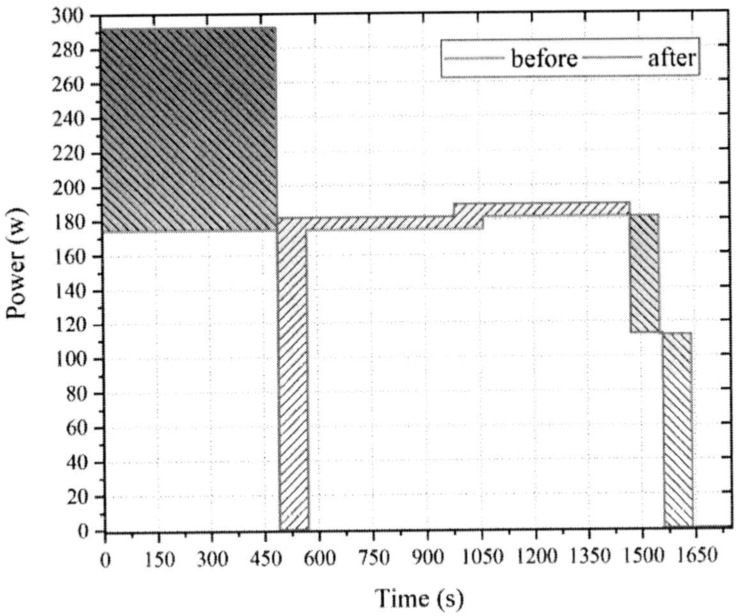

Figure 30. Power contrast curve of M_3 after adopting the hybrid energy saving strategy.

However, the reduction in E_c is much smaller than that in E_{Add} in terms of energy consumption and has little influence on the total energy consumption. The decrease in E_{Add} is mainly attributed to the integration of the cutting-tool change and machine tool turn-on/off processes, which leads to the reduction in the makespan, thus reducing the energy consumption of additional equipment. However, the cutting-tool change and machine tool turn-on/off processes were not eliminated; hence, their energy consumption did not change. In summary, the hybrid energy-saving strategy effectively reduced energy consumption and optimized the makespan, making it vital within the acceptable degree of reduction in the cutting-tool processing capacity.

CONCLUSIONS

Production planning and scheduling are usually the most critical activities in intelligent manufacturing enterprises. In the manufacturing process, manufacturers not only need to use the minimum resources to meet the production demand with as little energy consumption and in as short a time as possible but also face the challenge of the lack of mutual responsibility between the scheduling system and the single machine, which often leads to a large deviation between the scheduling optimization results and the actual application. Therefore, a new FJSP–CTD–ESM method is proposed in this paper to provide strong support for intelligent manufacturing enterprises to reduce the time and energy consumption in the production process. Through analyzing the coupling relationship between shop scheduling, single-machine tool energy consumption and tool life prediction, and organically integrating the three to achieve deeper shop consumption reduction. The resulting effect is as follows:

(1) Cutting-tool degradation during shop scheduling was analyzed. Based on the experimental data, exponential regression models of the dynamic power and cutting-tool life were established under certain machining conditions, with an error of approximately 6.5%.

(2) A dynamic cutting-tool change strategy by monitoring the RUL was proposed to change the cutting tool before it becomes blunt. This makes the optimization model closer to the real machining situation.

(3) Oriented towards low-carbon production objectives, the conventional machine tool turn-on/off schedule can reduce the non-processing energy consumption by 93.5%. Integrating the cutting-tool change strategy into the conventional machine tool turn-on/off schedule further reduces the total energy consumption by 4.44% and production cost by 2.44%. It was proved that this hybrid energy-saving strategy effectively reduces the energy consumption of workshops and has great application prospects.

In terms of the defects in this study, the proposed model does not consider the constraints of transport, clamping, and assembly on shop scheduling. In addition, the establishment of the machining power model and the tool life model of each machine tool in the workshop needs to spend a lot of time on the cutting wear experiment (about 45 h), which brings a lot of work to the preparation of the early production. When the shop changes the machine tool or changes a different type of tool, the models need to be rebuilt. Based on the above limitations, some suggestions are recommended as follows:

(1) To explore a fast method to obtain the machining power model and the tool life model and make these models have a certain universal applicability.

(2) To integrate more practical constraints such as transport, clamping, assembly, random breakdown or rush orders into the optimization model.

(3) To design an efficient solution algorithm to solve multi-objective and many-objective optimization problems.

AUTHOR CONTRIBUTIONS

Conceptualization, Y.T. and Z.G.; methodology, Y.T. and Z.G.; software, Z.G.; validation, Z.G.; formal analysis, Z.G.; investigation, Y.T., Z.G., L.Z., Y.C. and T.W.; resources, Y.T., L.Z. and T.W.; data curation, Z.G. and Y.C.; writing—original draft preparation, Y.T. and Z.G.; writing—review and editing, Y.T., Z.G. and T.W.; visualization, Z.G.; supervision, Y.T. and Z.G.; project administration, Y.T., L.Z. and Z.G.; funding acquisition, Y.T. All authors have read and agreed to the published version of the manuscript.

REFERENCES

1. Zhou, L.; Li, J.; Li, F.; Meng, Q.; Li, J.; Xu, X. Energy consumption model and energy efficiency of machine tools: A comprehensive literature review. *J. Clean. Prod.* 2016, *112*, 3721–3734.
2. Danil, Y.P.; Mozammel, M.; Munish, K.G.; Álisson, R.M.; Giuseppe, P.; Deepak, R.U.; Navneet, K.; Aqib, M.K.; Ítalo, T.; Szymon, W.; et al. Resource saving by optimization and machining environments for sustainable manufacturing: A review and future prospects. *Renew. Sustain. Energy Rev.* 2022, *166*, 112660.
3. Bi, Z.M.; Wang, L.H. Optimization of machining processes from the perspective of energy consumption: A case study. *J. Manuf. Syst.* 2012, *31*, 420–428.
4. Zeng, L.L.; Zhou, F.X.; Xu, X.H.; Gao, Z. Dynamic scheduling of multi-task for hybrid flow-shop based on energy consumption. In Proceedings of the 2009 International Conference on Information and Automation, Zhuhai/Macau, China, 22–24 June 2009; pp. 478–482.
5. Guzman, E.; Andres, B.; Poler, R. Models and algorithms for production planning, scheduling and sequencing problems: A holistic framework and a systematic review. *J. Ind. Inf. Integr.* 2022, *27*, 100287.
6. Feng, Y.; Hong, Z.; Li, Z.; Zheng, H.; Tan, J. Integrated intelligent green scheduling of sustainable flexible workshop with edge computing considering uncertain machine state. *J. Clean. Prod.* 2020, *246*, 119070.
7. Guzman, E.; Andres, B.; Poler, R. Matheuristic algorithm for job-shop scheduling problem using a disjunctive mathematical model. *Computers* 2021, *11*, 1.
8. Mula, J.; Díaz-Madroñero, M.; Andres, B.; Poler, R.; Sanchis, R. A capacitated lot-sizing model with sequence-dependent setups, parallel machines and bi-part injection moulding. *Appl. Math. Model.* 2021, *100*, 805–820.
9. Rakovitis, N.; Li, D.; Zhang, N.; Li, J.; Zhang, L.; Xiao, X. Novel approach to energy-efficient flexible job-shop scheduling problems. *Energy* 2022, *238*, 121773.
10. Mouzon, G.; Yildirim, M.B.; Twomey, J. Operational methods for minimization of energy consumption of manufacturing equipment. *Int. J. Prod. Res.* 2007, *45*, 4247–4271.
11. Wu, X.; Sun, Y. A green scheduling algorithm for flexible job shop with energy-saving measures. *J. Clean. Prod.* 2018, *172*, 3249–3264.
12. Gong, G.; Chiong, R.; Deng, Q.; Gong, X.; Lin, W.; Han, W.; Zhang, L. A two-stage memetic algorithm for energy-efficient flexible job shop scheduling by means of decreasing the total number of machine restarts. *Swarm Evol. Comput.* 2022, *75*, 101131.
13. Cheng, L.; Tang, Q.; Zhang, L.; Meng, K. Mathematical model and enhanced cooperative co-evolutionary algorithm for scheduling energy-efficient manufacturing cell. *J. Clean. Prod.* 2021, *326*, 129248.
14. An, Y.; Chen, X.; Zhang, J.; Li, Y. A hybrid multi-objective evolutionary algorithm to integrate optimization of the production scheduling and imperfect cutting tool maintenance considering total energy consumption. *J. Clean. Prod.* 2020, *268*, 121540.
15. Setiawan, A.; Wangsaputra, R.; Martawirya, Y.Y.; Halim, A.H. An FMS Dynamic Production Scheduling Algorithm Considering Cutting Tool Failure and Cutting Tool Life. *IOP Conf. Ser. Mater. Sci. Eng.* 2016, *114*, 012052.
16. Liu, F.; Wang, L.Q.; Liu, G.J. Content architecture and future trends of energy efficiency research on machining systems. *J. Mech. Eng.* 2013, *49*, 87–94.
17. He, Y.; Tian, X.; Li, Y.; Wang, S.; John, W. Modeling machining energy consumption including the effect of toolpath. *Procedia CIRP* 2020, *90*, 573–578.

18. He, Y.; Tian, X.; Li, Y.; Wang, Y.; Wang, Y.; Wang, S. Modeling and analyses of energy consumption for machining features with flexible machining configurations. *J. Manuf. Syst.* 2022, *62*, 463–476.
19. Shailendra, P.; Girish, K.G.; Srikanta, R. Modelling of Variable Energy Consumption for CNC Machine Tools. *Procedia CIRP* 2021, *98*, 247–251.
20. Haruhiko, S.; Tetsuo, S. Energy Efficiency in Machining Systems Based on Power-Law Model for Specific Energy Consumption. *Procedia CIRP* 2022, *107*, 931–936.
21. Mikołajczyk, T.; Nowicki, K.; Bustillo, A.; Pimenov, D.Y. Predicting tool life in turning operations using neural networks and image processing. *Mech. Syst. Signal Process.* 2018, *104*, 503–513.
22. Sun, H.; Liu, Y.; Pan, J.; Zhang, J.; Ji, W. Enhancing cutting tool sustainability based on remaining useful life prediction. *J. Clean. Prod.* 2020, *244*, 118794.
23. Castejón, M.; Alegre, E.; Barreiro, J.; Hernández, L.K. On-line tool wear monitoring using geometric descriptors from digital images. *Int. J. Mach. Tools Manuf.* 2007, *47*, 1847–1853.
24. Bagga, P.J.; Bajaj, K.S.; Makhesana, M.A.; Patel, K.M. An online tool life prediction system for CNC turning using computer vision techniques. *Mater. Today Proc.* 2022, *62*, 2689–2693.
25. Shi, K.; Zhang, D.; Liu, N.; Wang, S.; Ren, J.; Wang, S. A novel energy consumption model for milling process considering tool wear progression. *J. Clean. Prod.* 2018, *184*, 152–159.
26. Zhang, X.; Yu, T.; Dai, Y.; Qu, S.; Zhao, J. Energy consumption considering tool wear and optimization of cutting parameters in micro milling process. *Int. J. Mech. Sci.* 2020, *178*, 105628.
27. Muhammad, Y.; Syed, J.; Ashfaq, K.; Mushtaq, K. Development and analysis of tool wear and energy consumption maps for turning of titanium alloy (Ti6Al4V). *J. Manuf. Process.* 2021, *62*, 613–622.
28. Tian, C.; Zhou, G.; Zhang, J. Optimization of cutting parameters considering tool wear conditions in low-carbon manufacturing environment. *J. Clean. Prod.* 2019, *226*, 706–719.
29. Tian, Y.; Shao, W.; Wang, T. Energy Footprint Modeling and Parameter Optimization in Workshop Manufacturing Process. *China Mech. Eng.* 2021, *33*, 1–10. (In Chinese)
30. *ISO 8688-2: 1989*; Tool Life Testing in Milling-Part 2: End Milling. IX-ISO: Geneva, Switzerland, 1989.
31. Deb, K.; Pratap, A.; Agarwal, S.; Meyarivan, T. A fast and elitist multiobjective genetic algorithm: NSGA-II. *IEEE Trans. Evol. Comput.* 2002, *6*, 182–197.
32. Zhang, G.; Gao, L.; Li, P.; Zhang, C. Improved Genetic Algorithm for the Flexible Job-shop Scheduling Problem. *J. Mech. Eng.* 2009, *45–47*, 145–151.
33. Leng, J.; Gao, X.; Zhu, J. The application of multivariate linear regression forecast model. *J. Stat. Decis.* 2016, *7*, 82–85. (In Chinese)
34. Chu, H.; Dong, K.; Li, R.; Cheng, Q.; Zhang, C.; Huang, K.; Yang, C.; Zheng, Y. Integrated modeling and optimization of production planning and scheduling in hybrid flow shop for order production mode. *Comput. Ind. Eng.* 2022, *174*, 108741.
35. Ramya, G.; Chandrasekaran, M.; Arulmozhi, P. Optimization of production cost for integrating job shop scheduling with production resources. *Mater. Today Proc.* 2021, *37*, 1839–1844.

8

Data-Mining-Based Real-Time Optimization of the Job Shop Scheduling Problem

Anran Zhao, Peng Liu , Xiyu Gao, Guotai Huang, Xiuguang Yang, Yuan Ma, Zheyu Xie, and Yunfeng Li

School of Mechanical and Aerospace Engineering, Jilin University, Changchun 130025, China

ABSTRACT

In the job-shop scheduling field, timely and proper updating of the original scheduling strategy is an effective way to avoid the negative impact of disturbances on manufacturing. In this paper, a pure reactive scheduling method for updating the scheduling strategy is proposed to deal with the disturbance of the uncertainty of the arrival of new jobs in the job shop. The implementation process is as follows: combine data mining, discrete event simulation, and dispatching rules (DRs), take makespan and machine utilization as scheduling criteria, divide the manufacturing system production period into multiple scheduling subperiods, and build a dynamic scheduling model that assigns DRs to subscheduling periods in real-time; the scheduling strategies are generated at the beginning of each scheduling subperiod. The experiments showed that the method proposed enables a reduction in the makespan of 2–17% and an improvement in the machine utilization of 2–21%. The constructed scheduling model can assign the optimal DR to each scheduling subperiod in real-time, which realizes the purpose of locally updating the scheduling strategy and enhancing the overall scheduling effect of the manufacturing system.

Keywords: *Pure Reactive Scheduling, Subscheduling Period, Dispatching Rule (DR), Decision Tree, Scheduling Model*

INTRODUCTION

Scheduling is an important part of job shop manufacturing systems and a decisive factor affecting production efficiency [1]. As a classic combinatorial optimization problem, job shop scheduling has attracted scholars for more than 60 years because of its NP-hard characteristics [2]. Industries with high discreteness and strong customization, such as crystal ornaments and toys, often lead to unbalanced technological processes in the production process due to the variety of technological processes and large differences in processing time. Good scheduling strategies play a huge role. Due to disturbances encountered being more frequent and diverse in manufacturing systems, it is clear that static scheduling models can no longer fully meet manufacturing requirements. Dynamic scheduling needs to consider to machine degradation and the random arrival of products in the production process [3]. These disturbances are difficult to predict precisely or predictably in the early stage of scheduling, which may make the original scheduling strategy unsuitable. Due to the existence of the abovementioned disturbances, the complexity of scheduling increases rapidly. Therefore, research on the dynamic job shop scheduling problem (JSSP) remains a topic of considerable interest in the manufacturing industry, with strong application value and theoretical significance.

In increasingly complex manufacturing systems, uncertain events cause information asymmetry between the actual production process and pre-established scheduling strategies, affecting the execution of the pre-established scheduling strategies. Predictable disturbances can be dealt with in advance while unpredictable disturbances, such as the random arrival of jobs, can have a catastrophic impact on production efficiency in the case of improper scheduling. Dealing with these unpredictable disturbances rapidly and accurately ensures the smooth execution of the manufacturing system production process and is the key to improving production efficiency. However, the following challenges are encountered in the current research process:

(1) The metaheuristics [4], heuristic methods [5], and exact methods [6] used to optimize scheduling problems are often affected by computing resources, thus yielding poor performance of the scheduling strategies generated in a short time [7]. Moreover, these methods cannot evolve with state changes in the manufacturing system, and they are insufficient to cope with disturbance factors in the manufacturing system continuously and efficiently.

(2) Makespan as the scheduling goal has an extensive engineering background and is widely used in academic research and industrial practice [8]. However, in actual production processes, the value-added time only accounts for a small part of the production cycle, and most of the wasted time is nonvalue-added time, such as waiting and storage [9]. Reducing the proportion of nonvalue-added time is an effective way to optimize makespan and improve production efficiency.

(3) The unknown moment when the job is released to the manufacturing system and the unpredictability of its processing attributes make it impossible to obtain all of the job information that needs to be processed at the initial moment of the manufacturing system; thus, it is impossible to optimize the JSSP from a global perspective.

To address these challenges, the computational efficiency of the solution and the adaptive capacity of the obtained scheduling strategies should be considered. In this study, we apply data mining (DM) techniques to scheduling and mine scheduling knowledge from historical data to construct a scheduling model. This method can reduce the time consumption of the solution process and provide a basis for the intelligent generation of workshop scheduling strategies. The optimization problem of the entire manufacturing system can be divided into multiple subsystem optimization problems to be solved [10], thereby reducing the complexity of the entire manufacturing system. Scheduling newly released jobs with subsystem units can avoid or mitigate disturbances to the state of the entire manufacturing system. Moreover, the acquired scheduling knowledge can be used to partially update the manufacturing system scheduling strategies to achieve the goal of enhancing the overall scheduling efficiency of the manufacturing system.

Based on the above discussion, this study proposes a novel purely reactive scheduling method for optimizing the JSSP to overcome the negative impact of the randomness of job arrivals on production efficiency. The production scheduling cycle of the entire manufacturing system is divided into several scheduling subcycles, and scheduling strategies are generated at the beginning of each scheduling subcycle. The generated scheduling strategies are used to schedule newly released jobs and jobs transferred from previous processes in the previous scheduling subperiod. In executing the scheduling strategies in each scheduling subperiod, the original data containing scheduling knowledge are collected, and DM technology is used to mine the obtained scheduling knowledge. A scheduling model is then constructed in a data-driven manner, and a scheduling strategy is generated for each scheduling subcycle in real-time. The implementation of the above process can not only quickly generate a scheduling strategy at the beginning of each sub-scheduling cycle but can also actively schedule the inserted new jobs, avoiding the negative impact of the random release of a job on the manufacturing process.

REVIEW OF THE LITERATURE

This section provides a review of numerous studies, summarizes gaps in previous research, and continues to optimize the scheduling problem on the basis of previous studies. The summary of previous studies on scheduling problems and scheduling methods is shown in Table 1 and is described in detail in the following three sections.

Table 1. Summary of the literature

Literature	Scheduling	Description
[11,12,13,14,15,16]	Static scheduling	Propose advanced heuristic/metaheuristic algorithms to solve for better performance scheduling policies.
[17,18,19,20,21,22,23]	Robust scheduling	Construct a robust model in the early stages of scheduling to take into account possible perturbation problems.
[24,25,26,27,28]	Rescheduling	Monitor the moment a disturbance appears or the scheduling policy degrades and update the original scheduling policy with the set scheduling method.
[29,30,31,32]	Predictive reactive	Predict possible disturbances in real-time as production proceeds, and proactively update scheduling policies when disturbances are predicted.

[33,34,35,36,37,38]	Pure reactive scheduling	Generate scheduling policies in real-time and dynamically based on the current job information of the production system and the current production status without the need to generate scheduling policies in advance.

Data Mining and Its Application to the JSSP

Data mining (DM) is a technology that utilizes statistical computing, data management, machine learning, and artificial intelligence to extract hidden patterns or relationships from a large amount of data and apply them to future analysis [1]. It has been widely used in manufacturing, the service industry, and other fields [39,40]. With the ongoing application of DM technology in all walks of life, a large amount of experience has been accumulated. Scheduling is an integral part of manufacturing systems, and DM technology has been widely used to optimize production scheduling problems. DM technology provides new possibilities for solving dynamic scheduling problems and enhancing the responsiveness of manufacturing systems as it can rapidly obtain scheduling strategies. Alican et al. [39] proposed that DM technology could identify meaningful patterns and optimize problems encountered during the operation of a manufacturing system. Metan et al. [41] combined simulations, DM, and statistical process control chart technology to develop a real-time DR scheduling system to reduce the delivery delay time of jobs in a manufacturing system. Zahmani et al. extracted potential knowledge from scheduling strategies obtained using a genetic algorithm to reduce the computational load [42]. Shahzad et al. obtained a set of DR optimization job delays based on DM technology and confirmed their effectiveness in a static environment [43].

The above research shows that DM technology has been widely applied to solve scheduling problems in processing workshops and can directly generate scheduling strategies; however, the literature has mainly focused on static scheduling problems. In these cases, all of the job information to be scheduled is known, and the scheduling strategy is formulated before production starts. However, it is difficult to satisfy the production requirements in dynamic environments with frequent disturbances.

Job Shop Scheduling

Job shop scheduling includes both static and dynamic scheduling, and static scheduling can obtain a scheduling policy with superior performance in specific scenarios and stable production systems. Wei et al. [11] mixed a variable neighborhood equilibrium optimizer and a sticky bacterium algorithm to solve a JSSP, which accelerated the solution speed; Yu et al. proposed an improved particle swarm algorithm and compared the genetic algorithm and particle swarm. Yuraszeck et al. [12] proposed a heuristic algorithm to avoid falling into the local optimum when solving scheduling policies, which is suitable for solving small-scale scheduling problems. Szabó et al. [13] proposed a heuristic algorithm for Clique Search in Graphs of Special Class, which can obtain better scheduling policies than genetic algorithms. Luan et al. [14,15] successively improved the whale algorithm under different scheduling objectives and then obtained faster performance scheduling policies than variable neighborhood search methods and some scheduling benchmarks. Sauvey et al. [16] constructed a makespan as the scheduling objective for the job shop scheduling problem with mixed blocking constraints and used a mathematical model to solve the scheduling policy using Mosel Xpress software. It was able to obtain a scheduling strategy with superior performance in specific scenarios and stable production systems, but it did not consider the possible uncertainties in the production process and had limitations in scheduling production systems with poor stability.

Production environments are becoming increasingly complex and dynamic because manufacturing systems are often disturbed by real-time events, such as external order insertion and task changes during the production process. Traditional static scheduling generally cannot meet the production requirements of such systems, and research on dynamic scheduling problems is thus becoming increasingly crucial. At present, according to the literature, the primary methods for modeling and solving dynamic scheduling problems include robust scheduling, rescheduling, predictive reactive scheduling, and purely reactive scheduling.

The robust scheduling method is an optimization method that integrates uncertain factors into the scheduling model. The key to a robust scheduling method is the prediction of the occurrence of future disturbance factors. If the prediction is biased, two unfavorable outcomes can occur in the manufacturing system: First, if the predicted disturbance factor does not appear, it will lead to an increased idle time of processing equipment and result in a large number of wasted resources [17]; second, incorrect prediction of the disturbance factors can cause the performance of the original scheduling strategy to deteriorate such that it may no longer be suitable for the current production environment [18]. Xiao et al. [19] constructed a robust scheduling model to solve the dynamic scheduling problem of the job shop with a random processing time. Fantahun et al. [20] proposed a simulated annealing algorithm to better schedule irreplaceable operators in the production workshop and improve production efficiency. Taking makespan as the scheduling goal, Khurshid et al. [21] successively proposed an evolutionary algorithm and a hybrid evolutionary strategy to optimize the scheduling problem of the permutation flow shop. To address the dynamic scheduling problem of randomly arriving tasks, Zhou et al. proposed an event-triggered dynamic task scheduling method in which uncertain events were considered in the scheduling model [22]. Wang et al. proposed two robust scheduling formulas based on scenario sets and used an improved tabu search algorithm for their solution; they were then applied to an uncertain JSSP with the completion time as the performance index [23].

Rescheduling is a method of updating the original scheduling strategy when a disturbance event is encountered during the operation of a manufacturing system. When the product requirements or working conditions change, the current production information is input into the determined mathematical model or algorithm, and the scheduling strategy is regenerated [24]. In the dynamic scheduling process, the timing of rescheduling, performance of the initial scheduling strategy, guarantee of an efficient rescheduling model, and performance of generating new scheduling strategies are the keys to the scheduling method. Rescheduling is generally performed when disturbances are encountered, so disturbances are predicted in advance or monitored in real-time. Zhang et al. [25] proposed an improved Kalman algorithm that can solve problems in a shorter time than the genetic algorithm and can be used in dynamic scheduling. Gao et al. established a scheduling model for the new task disturbance problem encountered in a flexible job shop manufacturing system, which was divided into two stages: scheduling and rescheduling [26]. Yin et al. [27] constructed a fine-grained system state description model for timely response to the flexible job shop scheduling problem with cost loss as the scheduling objective. Vakhania et al. [28] considered the job release date and delivery date, constructed a dynamic scheduling framework, and proposed a polynomial solver algorithm to update the scheduling strategy within a short timeframe.

The predictive reactive scheduling method first generates an initial scheduling strategy then predicts disturbance factors in the actual production process and dynamically updates the scheduling strategy [29], mainly for predictable disturbance events such as the machine status. Ji and Qiu used DM technology to explore the potential failure modes of workshop equipment, predict the probability of machine failure when processing current or future tasks, and provide references for scheduling and rescheduling [30,31]. Zhang et al. [32] integrated a convolutional neural network and improved the imperialist competition algorithm to overcome the negative impact of machine failure on the production process, which had a very good reference value for dealing with predictable failures. This method differs from the robust scheduling method in that it uses real-time data to predict disturbances. The predictability of disturbances is the premise of using this method. The accuracy of the prediction is guaranteed. However, this method has limitations for unpredictable disturbances, such as the release of new jobs.

The purely reactive scheduling method applies the production information and current production status of the manufacturing system to generate a dynamic real-time scheduling strategy. Because the scheduling strategy does not need to be created in advance, this method is also called "online scheduling" [33]. A short calculation time along with the adaptive and self-learning abilities of scheduling strategies are the basis for the efficient application of purely reactive scheduling methods [34]. Multiagent scheduling is a representative method of purely reactive scheduling. Researchers have proposed agent-based scheduling systems [35,36]. Each agent aims to maximize its interests, leading to conflicts with other agents. Mezgebe et al. proposed a negotiation-based control method to address disturbances caused by machine failures in a manufacturing system and achieved significant improvements in reducing the makespan [37]. Zhang et al. designed a two-tier distributed dynamic workshop scheduling system with a workshop scheduling agent and a multiservice unit scheduling agent. The negotiation mechanism used DR, and the service unit scheduling used a multiagent scheduling method based on humoral immunity [38]. Due to the static characteristics of the negotiation mechanism and the algorithms used by each agent, this method easily led to insufficient adaptability in a dynamic environment. However, the purely reactive scheduling method has good application value for solving unpredictable disturbance factors, such as the release of new jobs, because of its strong reactivity to the state of the manufacturing system.

Dispatching Rules

A DR is a heuristic rule. Due to its simplicity, interpretability, and low computational load, it has a shorter execution time than heuristic and metaheuristic methods [44] and a solid ability to respond to dynamic events. Its working principle is as follows: Whenever a machine is idle, a priority function is used to prioritize the unscheduled jobs waiting to be processed on the machine, and the job with the highest priority is processed first. The parameters of the priority function are usually an attribute value of the job and the current state of the manufacturing system. It uses the current information to determine which jobs need to be scheduled and how these jobs are scheduled. Therefore, DRs have been widely and successfully used to solve dynamic scheduling problems. In addition, this method neither requires modifying the original scheduling nor increases production instability. Two methods have been developed to design a DR with excellent performance: human intervention design [45] and intelligent algorithm automatic design [46,47]. The first method requires repeated trial and error testing, and the designer must have extensive experience. The second design process is complex and unexplainable. Although many DRs have been created and applied, there is currently no DR that can solve a variety of problems or deal with a variety of disturbances with consistently excellent performance [7,45,48]. Researchers have extensively compared the performance of DRs and demonstrated that a suitable DR response can be obtained under different scheduling problems or disturbance situations.

In the literature, the application of DRs to optimize the JSSP is divided into two categories. The first category involves selecting different DRs based on different scheduling criteria. Kaban, Veronique, and Marko analyzed different scheduling criteria. The results demonstrated the performance of the DRs and confirmed that no DR could provide the best performance under all scheduling criteria [7,45,49]. The other category involves selecting different DRs or DR combinations for job shop manufacturing systems in different situations. Tavakkoli et al. considered 10 different DRs and compared their performance in different manufacturing systems using makespan as the scheduling criterion. Then, the best DR to deal with the JSSP was selected [50]. Azadeh et al. proposed assigning DRs on a machine basis in a manufacturing system, determining the job processing sequence to be processed, and using the DR combination to optimize the makespan criterion [8]. Metan et al. used the delay time as the scheduling criterion to select the optimal DR combination from a predetermined DR library to optimize the JSSP [41]. However, the above methods solve static scheduling problems, i.e., all of the job information is obtained before scheduling. When the job information cannot be obtained in advance, the performance of the DR assigned to a manufacturing system or machine cannot be determined. In other words, there is a lack of research on how to apply DRs to optimize the JSSP when a job shop manufacturing system encounters a random process, such as when the job release moment or its attribute information cannot be obtained in advance.

As discussed above, DM has been widely used to generate scheduling strategies and predict disturbances. However, the generated scheduling strategies are mostly used to solve static scheduling problems. Integrating metaheuristics and heuristic algorithms to optimize dynamic scheduling problems is mostly based on the premise that disturbances are predictable. In order to overcome unpredictable disturbances, such as the random arrival of jobs, this paper proposes a pure reactive scheduling method that can generate scheduling strategies actively and in real-time, quickly combining the advantages of data model generation scheduling strategies and DRs.

MATHEMATICAL MODEL CONSTRUCTION

Before constructing the mathematical model, the involved notations were first defined, as shown in Table 2.

In a job shop, the order in which jobs are processed is random. The process flow of each job is diversified and known when it is released into the workshop. Due to the different jobs, the priorities of the multiple operations that comprise each job will be different [51]. In the manufacturing process, if a disturbance is considered, the feasible scheduling strategies will increase sharply, and it is very difficult to select the optimal or near-optimal scheduling strategy.

Table 2. Indexes and parameters

Notations	Descriptions
Indexes	
i	Index of machine, $i \in \{1,2,\cdots,m\}$
j	Index of jobs, $j \in \{1,2,\cdots,n\}$
k	Index of the machine in the production system when it completes the currentoperation, $k \in \{0,1,\cdots,K\}$
Parameters	
C_i	Time for machine i to complete all tasks, the running time of machine i
o_{ij}	Machine i processes the operation of job j
C_{ij}	Completion time of operation o_{ij}
$C_{\max}$	Maximum completion time for jobs in the production system (makespan)
p_{ij}	Processing time required for operation o_{ij}
r_{ij}	The moment the operation o_{ij_k} is released to the machine i
j_k	The job to which the kth operation of the machine output in the production system belongs
j_{ki}	Job j output by machine j_k
o_{ij_k}	Machine i processes the operation of job j_k
$rp_{ij_{ki}}$	The remaining processing time of o_{ij_k}, if the machine is idle, $rp_{ij_{ki}} = 0$
rp_k	$rp_{ij_{ki}}$ on all machines in the production system at the kth presence with outflow operations
f_{Ki}	The moment when machine i finally flows out the last job
Δk_{ij}	Total number of outflows experienced by machine i in the course of completing operation o_{ij} of job j
Decision variables	
x_{ij}	whether the machine is processing operation o_{ij}, if yes, $x_{ij} = 1$, if no, $x_{ij} = 0$.
f_k	the $k-th$ moment when at least one machine in the production system has completed the current job
k_{ij}	The index of the outflow operation o_{ij} of machine i

The job shop scheduling objective set in this paper is to minimize makespan and maximize machine utilization, and the objective function is defined as shown in Equations (1) and (2). Equation (2) represents the average of the actual processing operation time $\sum_{j=1}^{n} p_{ij}$ of the machine in the job shop production system as a percentage of the machine operation time C_i.

$$Minimum\ C_{\max} = \max\{C_i | i = 1,2,\cdots,m\} \tag{1}$$

$$Maximum\ M_u = \frac{1}{m}\sum_{i=1}^{m}\frac{\sum_{j=1}^{n} p_{ij}}{C_i} \tag{2}$$

In constructing the mathematical model, two core parameters, $rp_{ij_{ki}}$ and f_k, are introduced, and the expression of the set rp_k composed of $rp_{ij_{ki}}$ is shown in Equation (3); the solution of B is shown in Equation (4) with an initial value of 0. Among them, if there are pending operations before the machine, each operation flowing out of the machine will immediately flow into another operation; if not, the machine carries out idling.

$$rp_k = \{rp_{1j_{k1}}, rp_{2j_{k2}}, \cdots, rp_{mj_{km}}\} \tag{3}$$

$$f_k = \begin{cases} 0 & if\ k = 0 \\ \min\{rp_k | rp_{ij_{ki}} \neq 0\} & if\ k \neq 1 \end{cases} \tag{4}$$

Because machines take different amounts of time to process the job at hand, one machine may complete multiple jobs while another machine may not have completed one yet. Therefore, during the job flow, when jobs are flowing out of the machine, some machines may have some time remaining for the processing of the job at hand, and the remaining processing time experienced by the job during the machine processing will constitute a set rp_k which is obtained by Equation (3). When a machine completes a job, if there is a pending job next to that machine, the pending job immediately begins to be processed, at which point the time remaining for the machine to process the job is equal to the processing time for that job. The machine with the minimum remaining processing time among all machines in the production system gives priority to outflow jobs, and the inflow and outflow of jobs from the machine are expressed as a flow process, and the kth flow process is represented by Equation (4). After all the jobs flow out of the system, the task is completed and the time of the last job flowing out is the completion time, and the time of the last job flowing out of machine *i* is the time of machine *i* completing the task. Thus, Equations (1) and (2) are transformed into Equations (5) and (6).

In this paper, when solving the scheduling strategy, because the process of job flow is determined by the remaining time that the machine processes the current job, the relationship between the time that the machine processes the job and the job flow is shown in Equation (8). The time for each job to flow from the inflow to the outflow machine is equal to the time for the machine to process the job. Each operation o_{ij} is completed in a process in which the outflow of jobs has already occurred in other machines in the system, thus establishing the relationship between the time p_{ij} for each operation o_{ij} to be processed and the job flow process in the system, as shown in Equation (8).

The scheduling criterion makespan can be described as the time when the last operation of the last job in all tasks flows out of the production system, and C_i can be described as the time when the last operation flows out of machine i. According to the "outflow" characteristic, the objective function (2) can be transformed into the form shown in Equation (5), the objective function (3) can be transformed into the form shown in (6), and the whole mathematical model is shown in Equations (5)–(11).

$$Minimum\ C_{\max} = \sum_{k=0}^{K}(f_{k+1} - f_k) \tag{5}$$

$$Maximum\ M_u = \frac{1}{n}\sum_{i=1}^{u}\frac{\sum_{j=1}^{n} p_{ij}}{f_{Ki}} \tag{6}$$

Subject to

$$r_{ij} + p_{ij} \leq r_{(i+1)j}\ i = 1,2\ldots,m;\ j = 1,2,\ldots,n \tag{7}$$

$$\sum_{k=k_{ij}-\Delta k_{ij}}^{k_{ij}} f_k - f_{k-1} = p_{ij}\ i = 1,2\ldots,m;\ j = 1,2,\ldots,n \tag{8}$$

$$rp_{ij_{ki}} \leq p_{ij}\ i = 1,2\ldots,m;\ j = 1,2,\ldots,n \tag{9}$$

$$rp_K = \sum_{i=1}^{m} rp_{ij_{Ki}} = 0\ j = 1,2,\ldots,n \tag{10}$$

$$\sum_{i=1}^{m} x_{ij} = 1,\ x_{ij} \in \{0,1\}\ j = 1,2,\ldots,n \tag{11}$$

Constraint (7) indicates that operation o_{ij} of job j is processed by machine i before its next operation $o_{(i+1)j}$ is released to machine i+1; Constraint (8) ensures that all operations of all jobs will be completed in the production system; Constraint (9) ensures that the remaining processing time of operation o_{ij} during the flow of the production system does not exceed the total processing time; Constraint (10) ensures that each operation o_{ij} of each job j can be processed, determines the index K value, and then solves for the scheduling target value; Constraint (11) indicates that only a single operation o_{ij} of job j can be processed by the machine in the same moment.

To better explain the above mathematical model, we take four machines as an example. Information on the jobs to be completed is shown in Table 3, and the PS column in the Table 3 indicates the process flow of the job. At the beginning of scheduling, machine 1 has job 1 and job 5 next to it, and according to the selected scheduling method, machine 1 processes job 1 first, x_{11}=1, x_{15}=0; machine 2 has job 2 next to it, x_{22}=1; machine 3 has job 3 next to it, x_{33}=1; and machine 4 has job 4 next to it, x_{44}=1. No jobs are flowing from the machine in the production system, f_k=0. At this point, the remaining processing time for machine 1 processing job 1 is 14, the remaining processing time for machine 2 processing job 2 is 50, the remaining processing time for machine 3 processing job 3 is 28, and the remaining processing time for machine 4 processing job 4 is 24. Therefore, rp_0={14,50,28,24}, $minrp_0$=14, and the production system starts to run. The first job to flow out of the machine is machine 1, the time of flow out is 14, f_l=14, job 1 flows out from machine 1 to the side of machine 2, and job 5 flows into machine 1. At this point, rp_0={77,36,14,10}, $minrp_0$=10, k_{ij}=1, and Δk_{ij}=1 and continues to iterate.

Table 3. Job shop production system with four machines and five operations

Job	Machine 1	Machine 2	Machine 3	Machine 4	PS
1	14	87	31	43	1→2→4→3
2	90	50	60	56	2→1→3→4
3	21	46	28	55	3→4→2→1
4	81	54	44	24	4→2→1→3
5	77	65	32	76	1→3→4→2

In this study, the job shop system only considers two production factors: machines and materials. Only one machine is responsible for each process, and any technological process can be allowed. The moment when job *i* is released to the manufacturing system is random, and the processing information of the job before its release is unknown. The movement time of the job in the manufacturing system, machine degradation, and failures are not considered. When the job is released to the manufacturing system, its process flow and operating time on each machine become known. Due to the randomness of job release and its unpredictable characteristics, it is impossible to obtain a suitable scheduling strategy in the early stage of scheduling. The purpose of this paper is to reasonably solve the disturbance of job release randomness.

PROPOSED APPROACH

In this study, the implementation process of the proposed method is based on the general process of data mining technology. The original data with scheduling knowledge are initially obtained based on historical production data. Second, the available data with scheduling knowledge suitable for machine learning algorithms are obtained after data processing. Subsequently, the scheduling knowledge contained in the data is made explicit. Finally, a scheduling model is constructed, and the scheduling problem of the manufacturing system is optimized through the application of the model. The overall process of the proposed method is shown in Figure 1. The method is based on data collection and processing; knowledge extraction is the key to the proposed method; knowledge is obtained to solve the manufacturing system scheduling problem. To realize the above process, the following steps are performed: (1) relevant production data for the manufacturing system are collected, the scheduling goals are clarified, and factors affecting the pros and cons of the selected scheduling target values are analyzed to determine the optimal scheduling problem; (2) scheduling strategies to eliminate or reduce the influence of factors affecting the pros and cons of the scheduling target value (determined in step (1)) in the production scheduling process are determined to obtain the original data with scheduling knowledge; (3) the data foundation is consolidated for knowledge extraction to obtain the available data with scheduling knowledge; (4) a scheduling model that can generate scheduling strategies in real-time is constructed to allow for iterative scheduling of waiting jobs in the production process. The specific implementation process is described below.

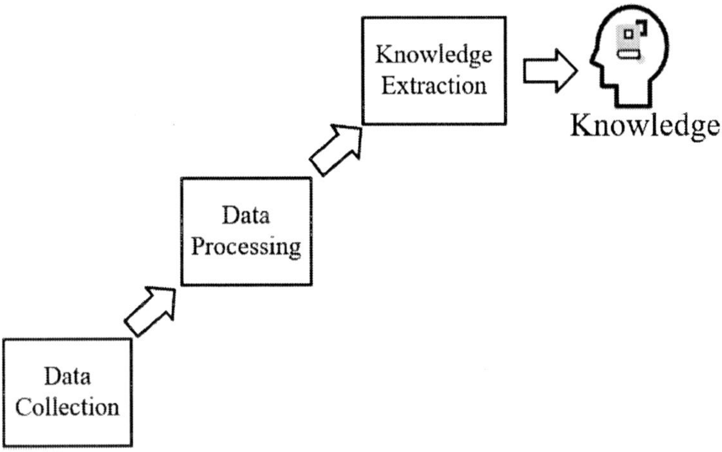

Figure 1. Overall process of the proposed method.

Scheduling Subperiod Division

The purpose of dividing scheduling subperiods is to achieve local scheduling of known jobs and to generate scheduling strategies in the early stage of subscheduling. Due to the differences in different manufacturing systems and the uncertainty of the time of encountering disturbances, the division of scheduling subperiods should be active, dynamic, and carried out with the production process.

This study considers two goals in the production schedule. The first goal is to minimize the makespan of the manufacturing system and reduce the job waiting time, and the second goal is to continue increasing the actual load rate of each machine after obtaining the first target optimal value to reduce the idle time of the machine. The four-machine job shop problem is considered an example. As shown in Figure 2, the filled circles represent operation o_{ij} of the job waiting to be processed, and the open circles represent the next operation $o_{(i+1)j}$ of the job waiting to be processed. Assuming that Figure 2 represents a moment (m_t) in the job shop, it can be seen that there are pending operations in queues 0, 1, and 2. Machines 0, 1, and 2 will change to the working state at the next moment, queue 4 is empty, and machine 3 remains idle at the next moment. In the absence of new jobs released into the manufacturing system, if machine 0 processes operation o_{11} first, machine 3 will change from idle to working at m_t+p_{11}; if machine 0 processes operation o_{42} first, machine 3 will change from idle to working at $m_t+p_{42}+p_{11}$. The order in which machine 0 processes the operations in queue 0 will not only affect the load rate of machine 3 but also increase the makespan of the entire manufacturing system. Using specific methods or rules to determine the processing sequence for operations waiting to be processed in front of a machine can reduce the makespan of the manufacturing system and increase the actual load rate of the machine.

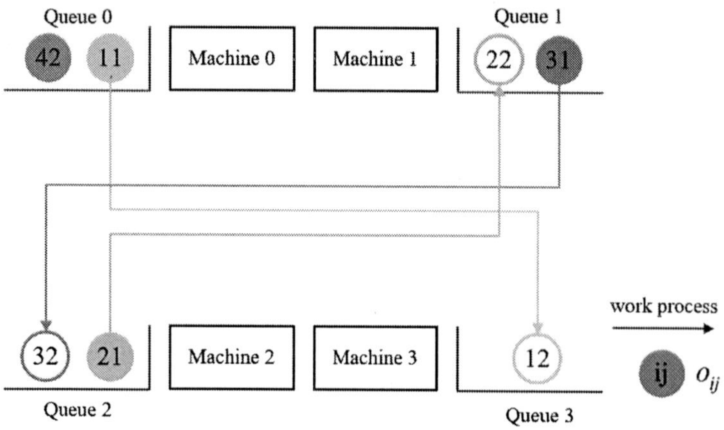

Figure 2. Job processing flow.

When the state of the machine changes from working to idle, the selected DR sorts the jobs waiting for processing next to each machine according to parameter values such as the job attribute or process flow, determines the priorities of the operations to be processed, and processes the operations with the highest priority until the queue is empty. Many studies have shown that no DR can effectively optimize multiple scheduling problems [52], and no DR can be adapted to different manufacturing systems under the same scheduling problem [7]. However, frequently switching DRs for scheduling problems to adapt to the scheduling of different manufacturing systems can effectively improve the production efficiency of the manufacturing system [53]. In the production process of the entire manufacturing system, taking the machine as a unit, the overall running time of each machine is iteratively divided into multiple scheduling subperiods, and all of the scheduling subperiods constitute the manufacturing system scheduling period. A DR generation scheduling strategy with excellent performance is selected at the beginning of each scheduling subperiod. Therefore, determining the scheduling subperiod is the key to using DRs to optimize production scheduling.

The number of scheduling subperiods in the manufacturing system scheduling period is the number of times DRs are assigned. Each DR assignment is defined as a decision point. For the running process of a machine, the time between two adjacent decision points is a scheduling subperiod. As shown in Figure 3, a machine in the manufacturing system is considered an example. At m_1, there are two operations waiting to be processed in front of the machine. At this moment, a DR with good performance is selected to determine the priorities of the two operations to be processed, the first decision is made, and m_1 is decision point 1. When the machine processes the operation, it is immediately transferred to the operation queue of jobs to be processed in front of the machine that processes the next operation. After both operations are processed, the time shifts to m_2. Between m_1 and m_2, as a result of operations completed by other machines and jobs newly released to the manufacturing system, a new queue of jobs to be processed will be formed next to the machine. At this time, the second decision is made, and m_2 is decision point 2. This decision point will schedule the newly released job in the manufacturing system, avoiding the adverse effect of the release of a new job disturbing the overall operation process of the manufacturing system. The time between m_1 and m_2 is defined as a scheduling subperiod of the manufacturing system scheduling period. The above process is iterated continuously, and each scheduling subperiod of the machine operation process can be obtained. The method for determining the scheduling subperiod for the unit machine in the production scheduling system is the same as that described above. After determining each scheduling subperiod, selecting a DR with good performance at the beginning of each scheduling subperiod is the most critical issue for optimizing production scheduling.

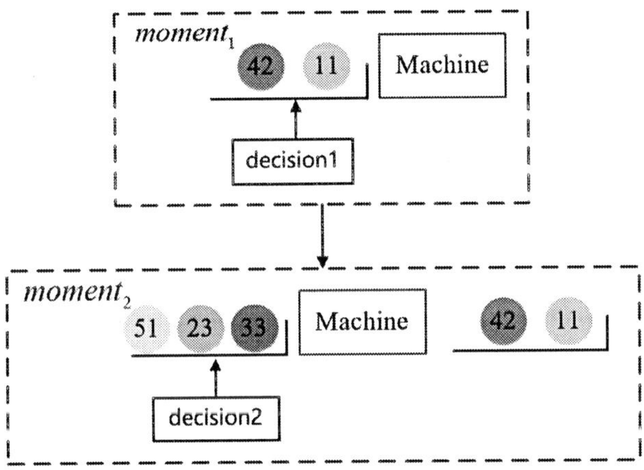

Figure 3. Determination of the scheduling subperiod.

Schedule Data Collection Method

Each scheduling subperiod has job processing data and scheduling strategies, and these data contain rich scheduling knowledge. Simulation technology is a powerful tool for evaluating the efficiency of different scheduling strategies. These methods can simulate processes in a short time without changing the state of physical entities to obtain the results of applying different scheduling strategies in the future [52]. As shown in Figure 3, the determination of the scheduling strategies for each scheduling subperiod affects the production efficiency of the entire manufacturing system.

To collect the original data with scheduling knowledge, simulation technology was used in this study to determine the optimal DR for each scheduling subperiod. In this process, it is necessary to simulate the production scheduling cycle of the entire manufacturing system. A DR is suitable for the scheduling subperiod only if it results in better performance in the entire production scheduling period. In obtaining the DR combination, the equation for solving the simulation number (N_s) of the manufacturing system production cycle is shown in Equation (12), where N_{sp} represents the number of subperiods and N_{dr} represents the number of DRs that can be selected. As N_s and N_{sp} increase, the number of simulations will increase exponentially.

In the actual application process, when facing a complex manufacturing system, an excessive number of simulations will be required, which will lead to a time-consuming method of selecting the optimal DR combination using the simulation method; as a result, it will be difficult to ensure the fluency of the production process. Metan et al. [41] noted that a long time is required to calculate simulation results when real-time decision-making is necessary; thus, the simulation method will become useless. Accelerating the selection of the optimal DR combination to ensure a smooth production process is the key to using DRs to solve the dynamic scheduling problem in complex manufacturing systems. In addition, when applying simulation technology, all of the production information in the manufacturing system should be known. Therefore, it is not feasible to apply simulation technology to time consumption and generation-scheduling strategies. However, simulation technology can be used to obtain the original data containing scheduling knowledge from historical production data. The NP-hard characteristics of the JSSP result in relatively good DR combinations. The better the performance of the DR combination, the better the collected data will be and the higher the quality of the scheduling knowledge contained in the data.

$$N_s = (N_{dr})^{N_{sp}} \tag{12}$$

Construction of the Scheduling Model

To solve the scheduling problem of rapidly assigning a DR in the scheduling subcycle, based on the original data that contain scheduling knowledge obtained using simulation technology, a machine learning algorithm is used to mine the scheduling knowledge contained in the operation of the entire manufacturing system, and a DR assignment model is constructed. Thus, a solution to the above problems is achieved.

As shown in Figure 4, this study divides the process of constructing the assigned DR model into three modules: data collection, simulation, and learning. The data collection module collects job attribute data and processes the data in the job manufacturing system; the collected data is stored in database 1. The simulation module obtains the data containing scheduling knowledge. The realization process selects the optimal DR combination for each manufacturing system. The optimal DR combination is combined with the data collected by the data collection module to produce data with scheduling knowledge; these data are stored in database 2. The learning module accesses the knowledge in the learning data and builds a DR assignment model. The assigned DR model can be directly used in the scheduling process for a manufacturing system.

The scheduling model is the core of the method proposed in this study. This ensures that a scheduling strategy can be generated in real-time. The construction process for the scheduling model is shown in Figure 5, including the collection of raw data containing scheduling knowledge, the assembly of high-quality available data, and the training and prediction of multiclassification models. The specific implementation process is as follows.

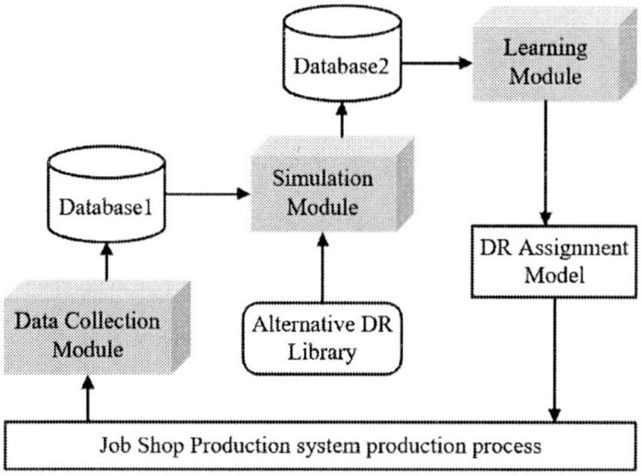

Figure 4. Assigned DR model construction process.

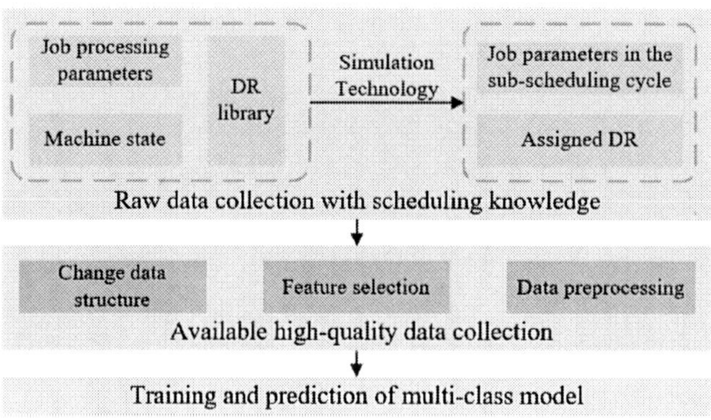

Figure 5. Decision model construction process.

Collect raw data with scheduling knowledge: Historical production data include processing parameters, such as the processing time of the job on each machine, the process flow in the manufacturing system, the state of each machine in the manufacturing system, and a DR library composed of multiple DRs. Of these, this study only considers the idle and working states of the machine. The above data can be collected directly; however, they contain no scheduling knowledge. As described in the previous section, the determined scheduling decision moment divides the scheduling period of the entire manufacturing system into multiple scheduling subperiods. The job processing data are linked to the DRs in the DR library based on simulation technology. The relevant parameter data of the job in each scheduling subperiod and the assigned DR in the scheduling subperiod are combined to form an instance sample, and the data contain rich scheduling knowledge. The job parameter data in the scheduling subcycle are defined as the attribute data of the instance samples, and the assigned DR is defined as the label of the instance samples. Simulating multiple manufacturing systems in the same category can ensure sufficient historical instance samples. Because the times when the job is released and the job release moment are unknown, the collection of original data with scheduling knowledge is based on historical production data.

Collect high-quality available data: Before using machine learning algorithms to mine the knowledge contained in the data, it is necessary to ensure the availability of data and their suitability for input into machine learning classification algorithms; it is also necessary to ensure the data are of a high quality so that the constructed model will have good performance. For the former, this study adopts the method of changing the data structure because the attribute data of the collected sample data are n rows and m columns. If n is equal to 1, the sample data of this instance do not contain scheduling knowledge because when a scheduling subperiod only includes one job to be scheduled, the effect of assigning any DR is indistinguishable. When n is greater than 1, the sample data contains scheduling knowledge, but this example sample is not suitable as the input data for the machine learning classification algorithm because the attribute data structure of the input data of the machine learning classification algorithm should be one row and m columns. Therefore, the structure of the attribute data of the collected data with scheduling knowledge needs to be changed, and there is a need to transform the original data structure $(n*m)\times d$ into an $n*(m+1)$ structure. This study employs data feature selection and data preprocessing methods for this purpose. The data preprocessing includes removing duplicate values, filling in missing values, and deleting outliers. The feature selection process is mainly used to eliminate features that are of no value in the data and prevent such features from affecting the performance of the model, such as the time when a job is released to the system.

Training and prediction of multiclassification models: A typical problem in supervised learning is classification [53]. In classification problems, supervised learning is used to construct a classifier that can label new instances based on experience with known labeled instance samples. The problem in this study is a classification problem because the label of the example sample comprises multiple values, and the constructed decision model is a multiclassification model [54]. The DT algorithm has been widely used in the establishment of classification models due to its ease of understanding, fast calculation speed, high accuracy, and lack of required domain knowledge or parameter assumptions [55]. Based on the above advantages, this study uses a DM algorithm to build a decision model to realize the real-time assignment of DRs to each scheduling subperiod of the manufacturing system scheduling period. The available high-quality data are divided into training and test sets in proportion to the construction process. The training data are used to build the model, and the test data are used to evaluate the performance of the trained model. The cooperation between the training and prediction processes ensures a stronger prediction performance of the model.

Application of the Scheduling Model

After the construction of the decision model is completed, the next step is the application of the decision model. According to the method described in the previous section, the model is used at each decision time. The processing parameters of the job to be scheduled on the machine at the decision time comprise the data input to the decision model before processing. If there is no job to be scheduled on the machine at the decision time, the machine state becomes idle, and the new decision time becomes the time before the job is released or transmitted to the machine. If there is only one job to be scheduled on the machine at the decision time, the decision model is not used, and the job is processed directly by the machine. If there are multiple jobs to be scheduled on the machine at the decision time, the parameter data of the jobs are combined to create the original data input to the decision model. After processing the data using the same method as when the model was constructed, the data are processed to produce usable, high-quality data that can be directly input into the decision model. The decision model then outputs the DR, which generates the scheduling strategy for the scheduling subperiod.

EXPERIMENTS AND RESULTS

Experiment Setup

In this paper, the experiment used an 8G running memory, i5cpu personal computer. To verify the feasibility of the proposed method and the efficiency of the constructed decision-making model, a set of control experiments were designed and executed for different manufacturing systems. The method of integrating Taillard and Marko to generate the JSSP is consistent with actual-scale industrial problems [49,51]. Because the output scheduling strategy time of the decision model is significantly shorter than the processing time of the job operation, the precondition was to ignore the decision time of the decision model. Before generating the scheduling problem, the following assumptions were made:

- the delivery dates of all operations will be ignored;
- the transportation time between machines is zero;
- no faults occur during machine processing.

In the specific generation method, the number of jobs, attributes of the jobs, number of machines, and technological process of the jobs comprised a manufacturing system. With the goal of minimizing the makespan and maximizing the actual utilization of machines, the scheduling of each manufacturing system was defined as a JSSP. In the manufacturing system, the job attributes included the job processing time on the machine and the moment when the job is released to the manufacturing system. The processing time, pt_{ij}, of each operation on each machine required to complete the job satisfied the geometric distribution of $(0,\phi)$, and the size of ϕ controlled the difference in the processing time of the operation to complete the job on the machine. The greater the value of ϕ, the greater the time difference between machine processing operations, and thus, the greater the heterogeneity of the jobs. The release moment, r_j, when the job is released to the manufacturing system was random, but the upper limit should be the total production time of the manufacturing system. This study assumes that the release moment, r_j, satisfied the geometric distribution of $(0,\varphi)$. The value of φ controlled the load rate of the manufacturing system. The smaller the value of φ, the higher the load rate of the manufacturing system. The number of machines was n, and the machines were numbered as $\{0,1,\cdots,n-1\}$. The process flow of the job involved selecting one or more machines in the manufacturing system and rearranging and combining them; each machine only processed each job once. From the above, the generated manufacturing system included the following four categories: high job heterogeneity and a high manufacturing system load rate, low job heterogeneity and a low manufacturing system load rate, high job heterogeneity and a low manufacturing system load rate, and low job heterogeneity and a high manufacturing system load rate.

Table 4 gives an example of the manufacturing system data for four machines and 10 jobs. Each row represents a job. The values in column R_j represent the release moment, r_j, when the job is released to the manufacturing system; the empty cells in column R_j represent that the job to be processed on the machine was transferred to the previous machine after processing. The values in column PT_j represent the time for the job to be processed on the machine. If the value of PT_{ij} is 0, job j does not need to be processed on machine i. The value in column M_i represents the order of operations for processing the job. For example, for job 0, the job was released to the system at time 65, and the process flow proceeded through M_3, M_2, M_0, and M_1 in sequence; the processing times on M_3, M_2, M_0, and M_1 were 26, 5, 14, and 87, respectively.

Table 4. Manufacturing system data example (four machines and ten jobs)

No.	M0	R0	PT0	M1	R1	PT1	M2	R2	PT2	M3	R3	PT3
0	2		14	3		87	1		5	0	65	26
1	2		90	3		50	1		31	0	0	5
2	0	0	21	1		6	2		10	3		43
3	1		1	0	4	54	3		28	2		56
4	2		77	1		51	0	0	44	3		15
5	0	6	32	3		46	2		80	1		24
6	2		11	0	4	9	1		48	3		77
7	0	6	90	1		93	3		78	2		58
8	3		60	1		79	0	37	27	2		33
9	3		49	0	0	40	2		83	1		54

After the historical production data of the manufacturing system were collected, a DR library was constructed to schedule the jobs in the manufacturing system, and a group of highly adaptive DR combinations was selected from the DR library to guide the generation of scheduling strategies for the manufacturing system. The parameter value of the DR was obtained through the job properties. According to the characteristics of the generative manufacturing system in this study, the job attributes were as follows:

- Processing time (PT): the time required for the operation of the job to be processed on the machine;
- Processing sequence (PS): the total number of operations required by the job in the manufacturing system;
- Total processing time (TPT): the total time the job was processed in the manufacturing system; the total processing time, TPT_j, of job j is given in Equation (13):

$$TPT_j = \sum_{i=1}^{m} pt_{ij} \tag{13}$$

- Remaining total processing time (RPT): the total remaining processing time of the job in the manufacturing system; the remaining total processing time, RPT_j, of job j is shown in Equation (14), where $\hat{j}$ represents the number of operations to be performed in the current job:

$$RPT_j = \sum_{j=\hat{j}}^{n} pt_{ij} \tag{14}$$

- Remaining total processing sequence (RPS): the number of operations remaining in the manufacturing system for the job; the remaining total processing sequence of job j is shown in Equation (15):

$$RPS_j = n - \hat{j} \tag{15}$$

Based on the attributes of the above job, 10 DRs were defined to create the single-parameter DR library, as summarized in Table 5. The first six DRs in Table 5 were static single-parameter DRs, and their parameter values did not change with the job process; the last four DRs were dynamic single-parameter DRs, and their parameter values did change with the job process. The constructed DR library contained static single-parameter DRs and dynamic single-parameter DRs, which ensures that the DRs can solve various dynamic scheduling problems.

Table 5. Single-parameter DRs

No.	DR	Parameter	Description
1	SPT	Processing time	Priority processing for jobs with the shortest processing time
2	LPT	Processing time	Priority processing for jobs with the longest processing time
3	SPS	Processing sequence	Priority processing for jobs with the shortest processing sequence
4	LPS	Processing sequence	Priority processing for jobs with the longest processing sequence
5	STPT	Total processing time	Priority processing for jobs with the shortest total processing time
6	LTPT	Total processing time	Priority processing for jobs with the longest total processing time
7	SRPT	Total remaining processing time	Priority processing for jobs with the shortest total remaining processing time
8	LRPT	Total remaining processing time	Priority processing for the job with the longest total remaining processing time
9	SRPS	Total remaining processing sequence	Priority processing for jobs with the shortest total remaining processing sequence
10	LRPS	Total remaining processing sequence	Priority processing for jobs with the longest total remaining processing sequence

$$P = P_1 \times P_2 \tag{16}$$

Based on the current knowledge, no single-parameter DR can adapt to the scheduling process of an entire manufacturing system. The method for constructing a new DR proposed by Kaban [45] was applied to construct the DR library required in this study. The second category of DRs in the constructed DR library was composed of mixed-parameter, in which two job attributes were combined. The equation for solving the parameter value of the mixed-parameter DR is given in Equation (16), where P_1 is one value of a job attribute, and P_2 is another value of a job attribute. For example, P_1 is the value of the processing time PT, and P_2 is the value of the total processing time TPT; the value of PT∗TPT is the parameter value of the hybrid DR. If the value of PT∗TPT for the job waiting to be processed by the machine is small, the mixed-parameter DR corresponding to the priority being processed is S_PT_TPT. If the value of PT∗TPT for the job waiting to be processed by the machine is large, the mixed-parameter DR corresponding to the priority being processed is L_PT_TPT. The job attributes and the hybrid DRs' parameters which calculated by Equation(16) are listed in Table 6 resulting in a total of 10 hybrid parameters. Different DRs were constructed by sorting the priority of the jobs according to the parameter values from small to large and from large to small, and each parameter value could create two mixed-parameter DRs.

Table 6. Mixed parameter DR

Parameter	PT	PS	TPT	RPT	RPS
PT	×	√	√	√	√
PS	×	×	√	√	√
TPT	×	×	×	√	√
RPT	×	×	×	×	√
RPS	×	×	×	×	×

In summary, the DR library constructed in this study contains 10 single-parameter DRs and 20 mixed-parameter DRs, totaling 30 DRs.

$$\hat{P} = \max\left(\sum_j p_{0j}, \sum_j p_{1j}, \sum_j p_{2j}, \sum_j p_{3j}\right) \quad (17)$$

$$\varphi = \frac{\hat{P}}{\lambda} \quad (18)$$

To verify the performance of the proposed method for the four manufacturing system categories, 20 sets of data were generated for each manufacturing system category. Each manufacturing system contained four machines and 50 operations. The attribute data of each category of the manufacturing system were determined based on the geometric distribution in a specific interval, as summarized in Table 7. The equations for the upper limit value, φ, of the geometric distribution interval subject to the release moment of the job are given in Equations (17) and (18), where $\hat{P}$ represents the ideal makespan of the manufacturing system, which is equivalent to the maximum actual working time for a machine to complete all tasks in the manufacturing system.

Table 7. Attribute value ranges of a job in the manufacturing system

No.	Category	R	PT
1	High job heterogeneity and high manufacturing system load rate	$[0,\hat{P}/2]$	[1,100]
2	Low job heterogeneity and low manufacturing system load rate	$[0,\hat{P}]$	[1,100]
3	High job heterogeneity and low manufacturing system load rate	$[0,\hat{P}/2]$	[1,1000]
4	Low job heterogeneity and high manufacturing system load rate	$[0,\hat{P}]$	[1,1000]

Because of the large number of different DR combinations in the entire manufacturing system, it was unrealistic to use simulation technology to search all of the possible DR combinations to obtain the optimal DR combination. Therefore, this study used a local search method to identify the optimal DR combination. To verify the performance of the searched DR combination, the minimum limit value of the makespan was considered. The value of the minimum makespan limit, L_Makespan, was equal to the value of $\hat{P}$.

The implementation tool of all the above experimental processes was Spyder software, and the programming language was Python. Among them, the DR in the DR library was written as a function that reproduced the production process of the job shop and simulated the performance of each DR combination, and automatically output the scheduling target value and collect data with scheduling knowledge.

Acquisition of Data with Scheduling Knowledge

The data with scheduling knowledge were obtained through simulation, and a DR was assigned to each subscheduling period by means of a full search, and then a DR combination was assigned to the entire scheduling period. In this study, 10,000 DR combinations were randomly obtained from the DR library for each manufacturing system. As the scheduling subperiod was divided, the number of DRs in different DR combinations might have differed due to the influence of each DR on the scheduling subperiod. For 20 manufacturing systems generated under the same category, the best and worst DR combinations from 10,000 DR combinations were selected; the large differences between the optimal and worst scheduling objective values verify the sensitivity of the DR combinations to the optimal scheduling problem. Figure 6, Figure 7, Figure 8 and Figure 9 show comparisons of the optimal makespan limit value, the makespan value under the optimal DR combination, and the makespan value under the worst DR combination as well as the sum of the best actual machine utilization rate under the optimal makespan value and the sum of the optimal actual machine utilization rate under the optimal makespan value for different categories of manufacturing systems.

The makespan value of the optimal DR combination was close to or equal to the optimal limit valuc of the makespan, which confirms that the optimal DR combination among the 10,000 DR scheduling combinations exhibited excellent scheduling performance. However, it was also possible to continue expanding the DR search range to obtain the optimal DR in order to obtain a better DR combination. Figure 6 shows a comparison of the performance of different DR combinations for a high job heterogeneity and high manufacturing system load rate.

The optimization range of the makespan value was 3–15%, and the improvement in the machine utilization of the manufacturing system was 3–17%. Figure 7 shows a comparison of the performance of different DR combinations for a low job heterogeneity and low manufacturing system load rate. The optimization range of the makespan value was 5–15%, and the improvement in the machine utilization of the manufacturing system was 2–16%. Figure 8 shows a comparison of the performance of different DR combinations for a high job heterogeneity and high manufacturing system load rate. The optimization range of the makespan value was 5–16%, and the improvement in the machine utilization of the manufacturing system was 2–21%. Figure 9 shows a comparison of the performance of different DR combinations for a high job heterogeneity and low manufacturing system load rate. The optimization range of the makespan value was 6–13%, and the improvement in the machine utilization of the manufacturing system was 3–14%. The above results verify the effectiveness of the scheduling method proposed in this study for handling uncertain disturbances in the job release.

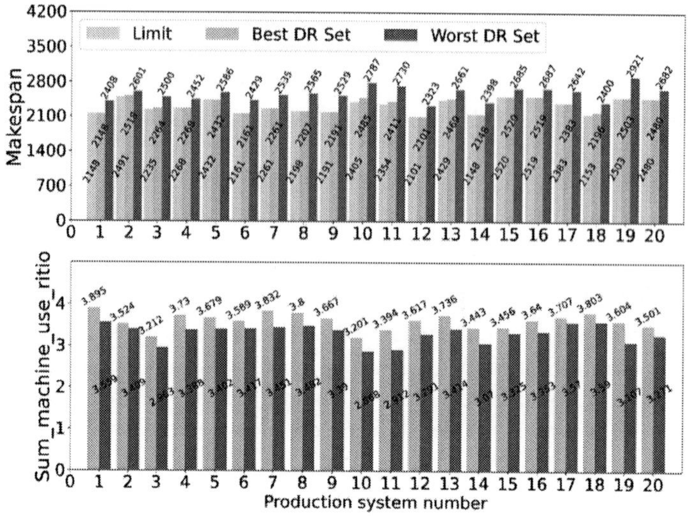

Figure 6. Low job heterogeneity and a high manufacturing system load rate.

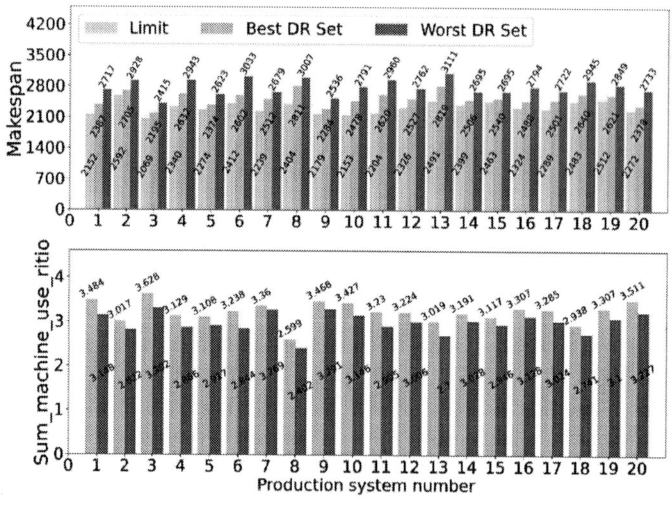

Figure 7. Low job heterogeneity and a low manufacturing system load rate.

Additionally, based on Figure 10, Figure 11, Figure 12 and Figure 13 we analyzed the difference between using dispatching rule combination performance and genetic algorithm performance. The genetic algorithm used real number coding, and the individual coding adopted the method of random ordering of all processes. The mutation was a random exchange of the serial numbers of the two processes. The fitness was determined according to the calculation time of each individual coding. The evaluation indicators used mean deviation and coefficient of variation. The purpose of using the average deviation as the evaluation index was to express the difference in the overall performance of the two methods, and the purpose of using the coefficient of variation as the evaluation index was to express the overall stability of the performance of the two methods. When using makespan as the scheduling target, the average performance deviations of the combination of variable coefficient rules and the genetic algorithm under the four categories were −5.5, −16.8, −40.65, and −38.5, respectively. Continue to take the sum of machine utilization as the scheduling target.

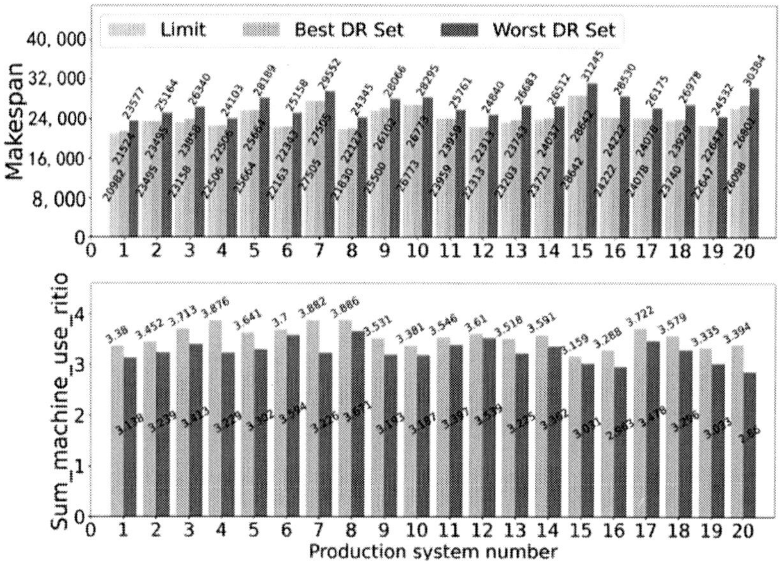

Figure 8. High job heterogeneity and a high manufacturing system load rate.

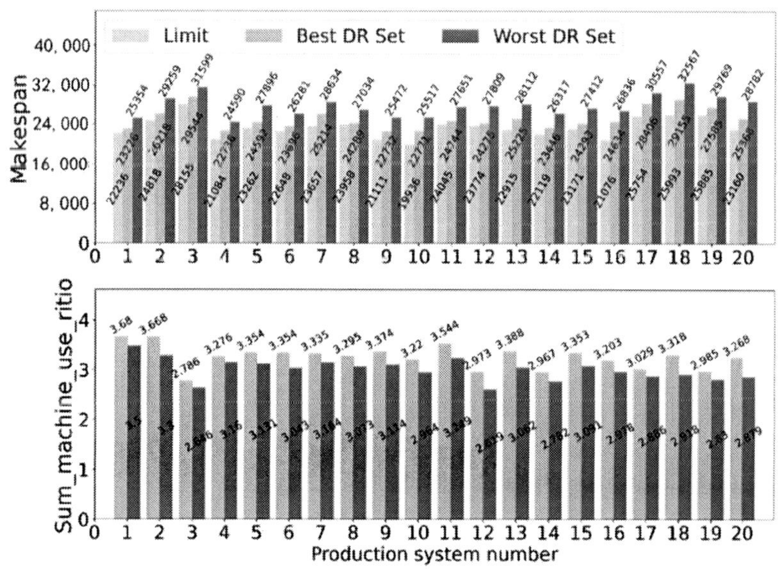

Figure 9. High job heterogeneity and a low manufacturing system load rate.

For the four categories of job shop scheduling systems, the average performance deviations of using the dispatching rule combination and the genetic algorithm were 0.006, 0.017, 0.028, and 0.021, respectively, which proves the overall superiority of using the dispatching rule combination to optimize the job shop scheduling problem. It can be seen from Table 8 that the overall performance stability of the dispatching rule combination optimization method was worse than that of the genetic algorithm when the makespan was used as the scheduling target.

The combination of Figure 10, Figure 11, Figure 12 and Figure 13 does not hide the performance of the dispatching rule combination optimization method, even if the genetic algorithm used in optimizing some job shop scheduling problems showed better performance; when we continue to optimize machine utilization, the dispatching rule combination optimization method showed better stability.

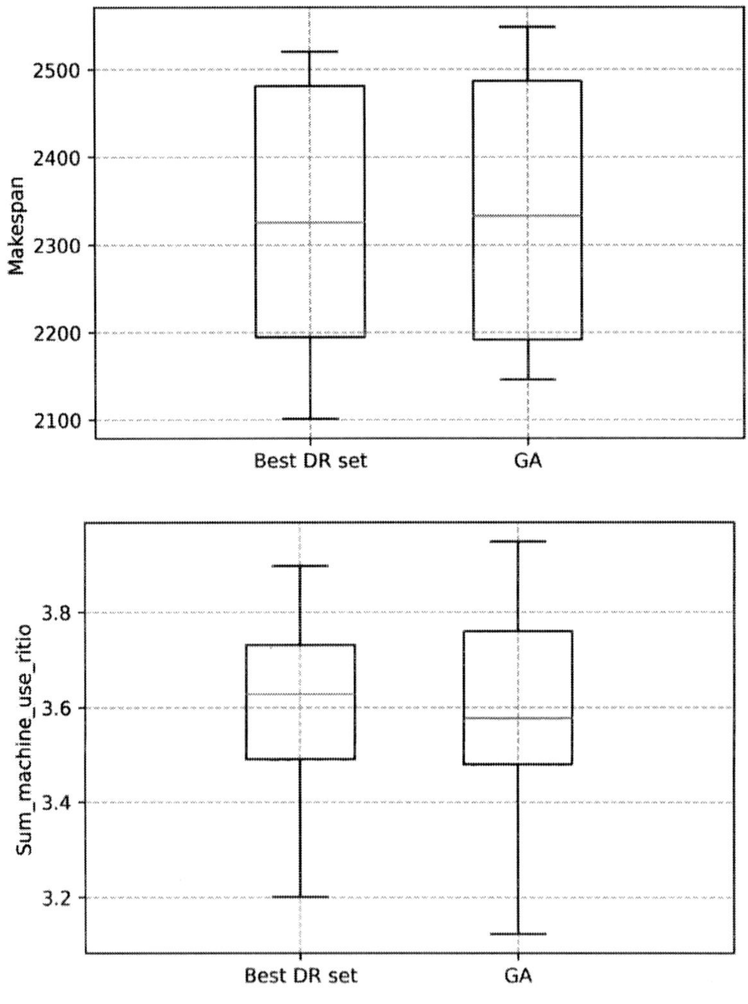

Figure 10. Low job heterogeneity and a high manufacturing system load rate.

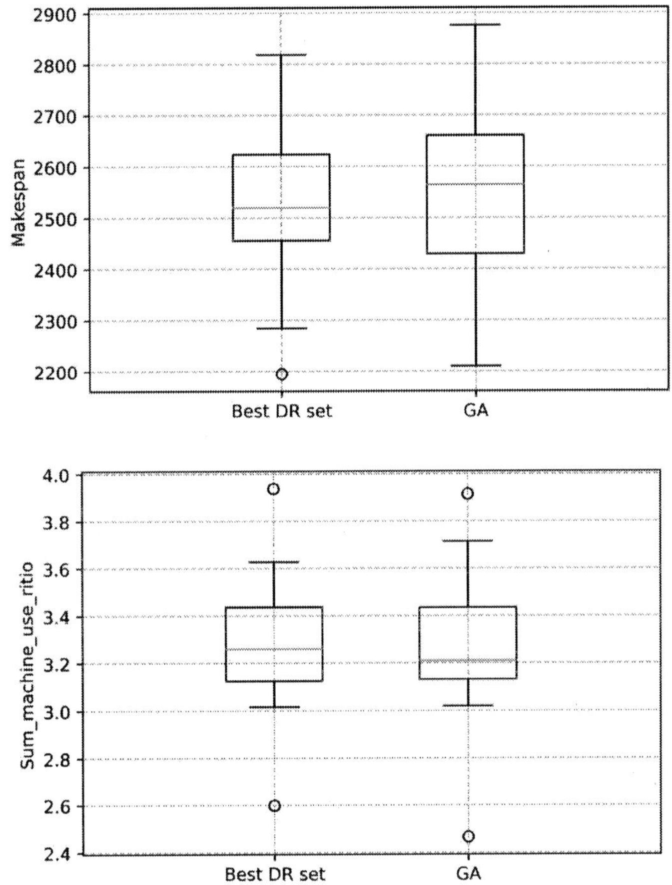

Figure 11. Low job heterogeneity and a low manufacturing system load rate.

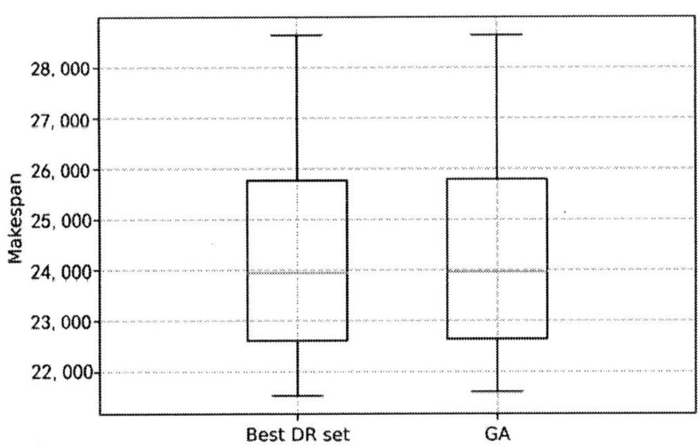

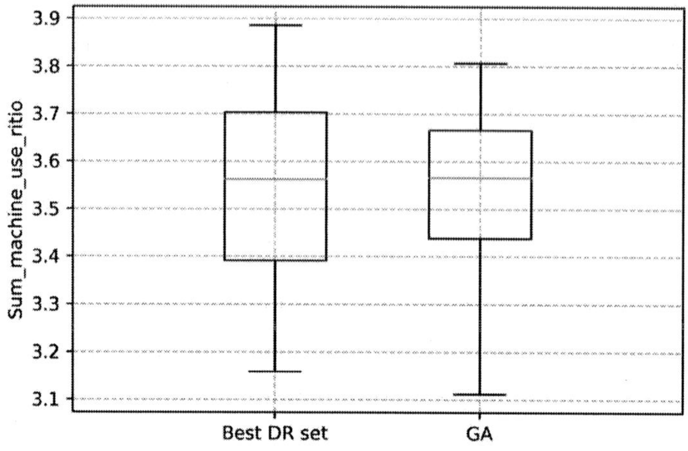

Figure 12. High job heterogeneity and a high manufacturing system load rate.

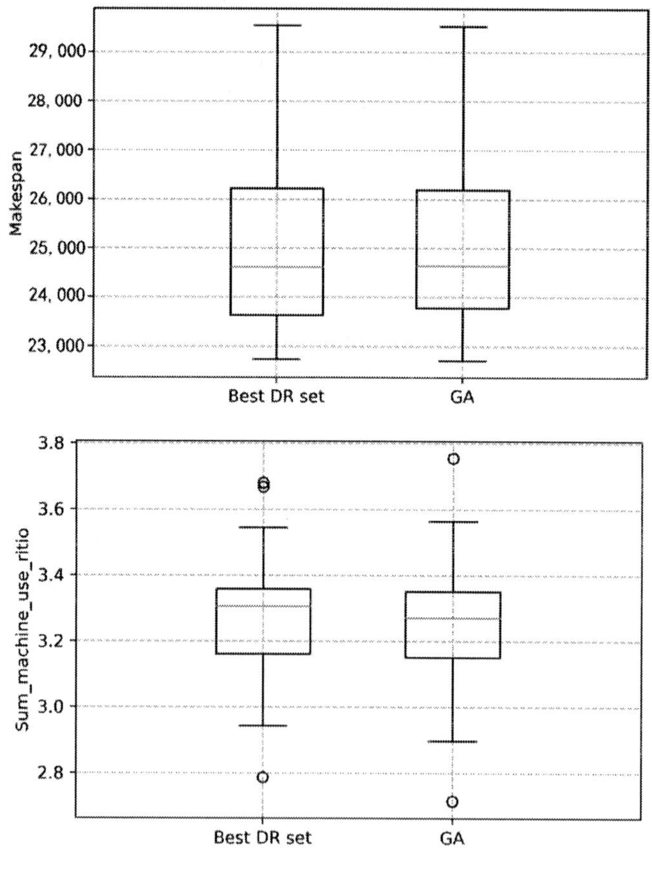

Figure 13. High job heterogeneity and a low manufacturing system load rate.

Table 8. Overall stability comparison of scheduling rule combination and genetic algorithm performance

Scheduling Criterion	Method	Low Job Heterogeneity and High Load Rate	Low Job Heterogeneity and Low Load Rate	High Job Heterogeneity and High Load Rate	High Job Heterogeneity and Low Load Rate
Makespan	Best DR set	9.324	9.563	152.774	165.438
	GA	8.994	12.169	148.959	163.826
Machine use ratio	Best DR set	0.01	0.21	0.1	0.016
	GA	0.011	0.27	0.11	0.017

To sum up, the quality of the scheduling data with scheduling knowledge collected by the method in this paper can be guaranteed, thereby ensuring the availability and superiority of the constructed dispatching rule assignment model.

Data Preprocessing

After collecting the production data related to the manufacturing system and using simulation technology to search for the optimal DR combination for the manufacturing system from the DR library, the original data with scheduling knowledge could be collected. The attributes of these data comprised the processing parameters of the jobs in the manufacturing system and the parameters of each DR.

The manufacturing system described in Table 4 is considered as an example. Three DRs (SPT, STPT, and STWR) were set in the DR library. After the simulation, they were divided into 29 scheduling subperiods, as listed in Table 9. Each sample data point represented a scheduling subperiod. The data structure contained sample data with a single attribute corresponding to one label and sample data with multiple attributes corresponding to one label. For the former, only one job was scheduled in the scheduling subperiod, which did not contain scheduling knowledge. The latter indicates that multiple jobs were scheduled in the scheduling subperiod, which contain scheduling knowledge. Because the data input to the machine learning algorithm should comprise a label corresponding to a row of attribute data, this type of datum cannot be directly input into the machine learning algorithm. Before using the DM algorithm to build a decision model, it is necessary to process the original data with scheduling knowledge using the methods of high-quality data collection described in the previous section. Given the characteristics and structure of the original data, the specific processing flow is described below.\

The data feature selection process is illustrated in Figure 14. Because assigning DRs and then generating the scheduling strategy is based on the machine as the unit and dividing the scheduling subperiod is also based on the machine, the decision-making times on each machine were independent of each other. The attribute data of the original data with scheduling knowledge were grouped by machine and processed in the same manner. For the original data with scheduling knowledge in this study, the release time attribute column (columns R0, R1, R2, and R3) and machine columns (columns M0, M1, M2, and M3) were removed, and the grouped data were combined vertically. In this process, the number (quantity) of jobs in each scheduling subperiod was added manually, and the resulting data were defined as the data after feature selection.

Table 9. Raw data with scheduling knowledge (four machines and 10 jobs)

No.	M0	R0	PT0	M1	R1	PT1	M2	R2	PT2	M3	...	DR	No.
0	0	0	21	1		6	2		10	3	...	STWR	0
1	3		49	0	0	40	2		83	1	...	SPT	1
2	2		77	1		51	0	0	44	3	...	STPT	2
3	2		90	3		50	1		31	0	...	STWR	3
4											...	STPT	4
5	0	6	32	3		46	2		80	1	...	SPT	5
	0	6	90	1		93	3		78	2	...		
6											...	STWR	6
7	0	0	21	1		6	2		10	3	...	SPT	7
	2		11	0	4	9	1		48	3	...		
	1		1	0	4	54	3		28	2	...		
8	3		49	0	0	40	2		83	1	...	SPT	8
9	2		90	3		50	1		31	0	...	STPT	9
	3		60	1		79	0	37	27	2	...		
10	2		14	3		87	1		5	0	...	STPT	10
	0	6	32	3		46	2		80	1	...		
11	0	0	21	1		6	2		10	3	...	SPT	11
	2		11	0	4	9	1		48	3	...		
	3		49	0	0	40	2		83	1	...		
....													....
29	0	6	90	1		93	3		78	2	...	SPT	29

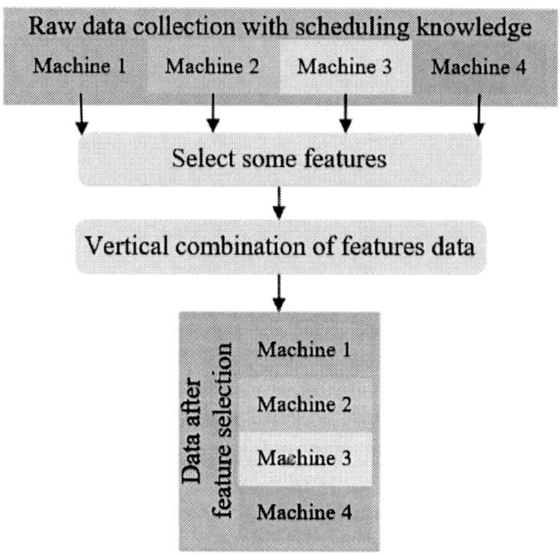

Figure 14. Feature selection process.

The second step was a transformation of the data structure. Before the transformation, data preprocessing operations were performed to delete abnormal sample data that did not contain scheduling knowledge. Then, the data with scheduling knowledge were transformed into a structural form in which a row of attribute data corresponded to the label data. Commonly used mathematical and statistical methods include the sample mean, sample standard deviation, coefficient of variation, and classic machine learning dimensionality reduction algorithms. In this study, the PCA algorithm was used, transforming the original data structure $(n*m)\times d$ into a $n*(m+1)$ structure. Finally, the available data with scheduling knowledge were preprocessed, including the elimination of repeated values and deletion of outliers. The outlier deletion process employed the 3σ principle.

The Construction of the Scheduling Model

After obtaining the available high-quality data, the data were divided into a training set and a test set at a ratio of 7:3, and the DM algorithm was used to build a multiclassification model. In constructing the model, a grid search method was used to obtain the optimal parameters of the DR algorithm. The accuracies of the decision-making models constructed for manufacturing systems of different categories obtained after five rounds of crossvalidation are listed in Table 10.

Table 10. Classification model accuracy results

Production System Category	Low Job Heterogeneity, High Load Rate	Low Job Heterogeneity, Low Load Rate	High Job Heterogeneity, High Load Rate	High Job Heterogeneity, Low Load Rate
Acc. (%)	79.96	77.99	85.92	83.81

Analysis of Model Performance

To verify the effectiveness of the constructed decision model for solving the scheduling problem in response to the disturbance factor of the job release moment with unknown released job information, 20 sets of data were collected for each manufacturing system category and randomly combined into 10,000 DR combinations. Simulation technology was used to search for the optimal DR combination with the goal of maximizing the sum of the utilization rate of each machine in the makespan and the manufacturing system. Then, the constructed decision model was used to iteratively assign DRs at each decision moment in the production process, and the generated scheduling strategy was used to assign the jobs in the scheduling subperiod. After all of the processing tasks of the manufacturing system were completed, the makespan value and sum of the utilization rate of each machine in the manufacturing system were calculated.

Figure 15, Figure 16, Figure 17 and Figure 18 show comparisons between the makespan values and total machine utilization values of the manufacturing system obtained under the optimal DR combination identified through global search and the DR combination produced by the iterative assignment of the decision-making model for different categories of manufacturing systems. Although the effect is less than that of the optimal DR combination obtained through the global search, the difference is insignificant, and the effect is the same in some manufacturing systems. Thus, the proposed method can solve the disturbance problem of the new job release in the manufacturing system efficiently and in real-time. A comparison of the decision-making effect of the decision model and the optimal DR combination obtained through the global search is shown in Figure 19 for each type of manufacturing system (Figure 19a represents high job heterogeneity and a high manufacturing system load rate, Figure 19b shows low job heterogeneity and a low manufacturing system load rate, Figure 19c shows high job heterogeneity and a high manufacturing system load rate, and Figure 19d represents high job heterogeneity and a low manufacturing system load rate); the statistical analysis of the comparison is summarized in Table 11. For the manufacturing system category of low job heterogeneity and a high manufacturing system load rate, compared with the most optimal DR combination, over half of the manufacturing system makespan increase rates were less than 1%; the average increase rate was 1.059%, and the median was 0.298%. The attenuation rates of the sum of the utilization values for each machine in half of the manufacturing systems were less than 1%; the average attenuation rate was 1.218%, and the median was 1.041%. For the manufacturing system category of low job heterogeneity and a low manufacturing system load rate, the average increase rate of the makespan value compared to the optimal DR combination was 3.139%, and the median was 3.276%; the average attenuation rate of the sum of the utilization values of each machine was 2.993% with a median of 3.276%. For the manufacturing system category of high job heterogeneity and a high manufacturing system load rate, compared with the most optimal DR combination, nearly half of the manufacturing system makespan increase rates were less than 1%; the average increase rate was 2.287%, and the median was 1.979%.

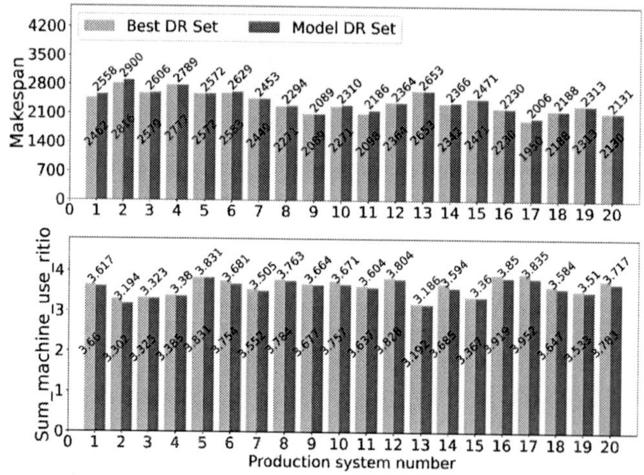

Figure 15. Low job heterogeneity and a high manufacturing system load rate.

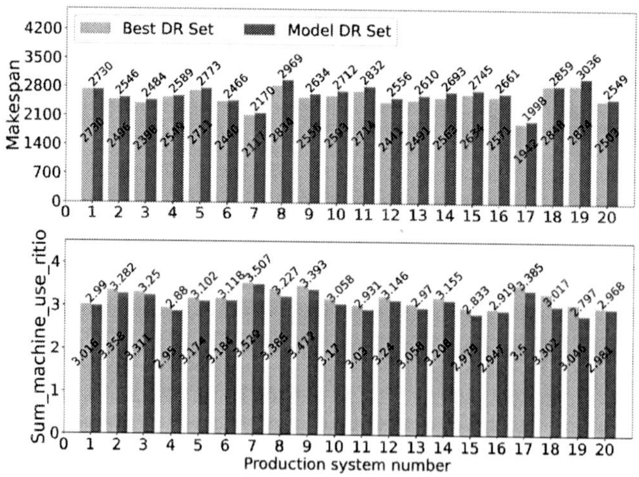

Figure 16. Low job heterogeneity and a low manufacturing system load rate.

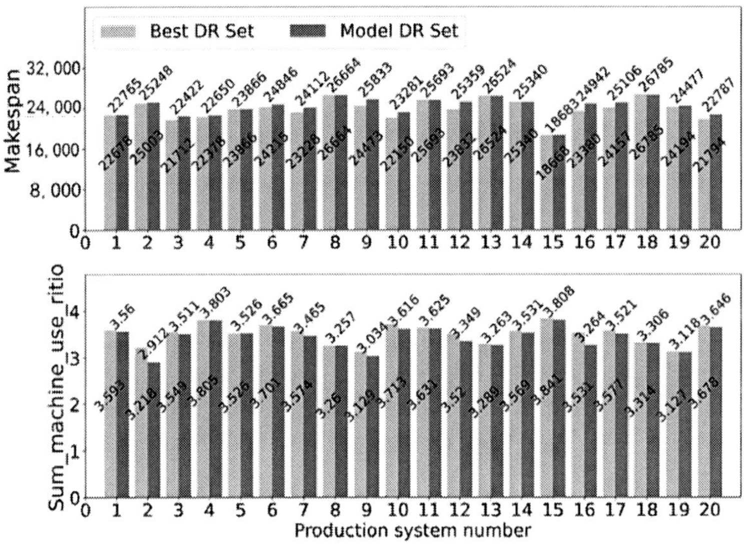

Figure 17. High job heterogeneity and a high manufacturing system load rate.

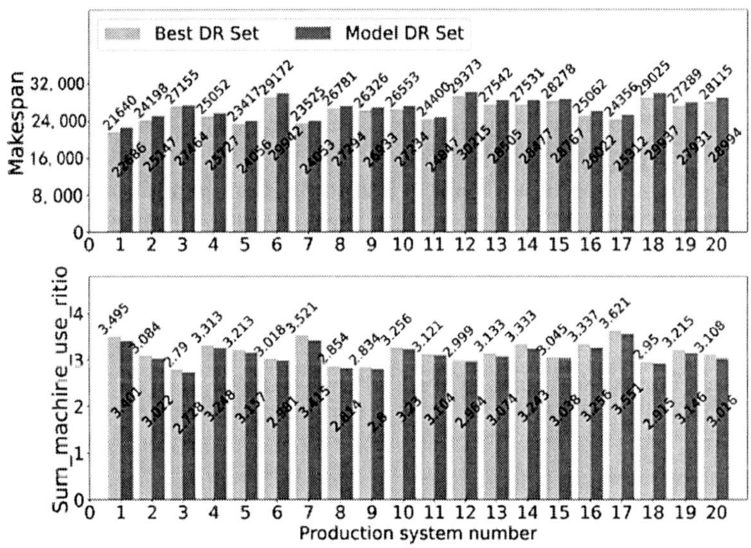

Figure 18. High job heterogeneity and a low manufacturing system load rate.

The attenuation rates of the utilization value for each machine in over half of the manufacturing systems were less than 1%; the average attenuation rate was 2.287%, and the median was 1.979%. For the manufacturing system category of high job heterogeneity and a low manufacturing system load rate, compared with the most optimal DR combination makespan value, the average increase rate was 2.836%, and the median was 1.772%. Compared with the most optimal DR combination, the average attenuation rate of the utilization value for each machine was 2.712%, and the median was 1.908%.

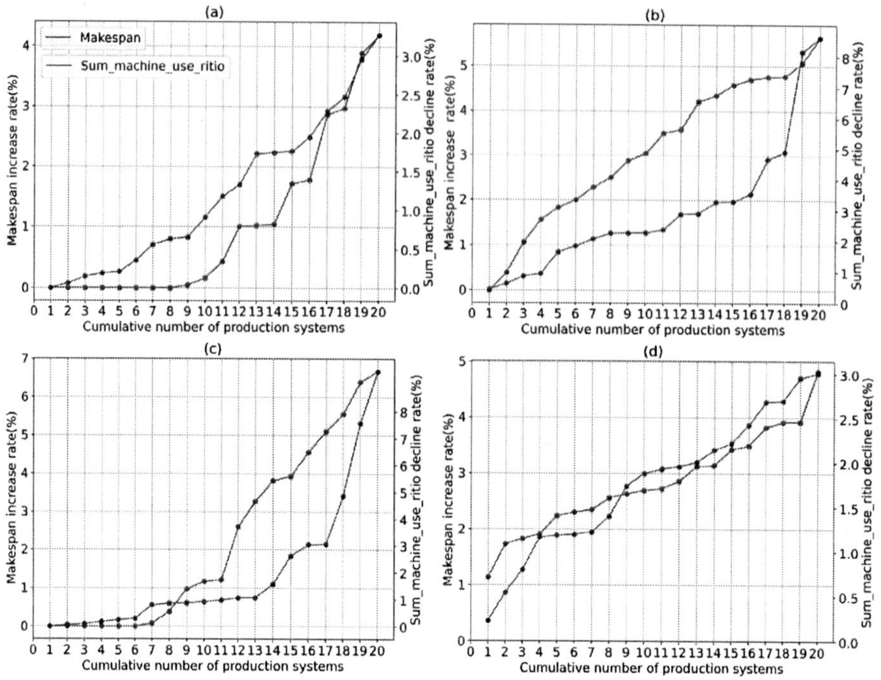

Figure 19. Comparison of the decision-making model and optimal DR combination results ((a) represents high job heterogeneity and a high manufacturing system load rate, (b) shows low job heterogeneity and a low manufacturing system load rate, (c) shows high job heterogeneity and a high manufacturing system load rate, and (d) represents high job heterogeneity and a low manufacturing system load rate).

Table 11. Statistics of the comparison between the decision model and optimal DR combination results

Scheduling Criterion	Statistical Indicators	Low Job Heterogeneity and High Load Rate	Low Job Heterogeneity and Low Load Rate	High Job Heterogeneity and High Load Rate	High Job Heterogeneity and Low Load Rate
Makespan	Avg. (%)	1.059	3.139	2.287	2.836
	Med. (%)	0.298	3.276	0.193	2.712
Machine use ratio	Avg. (%)	1.218	2.993	1.979	1.772
	Med. (%)	1.041	2.324	0.946	1.908

In summary, the decision-making model constructed in this study had significant effects, and the decision-making effects of models for different categories were similar to those obtained using the optimal DR simulation. The time range for each decision and generation of a locally optimal scheduling policy was 0.12–0.21 s, which is much less than the processing time of the job on the machine. This verifies that the proposed method can provide an efficient and real-time response to the impact of the randomness of the new job release on the manufacturing system.

CONCLUSIONS

Data mining (DM) technology provides a novel and effective solution for real-time job shop disturbance problems. In this paper, a purely reactive scheduling approach is proposed based on the data mining process. Firstly, a novel DR combination method was used to collect data with scheduling knowledge; secondly, the collected data were used to construct a decision model that can assign DR in real-time; finally, a four-machine scale JSSP was used to verify the effectiveness of the proposed method. The main contributions of this paper are as follows.

- A novel DR combinatorial optimization JSSP mixed-integer linear programming model was constructed, and a DR combinatorial optimization method is proposed.
- A decision tree algorithm was used to train a decision model for assigning DRs from the collected data. The model assigned DRs at the beginning of each subscheduling cycle, which achieved an optimal overall scheduling policy by generating a locally optimal scheduling policy and overcame the adverse effects of the dynamic perturbation problem of midjob release.
- The performance of the decision model DR combination method for assigning DR is similar under the scheduling objectives of makespan and machine utilization, demonstrating the superior performance of the scheduling policy generated using the DM technique.

However, the method proposed in this paper still has significant limitations. The construction of scheduling decision models using DM depends on the quality of the collected scheduling data, and further research is needed on how to generate scheduling data using the DR combination method; in terms of application scenarios, this paper only verifies the value of DM for optimizing dynamic scheduling problems on a classical job shop, and future research should focus on applications in more complex and wider production environments.

AUTHOR CONTRIBUTIONS

Conceptualization, A.Z.; data curation, A.Z.; formal analysis, A.Z.; funding acquisition, P.L.; investigation, P.L.; methodology, P.L.; project administration, X.G.; software, X.G.; resources, G.H.; supervision, G.H.; validation, X.Y.; visualization, X.Y.; writing—original draft, Y.M.; writing—review and editing, Z.X.; writing—review and editing, Y.L. All authors have read and agreed to the published version of the manuscript.

REFERENCES

1. Liu, Z.F.; Chen, W.; Zhang, C.X.; Yang, C.B.; Cheng, Q. Intelligent scheduling of a feature-process-machine tool supernetwork based on digital twin workshop. *J. Manuf. Syst.* 2020, *58 Part B*, 157–167.
2. Garey, M.R.; Johnson, D.S.; Sethi, R. The Complexity of Flowshop and Job shop Scheduling. *Math. Oper. Res.* 1976, *1*, 117–129.
3. Barenji, A.V.; Barenji, R.V.; Roudi, D.; Hashemipour, M. A dynamic multi-agent-based scheduling approach for SMEs. *Int. J. Adv. Manuf. Technol.* 2017, *89*, 3123–3137.
4. Mohsen, Z. A heuristic algorithm for solving flexible job shop scheduling problem. *Int. J. Adv. Manuf. Technol.* 2014, *71*, 519–528.
5. Perez, F.; Raupp, F. A Newton-based heuristic algorithm for multi-objective flexible job-shop scheduling problem. *J. Intell. Manuf.* 2016, *27*, 409–416.

6. Veronique, S.; Nele, G.; Mario, V. A comparison of priority rules for the job shop scheduling problem under different flow time- and tardiness-related objective functions. *Int. J. Prod. Res.* 2012, *50*, 4255–4270.
7. Zhang, J.; Deng, T.M.; Jiang, H.F.; Chen, H.J.; Qin, S.F.; Ding, G.F. Bi-level dynamic scheduling architecture based on service unit digital twin agents. *J. Manuf. Syst.* 2021, *60*, 59–79.
8. Azadeh, A.; Negahban, A.; Moghaddam, M. A hybrid computer simulation-artificial neural network algorithm for optimi-sation of dispatching rule selection in stochastic job shop scheduling problems. *Int. J. Prod. Res.* 2012, *50*, 551–566.
9. Gutowski, T.; Murphy, C.F.; Allen, D.; Bauer, D. Environmentally benign manufacturing: Observations from Japan, Europe and the United States. *J. Clean. Prod.* 2005, *13*, 1–17.
10. Wang, H.Y.; Wang, J.C.; Xu, H.T.; Zhao, S.W. Distributed stochastic model predictive control for systems with stochastic multi-plicative uncertainty and chance constraints. *ISA Trans.* 2021, *121*, 11–20.
11. Wei, Y.F.; Othman, Z.; Daud, M.K.; Yin, S.H.; Luo QFZhou, Y.Q. Equilibrium Optimizer and Slime Mould Algorithm with Variable Neighborhood Search for Job Shop Scheduling Problem. *Mathematics* 2022, *10*, 4063.
12. Yuraszeck, F.; Mejía, G.; Pereira, J.; Vilà, M. A Novel Constraint Programming Decomposition Approach for the Total Flow Time Fixed Group Shop Scheduling Problem. *Mathematics* 2022, *10*, 329.
13. Szabó, S.; Zaválnij, B. Clique Search in Graphs of Special Class and Job Shop Scheduling. *Mathematics* 2022, *10*, 697.
14. Luan, F.; Cai, Z.Y.; Wu, S.Q.; Jiang, T.H.; Li, F.K.; Yang, J. Improved Whale Algorithm for Solving the Flexible Job Shop Scheduling Problem. *Mathematics* 2019, *7*, 384.
15. Luan, F.; Cai, Z.Y.; Wu, S.Q.; Qiang, S.; He, Y. Optimizing the Low-Carbon Flexible Job Shop Scheduling Problem with Discrete Whale Optimization Algorithm. *Mathematics* 2019, *7*, 688.
16. Sauvey, C.; Trabelsi, W.; Sauer, N. Mathematical Model and Evaluation Function for Conflict-Free Warranted Makespan Minimization of Mixed Blocking Constraint Job-Shop Problems. *Mathematics* 2020, *8*, 121.
17. Wang, B.; Xie, H.X.; Xia, X.D.; Zhang, X.X. A NSGA-II Algorithm Hybridizing Local Simulated-Annealing Operators for a Bi-Criteria Robust Job-Shop Scheduling Problem Under Scenarios. *IEEE Trans. Fuzzy Syst.* 2019, *27*, 1075–1083.
18. Shen, X.N.; Han, Y.; Fu, J.Z. Robustness measures and robust scheduling for multi-objective stochastic flexible job shop scheduling problems. *Soft Comput.* 2017, *26*, 6531–6554.
19. Xiao, S.C.; Wu, Z.G.; Dui, H.Y. Resilience-Based Surrogate Robustness Measure and Optimization Method for Robust Job-Shop Scheduling. *Mathematics* 2022, *10*, 4048.
20. Fantahun, M.D.; Dolapo, O.; Alebachew, D.Y. Mathematical model and simulated annealing algorithm for setup operator constrained flexible job shop scheduling problem. *Comput. Ind. Eng.* 2022, *171*, 108487.
21. Khurshid, B.; Maqsood, S.; Omair, M.; Sarkar, B.; Saad, M.; Asad, U. Fast Evolutionary Algorithm for Flow Shop Scheduling Problems. *IEEE Access* 2021, *9*, 44825–44839.
22. Zhou, L.F.; Zhang, L.; Sarker, B.R.; Laili, Y.J.; Ren, L. An event-triggered dynamic scheduling method for randomly arriving tasks in cloud manufacturing. *Int. J. Comput. Integr. Manuf.* 2018, *31*, 318–333.
23. Wang, B.; Wang, X.Z.; Xie, H.X. Bad-scenario-set robust scheduling for a job shop to hedge against processing time uncertainty. *Int. J. Prod. Res.* 2019, *57*, 3168–3185.
24. Wang, Y.R.; Wu, Z.L. Model construction of planning and scheduling system based on digital twin. *Int. J. Adv. Manuf. Technol.* 2020, *109*, 2189–2203.

25. Zhang, H.K.; Buchmeister, B.; Li, X.Y.; Ojstersek, R. Advanced Metaheuristic Method for Decision-Making in a Dynamic Job Shop Scheduling Environment. *Mathematics* 2021, *9*, 909.
26. Gao, K.Z.; Suganthan, P.N.; Chua, T.J.; Chong, C.S.; Cai, T.X.; Pan, Q. A two-stage artificial bee colony algorithm scheduling flexible job-shop scheduling problem with new job insertion. *Expert Syst. Appl.* 2015, *42*, 7652–7663.
27. Yin, Y.; Kong, X.; Xia, C.Q.; Xu, C.; Jin, X. Low-Cost Emergent Dynamic Scheduling for Flexible Job Shops. *Mathematics* 2022, *10*, 1873.
28. Vakhania, N. Dynamic Restructuring Framework for Scheduling with Release Times and Due-Dates. *Mathematics* 2019, *7*, 1104.
29. Ouelhadj, D.; Petrovic, S. A survey of dynamic scheduling in manufacturing systems. *J. Sched.* 2009, *12*, 417–431.
30. Ji, W.; Wang, L.H. Big data analytics based fault prediction for shop floor scheduling. *J. Manuf. Syst.* 2017, *43 Part 1*, 187–194.
31. Qiu, Y.T.; Sawhney, R.; Zhang, C.Y.; Chen, S.; Zhang, T.; Lisar, V.G.; Jiang, K.; Ji, W. Data mining-based disturbances prediction for job shop scheduling. *Adv. Mech. Eng.* 2019, *11*, 1.
32. Zhang, G.H.; Lu, X.X.; Liu, X.; Zhang, L.T.; Wei, S.W.; Zhang, W.Q. An effective two-stage algorithm based on convolutional neural network for the bi-objective flexible job shop scheduling problem with machine breakdown. *Expert Syst. Appl. Int. J.* 2022, *203*, 117460.
33. Gupta, D.; Maravelias, C.T.; Wassick, J.M. From rescheduling to online scheduling. *Chem. Eng. Res. Des.* 2016, *116*, 83–97.
34. Dogan, A.; Birant, D. Machine learning and data mining in manufacturing. *Expert Syst. Appl.* 2021, *166*, 114060.
35. Zhou, Q.P.; Zhang, M.Z.; Ki-Hyung, B. Edge computing and financial service industry financing risk innovation based on data mining technology. *Pers. Ubiquitous Comput.* 2021, *25*, 19.
36. Gokhan, M.; Ihsan, S.; Henri, P. Real time selection of scheduling rules and knowledge extraction via dynamically controlled data mining. *Int. J. Prod. Res.* 2010, *48*, 6909–6938.
37. Zahmani, M.H.; Atmani, B. A Data Mining Based Dispatching Rules Selection System for the Job Shop Scheduling Problem. *J. Adv. Manuf. Syst.* 2019, *18*, 35–36.
38. Shahzad, A.; Mebarki, N. Data mining based job dispatching using hybrid simulation-optimization approach for shop scheduling problem. *Eng. Appl. Artif. Intell.* 2012, *25*, 1173–1181.
39. Sahin, C.; Demirtas, M.; Erol, R.; Baykasoğlu, A.; Kaplanoğlu, V. A multi-agent based approach to dynamic scheduling with flexible processing capabilities. *J. Intell. Manuf.* 2017, *28*, 1827–1845.
40. Xiong, W.; Fu, D.M. A new immune multi-agent system for the flexible job shop scheduling problem. *J. Intell. Manuf.* 2018, *29*, 857–873.
41. Zhou, Y.; Yang, J.J.; Zheng, L.Y. Multi-Agent Based Hyper-heuristics for Multi-objective Flexible Job Shop Scheduling: A Case Study in an Aero-engine Blade Manufacturing Plant. *IEEE Access* 2019, *7*, 21147–21176.
42. Mezgebe, T.T.; Bril El Haouzi, H.; Demesure, G.; Pannequin, R.; Thomas, A. Multi-agent systems negotiation to deal with dy-namic scheduling in disturbed industrial context. *J. Intell. Manuf.* 2019, *31*, 1–13.
43. Dalila, F.; Mahdi, H.; Jos'e, F.G. A Hybrid Particle Swarm Optimization and Simulated Annealing Algorithm for the Job Shop Scheduling Problem with Transport Resources. *Eur. J. Oper. Res.* 2022; *in press*.
44. Durasevic MJakobovic, D. Comparison of solution representations for scheduling in the unrelated machines environment. In Proceedings of the 39th International Convention on Information and Communication Technology, Electronics and Microelectronics (MIPRO), Opatija, Croatia, 30 May–3 June 2016; pp. 1336–1342.

45. Rohmah, D.S.; Othman, Z.; Kaban, A.K. Comparison of dispatching rules in job-shop scheduling problem using simulation: A case study. *Int. J. Simul. Model.* 2012, *11*, 129–140.

46. Đurasević, M.; Jakobović, D. Creating dispatching rules by simple ensemble combination. *J. Heuristics* 2019, *25*, 959–1013.

47. Li, X.N.; Olafsson, S. Learning effective new single machine dispatching rules from optimal scheduling data. *Int. J. Prod. Econ.* 2010, *128*, 118–126.

48. Ozturk, G.; Bahadir, O.; Teymourifar, A. Extracting priority rules for dynamic multi-objective flexible job shop scheduling problems using gene expression programming. *Int. J. Prod. Res.* 2019, *57*, 3121–3137.

49. Đurasević, M.; Jakobović, D. A survey of dispatching rules for the dynamic unrelated machines environment. *Expert Syst. Appl.* 2018, *113*, 555–569.

50. Tavakkoli, M.R.; Daneshmand, M.M. A computer simulation model for job shop scheduling problems minimizing makespan. *Comput. Ind. Eng.* 2005, *48*, 811–823.

51. Taillard, E. Benchmarks for basic scheduling problems. *Eur. J. Oper. Res.* 1993, *64*, 278–285.

52. Boris, J.; Patnaik, G.; Lee, M.Y.; Young, T.; Leitl, B.; Harms, F.; Schatzmann, M. Validation of an LES Urban Aerodynamics Model for Homeland Security. In Proceedings of the 47th AIAA Aerospace Sciences Meeting Including The New Horizons Forum and Aerospace Expo-Sition, Orlando, FL, USA, 5–8 January 2009.

53. Rokach, L. Ensemble-based classifiers. *Artif. Intell. Rev.* 2010, *33*, 1–39.

54. Read, J.; Reutemann, P.; Pfahringer, B.; Holmes, G. Meka: A Multi-label/Multi-target Extension to Weka. *J. Mach. Learn. Res.* 2016, *17*, 667–671.

55. Kotsiantis, S.B. Decision trees: A recent overview. *Artif. Intell. Rev.* 2013, *39*, 261–283.

9

Operator-Based Adaptive Tracking Capacity Control in Complex Manufacturing Processes

Ping Liu[1], Qiang Zhang[2], Aihui Wang[3], Shengjun Wen[1] and Jürgen Pannek[4]

[1]Zhongyuan-Petersburg Aviation College, Zhongyuan University of Technology, Zhengzhou 451191, China

[2]School of Intelligent Engineering, Zhengzhou University of Aeronautics, Zhengzhou 450015, China

[3]School of Electronic and Information, Zhongyuan University of Technology, Zhengzhou 451191, China

[4]Faculty of Mechanical Engineering, Technische Universität Braunschweig, 38106 Braunschweig, Germany

ABSTRACT

Nowadays, quickly changing customer demands are a big challenge in the manufacturing industry, especially for job shops, which are typical coupling and nonlinear multi-input–multi-output (MIMO) systems. In order to achieve good shop floor performance in the presence of short-term demand fluctuations, a key performance indicator—work in process (WIP)—is required to be effectively controlled in the vicinity of the desired levels. For this purpose, a machinery-oriented capacity adjustment approach via a reconfigurable machine tool (RMT) is employed to flexibly balance capacity and load in the case of a bottleneck. A mathematical model concerning the RMT and WIP was first established in the presence of uncertainty and delays. The operator-based robust right coprime factorization (RRCF) method was adopted to stabilize the uncertain system, and adaptive integral separated proportional–integral (ISPI) tracking controllers were further designed to improve the transient and robustness performance. The performance of the proposed ISPI-RRCF was analyzed and compared with that of a state-of-the-art method in a simulation. The results showed that both control systems could ensure that the WIP was within an allowed bound, while the former had lower overshoots, shorter setting times, and more concentrated distributions facing stochastic demands. This further indicated the effectiveness of the proposed algorithm in the avoidance of serious bottlenecks and unbalanced capacity distributions.

Keywords: *Operator Theory, Adaptive Tracking Capacity Control, Job Shop, Reconfigurable Machine Tool*

INTRODUCTION

With rapidly changing customer demand, along with the requirements of cost-effectiveness, high customization, and short delivery time, manufacturing processes have become more complex and dynamic [1,2]. Job shops are a typical flexible production mode for producing a variety of products with small lot sizes. However, they suffer from a high work-in-process (WIP) level, high costs, long lead times, and low productivity, which may lead to bottlenecks and cause performance deterioration [3,4]. To cope with these challenges and achieve good shop-floor performance in a job shop environment, as an effective supporting tool for compensating and balancing the capacity distribution, capacity adjustments are conducted on the operational layer. In [5], a decentralized capacity control structure was designed to deal with bottlenecks for the capacity balance between workstations in job shop systems. In [6], an improved centralized model predictive control (MPC) algorithm was proposed to optimize capacity adjustment processes to avoid serious bottlenecks. A local capacity adjustment was discussed based on the H_∞ algorithm to ensure that the WIP was in the vicinity of a planned level in [7]. These studies show that capacity adjustment is an effective way to improve performance, even with small modifications during a high load period. Instead of labor-oriented approaches (e.g., overtime), a reconfigurable machine tool (RMT) can be promoted as a new opportunity for a machinery-oriented capacity adjustment [8]. In [9], a harmonizing throughput–time capacity adjustment approach via an RMT was proposed to improve productivity while maintaining a certain flexibility in complex job shops. In [10], the WIP of workstations was also controlled by utilizing the flexibility of RMTs in the capacity adjustment of complex manufacturing processes.

Although RMTs play a vital role in terms of flexibility and reconfigurability, they are only an enabler for capacity adjustment. Therefore, an effective control method for the usage of RMTs is of crucial importance in the context of Industry 4.0 [11]. Due to its simplicity and wide applicability, the proportional–integral–derivative (PID) algorithm has been applied for single-input–single-output (SISO) systems. Kim and Duffie first adopted the PI algorithm in the backlog control of a single-workstation production system [12]. They further extended the application to the capacity control of a multi-workstation production system with disturbances [13]. In [14], the development of a PID method was discussed with respect to its incorporation with other advanced algorithms in practical applications, and the challenges in design and tuning for difficult problems, especially for systems with nonlinearities, coupling, disturbances, and delays (e.g., in a job shop), were also put forward.

In contrast to the PID, operator-based robust right coprime factorization (RRCF) is an advanced control method for a class of nonlinear systems that can be appropriately decomposed by using operator theory to design robust controllers via Bezout identity [15]. Deng proposed a new condition for the robust controller design of nonlinear systems with unknown bounded disturbances, which extended the application [16]. Improved RRCF algorithms were proposed to deal with delays, disturbances, and couplings [17,18]. This method was mathematically demonstrated and applied for a variety of fields, such as a highly nonlinear ionic polymer metal composite with hysteresis [19], a multi-joint manipulator [20], and a coupling multi-tank process [21], which was readily applicable for job shop systems for capacity control via RMTs. In previous work, this method was applied in capacity control. However, the performance still needs to be improved, especially for adaptive tracking control. To improve the tracking performance, a feedback-linearization-based PID method was proposed for the path tracking of micro-actuators to reduce the tracking error in [22]. Salehi Kolahi et al. designed a non-singular fast terminal sliding-mode control for the path tracking of nonlinear second-order systems with compound disturbances in [23]. For adaptive control, a neural network (NN) is an effective method. Nguyen et al. recommended an adaptive robust position control technique by integrating an radial basis function NN (RBF-NN) and NN-based disturbance observer for disturbed electro-hydraulic servo systems [24]. Ruan et al. also proposed an RBF-NN adaptive sliding-mode controller for nonlinear electromechanical actuator systems with uncertainty and disturbances [25].

Considering the key performance of job shops, WIP is essential, as it greatly influences many key performance indicators, e.g., energy efficiency, throughput, and delivery date reliability [26,27]. Hence, the purpose of control is to guarantee that the manufacturing process works on an expected WIP level via flexible capacity control with RMTs and to ensure the closed-loop stability in which the performance indicators (e.g., WIP) remain bounded while converging toward desired values or an acceptable stability region. In [28], the authors investigated the problem of WIP regulation via RMT assignment in a job shop with a constant flow probability. Desirable control performance and the stability of the closed-loop system were achieved by using MPC with terminal endpoint constraints. However, the preferred assignment of RMTs for capacity adjustment belonged to a continuous optimization case. To solve this problem, the authors further extended their work and employed MPC in association with a deterministic method (e.g., branch and bound) and stochastic optimization techniques (e.g., genetic algorithm) for the integer assignment of RMTs [29]. However, transportation delays were not taken into consideration, and the computational complexity of this method was very high due to the iterative online optimization. In [30], the complexity of workstations was described as a nonlinear operator, and the WIP was controlled by considering the productivity and customer requirements. This also indicated the applicability of operator theory in the capacity control process. To measure the control performance, transient and robustness were two key factors facing stochastic customer demands. As a key transient performance indicator, overshoot reflects the bottleneck level of workstations and the capacity distribution; therefore, it is expected to have a low value.

The above survey revealed that the integration of RMTs and RRCF was an effective means of capacity control. However, there is still much work to be done to improve the performance in capacity control systems while considering practical applications. This research is concerned with quickly solving the serious bottleneck represented by the high overshoot and unbalanced capacity reflected by the robustness in job shops facing stochastic demands. To solve this problem, an improved adaptive tracking capacity control algorithm is proposed by integrating the RRCF and ISPI with a single-neuron algorithm. The main contribution can be summarized as follows:

- To decrease the complexity of a high-coupling job shop manufacturing process and autonomously realize rapid responsiveness among workstations, a decoupling-controller-based operator was designed to decompose the complex MIMO system into multiple SISO systems.

- To ensure the steady-state performance and keep the WIP level for each workstation in the vicinity of the planned values while considering disturbances and delays, robust controllers were theoretically designed by using the RRCF method based on the Bezout identity.
- To effectively decrease the overshoot and excessive adjusting time in the face of large deviations, integral separated PI-type tracking controllers based on the RRCF (ISPI-RRCF) for the decomposed SISO systems were designed to improve the transient performance.
- To adaptively adjust the parameters of the ISPI-RRCF tracking controllers and enhance the performance in real time, a single neuron associated with the supervised Hebb learning algorithm was adopted, where the related weight coefficients were constantly updated in the presence of disturbances and delays.

Mathematical Model

In the process of adaptive capacity controller design for a job shop, a mathematical model is an important factor for the controller's design. In this section, a funnel-based development model is discussed, and it integrates the customized flexibility of RMTs within complex manufacturing processes [29,30]. In this model, the performance indicators considered are the input rate, output rate, and WIP level; these are not of interest for any single events or orders in the time domain. A general job shop manufacturing system, which consists of n workstations, is shown in Figure 1 [5]. The parameters and variables in the mathematical model of this system are shown in Table 1.

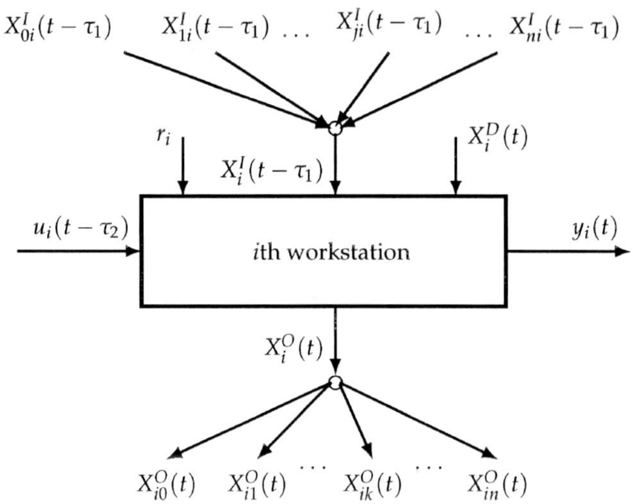

Figure 1. The general model structure of the n-workstation job shop system [31].

Due to the multiple parallel production paths of multiple products, the WIP levels of all workstations are generally higher than those in flow shop processes. Therefore, all machine tools are assumed to be working at the maximum productivity; then, the orders of the output rates of each workstation can be assumed to be the sum of all machines' capacities. Taking DMTs' high productivity into account, the capacity of a workstation includes the customizable part of DMTs and the changeable part of RMTs.

Table 1. Variables within a job shop system with RMTs

Variable	Description
$X^I_{ji}(t)$	Order input rate from the jth to the ith workstation for $j, i \in \{1,\ldots,n\}$
$X^I_i(t)$	Order input rate in the ith workstation for $i \in \{1,\ldots,n\}$
$X^O_{ij}(t)$	Order output rate from the ith to jth workstation for $i, j \in \{1,\ldots,n\}$
$X^O_i(t)$	Order output rate in ith workstation for $i \in \{1,\ldots,n\}$
p_{ij}	Order flow possibility from the ith to the jth workstation for $i, j \in \{0,\ldots,n\}$
p_{i0}	Order flow possibility from the ith workstation to final stage for $i \in \{1,\ldots,n\}$
p_{0i}	Order flow possibility from an initial stage to the ith workstation for $i \in \{1,\ldots,n\}$
n^R	Number of RMTs in the system
n^D_i	Number of DMTs in the ith workstation for $i \in \{1,\ldots,n\}$
v^D_i	Order output rate of DMTs in the ith workstation for $i \in \{1,\ldots,n\}$
v^R_i	Order output rate of RMTs in the ith workstation for $i \in \{1,\ldots,n\}$
$X^D_i(t)$	Disturbances in the ith workstation for $i \in \{1,\ldots,n\}$
$u_i(t)$	Number of RMTs in the ith workstation $i \in \{1,\ldots,n\}$
$y_i(t)$	WIP level in the ith workstation $i \in \{1,\ldots,n\}$
τ_1	Transportation delay between workstations in $X^I_i(t)$
τ_2	Reconfiguration delay of RMTs in $u_i(t)$

This is given by

$$\bar{c}_i(t) = n^D_i \cdot v^D_i + n^R_i \cdot v^R_i. \tag{1}$$

If the number of RMTs is considered as a single input, then the output rate of the ith workstation is approximately equal to the capacity, which could be adjusted by the assigned number of RMTs. Then, the output rate is represented by

$$X^O_i(t) = n^D_i \cdot v^D_i + u_i(t) \cdot v^R_i. \tag{2}$$

As one of the key performance indicators, WIP has a great influence on productivity, delivery date, throughput, and cost. Therefore, the purpose of a capacity adjustment is to guarantee that every workstation works on an expected WIP level. Then, the WIP of each workstation can be described as the output signal of the model given by

$$y_i(t) = y_i(0) + \int_0^t X^I_i(\tau) - (n^D_i \cdot v^D_i + u_i(\tau) \cdot v^R_i)d\tau. \tag{3}$$

However, customers' demands are volatile, and delays, including transportation delays between workstations and reconfiguration delays of RMTs, always exist; cf. Figure 1. Considering these factors, the mathematical model can be represented by

$$\begin{aligned} y_i(t) = y_i(0) + \int_0^t & X^I_{0i}(\tau - \tau_1) + X^D_i(\tau) \\ & + \sum_{j=1}^{n} p_{ji} \cdot (n^D_j \cdot v^D_j + u_j(\tau - \tau_2 - \tau_1) \cdot v^R_i) \\ & - (n^D_i \cdot v^D_i + u_i(\tau - \tau_2) \cdot v^R_i)d\tau, \end{aligned} \tag{4}$$

where the transportation time τ_1 is constant in this paper, and the reconfiguration delay τ_2 is δ when RMT changes its operation from one to another workstation, but it only exists in the object, not in the original one. Thus, the reconfiguration delay is asynchronous and can be represented by

$$\tau_2 = \begin{cases} \delta, & u_i(t^+) \geq u_i(t^-), \\ 0, & \text{else}. \end{cases} \tag{5}$$

Furthermore, though the machine tools are assumed to be working at the maximum production rate, the capacity of the whole system is limited, and it depends on the number of RMTs in the job shop. For a job shop with n workstations and n^R RMTs, the number of RMTs at the jth workstation $u_{i(t)}$ is a non-negative integer, which can be described with following constraints:

$$u_i(t) \in \mathbb{N}_0 \quad \text{and} \quad \sum_{i=1}^{n} u_i(t) \leqslant n^R. \tag{6}$$

For these constraints, the truncation $\lfloor\cdot\rfloor$ and fractional approach [5] are utilized with

$$\hat{u}_i(t) = \begin{cases} \lfloor u_i(t) \rfloor, & \text{if } \sum_{i=1}^{n} u_i(t) \leq n^R \\ \left\lfloor \dfrac{n^R}{\sum_{j=1}^{n} u_j(t)} u_i(t) \right\rfloor, & \text{else.} \end{cases}$$

Therefore, when the sum of the RMTs exceeds n^R, $\hat{u}_i(t)$ is obtained with the fractional discrete value. Otherwise, the truncated value $u_{i(t)}$ is chosen.

OPERATOR-BASED ADAPTIVE CAPACITY CONTROL

For the capacity controller design, an improved operator-based adaptive capacity control method is proposed. Within this method, the multi-workstation job shop system is firstly decoupled into a set number of SISO systems. Thereafter, a local controller of the decoupled SISO system is designed based on operator theory, where an ISPI tracking controller is proposed according to the RRCF (ISPI-RRCF) method, and a neuron algorithm is used to optimize the parameters of the ISPI-RRCF controller. In this section, the content includes the mathematical preliminaries of operator theory, the decoupling control of the MIMO system, and the local adaptive capacity control of the decoupled SISO systems.

Mathematical Preliminaries

In operator theory, a job shop manufacturing system can be represented by an operator Q, which is a mapping from the input space U to the output space Y. The domain and range of Q are defined with D(Q) and R(Q), respectively. N(U,Y) donates the set of all nonlinear operators, and the Lipschitz semi-norm of Q on N(Ds,Y) is defined via

$$\|Q\| := \sup_{x,\tilde{x}\in D_s \& x\neq\tilde{x}} \frac{\|Q(x) - Q(\tilde{x})\|_Y}{\|x - \tilde{x}\|_U}.$$

For such complex job shop systems, the purpose is to design an adaptive capacity controller to guarantee that the job shop works at a predefined level. When the semi-norm is finite, the system is called finite-gain input–output stable (simply called 'stable'). The operator-based definitions and theorems are given as follows; cf. [5] for details.

Definition 1. *Consider a causal and stabilizable operator* Q:D(Q)→R(Q). *It has the right factorization* Q=N∘D−1, *where N is causal and stable, while D is causal, stable, and invertible. Then, the right coprime factorization (RCF) of Q, which is shown in Figure 2, is defined based on the Bezout identity:*

$$R \circ N + S \circ D = M, \tag{7}$$

Where R:R(N)→D(Q) *and* S:R(D)→D(Q) *are causal and stable, and* M:D(Q)→D(Q) *is a unimodular operator.*

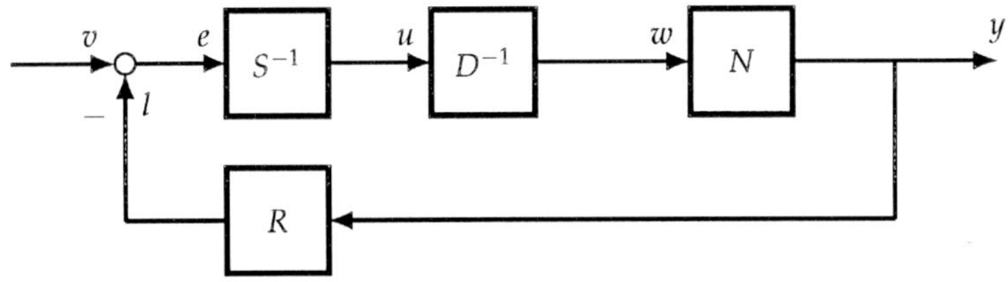

Figure 2. The right coprime factorization for an SISO system.

As shown in Figure 2, except for the input signal *u* and the output signal *y*, there exists a quasi-state signal *w* from the right factorization. *v* and *l* are the referred and feedback signals, and is the error. With this definition, the dynamics of this control system can be described with the following theorem [5].

Theorem 1. *Consider a causal and stabilizable operator* Q:D(Q)→R(Q). *If it has RCF, then this system is stable and can be equivalent to* $y=N\circ M^{-1(v)}$.

When considering bounded uncertainties or disturbances, if the above system *Q* still has the right factorization with

$$Q=(N+\Delta N)\circ D^{-1} \quad (8)$$

where ΔN is an unknown bounded operator, then the following definition is given.

Definition 2. *Consider a bounded disturbed system Q (8). If there exist two operators R and S satisfying the Bezout identity* $R\circ(N+\Delta N)+S\circ D=\tilde{M}$, *then, the system has robust right coprime factorization (RRCF), as shown in Figure 3, where* $\tilde{M}$, *is also a unimodular operator.*

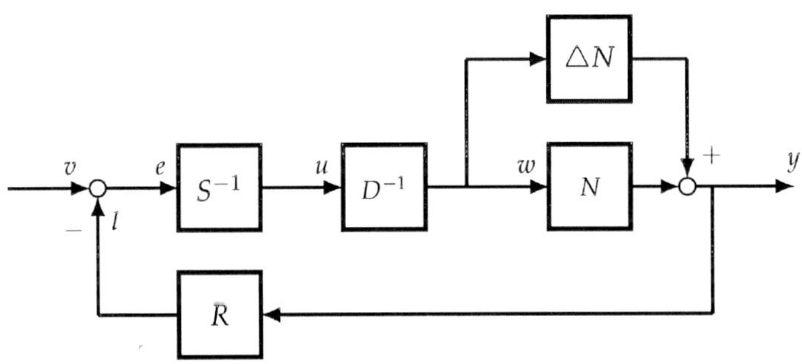

Figure 3. Nonlinear feedback system with disturbances.

Similarly to the Theorem 1, the RRCF of the disturbed system can be equivalent to $y=(N+\Delta N)\circ\tilde{M}^{-1}(v)$. These definitions provide an effective tool for the control and analysis of a class of nonlinear systems, especially for complex dynamic job shops. The details of the controller design process are introduced in the following; these include the decoupling controller design for MIMO systems and the local adaptive capacity control of SISO systems.

Decoupling Control for MIMO Systems

A multi-workstation, multi-product job shop manufacturing process is a typical MIMO system with various delays, uncertainties, and couplings. RRCF was adopted in the capacity control of this system. Based on the mathematical model in (4), the input rate from the initial stage $X_{0i}^I(t)$ was assumed to randomly change with a Gaussian distribution, which was considered the uncertainty of the system. The disturbance $X_i^D(t)$, e.g., the rush order, which was also from the initial stage, was included in the uncertainty $XD_{i(t)}$, which was represented by ΔN_i. Then, the right factorization of the complex MIMO system was $Q=(N+\Delta N)\circ D^{-1}$, where the N and D were designed with

$$\begin{aligned} w_i(t) &= D_i^{-1}(u_j(t-\tau_2-\tau_1))(u_i(t-\tau_2)) \\ &= X_{0i}^I(t-\tau_1)+\sum_{j=1}^{n} p_{ji}\cdot(n_j^D\cdot v_j^D+u_j(t-\tau_2-\tau_1)\cdot v_j^R) \\ &\quad -(n_i^D\cdot v_i^D+u_i(t-\tau_2)\cdot v_i^R) \end{aligned} \tag{9}$$

$$y_i(t) = N_i+\Delta N_i = y_i(0)+\int_0^t w_i(\tau)+X_i^D(\tau)d\tau. \tag{10}$$

In (9), there are couplings among the input signals u_i for $i\in\{1,\ldots,n\}$, which can be described as n linear equations. The solution is obtained with $u_i(\cdot)=\sum_{j=1}^{n} D_{ij}(w_j)(\cdot)$. In order to simplify the computation for the RRCF-based capacity control of the MIMO system, the following theorem is given for the decoupling controller design [5].

Theorem 2. *Consider the decoupling control system shown in Figure 4. If there exists a linear operator G and a stable and invertible operator Z with*

$$\sum_{j=1, j\neq i}^{n} [Z_{ij}(w_i)](w_j)+G_i\circ D_{ij}(w_j)=0 \tag{11}$$

$$Z_{ii}(w_i)+G_i\circ D_{ii}(w_i)=L_i(w_i) \tag{12}$$

to ensure that L_i *is stable and invertible, then the MIMO system is decoupled, where* L=(L1,…,Ln *is the decoupled operator with* vi=Li(wi).

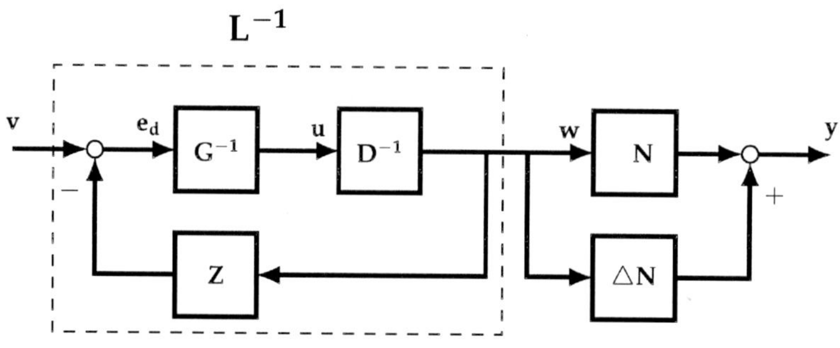

Figure 4. Decoupling structure of the MIMO system.

With this theorem, the stability of the decoupled job shop system can be proved based on the following proposition (cf. Proposition ! in [5] for a detailed proof).

Proposition 1. *Consider the system (4). Let the decoupling parameters* h_i *be finite with* $|h_i|\neq\frac{1}{v_i^R}$, *let* G=(G$_{1,\ldots,Gn)}$ *be the identity operator, and let* Zii *be unimodular for* i=1,…,n, *such that*

$$\sum_{j=1, j\neq i}^{n} [Z_{ij}(w_i)](w_j) = -\sum_{j=1, j\neq i}^{n} G_i\circ D_{ij}(w_j),$$

holds; then,

$$L_i(w_i) = (h_i - \frac{1}{v_i^R}) \cdot w_i - \frac{v_i^D n_i^D}{v_i^R} \tag{13}$$

holds. Furthermore, $L_{i(wi)}$ *is stable and invertible if* nR *is sufficiently large.*

Local Adaptive Capacity Control

The above decoupling controller transformed the MIMO system into *n* independent SISO systems. Then, while considering each decoupled SISO system, the local adaptive capacity controller is designed in two parts, namely, the RRCF controller and adaptive tracking controller for the robustness and tracking performance, respectively.

For the decoupled SISO system, the RRCF operators R_i and S_i are designed with the Bezout identity: $R_i \circ (N_i + \triangle N_i) + S_i \circ L_i = \tilde{M}_i$. Then, the following theorem is presented.

Theorem 3. *Consider the MIMO system (4) with the decoupling controller in Proposition 1. If the ith workstation has its local RRCF controller,*

$$R_i(s(\cdot)) = (1 - K_i) \cdot s(\cdot)' \tag{14}$$

$$S_i^{-1}(s(\cdot)) = \frac{(h_i v_i^R - 1)s(\cdot)}{v_i^R K_i} - \frac{v_i^D n_i^D}{v_i^R} \tag{15}$$

for i=1,2,⋯,n, *and the RRCF control parameter* $K_{i\in}(0,1)$, *then the feedback control system shown in Figure 5 is stable.*

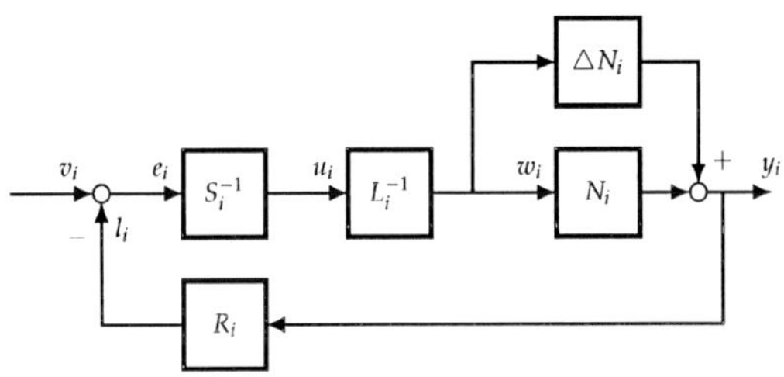

Figure 5. RRCF control of the decoupled MIMO systems.

Proof. The coupling system (4) can be represented with $y_i(t) = N_i L_i^{-1}$ for $i = 1, 2, \cdots, n$ by using Proposition 1. According to the definition of RRCF 2, let

$$L_i^{-1}(s(\cdot)) = \frac{s(\cdot)v_i^R + v_i^D n_i^D}{h_i v_i^R - 1} \tag{16}$$

$$(N_i + \triangle N_i)(s(\cdot)) = \int (s(\cdot))dt. \tag{17}$$

Additionally, according to Theorem 1, the control system can be equivalent, and its Lipschitz semi-norm is

$$\|N_i + \triangle N_i\| := \sup_{s,\tilde{s} \in D_s \& s \neq \tilde{s}} \frac{\|(N_i + \triangle N_i)(s) - (N_i + \triangle N_i)(\tilde{s})\|_{Y_s}}{\|s - \tilde{s}\|_{U_s}} < 1 + |X^D(t)|. \tag{18}$$

Because the uncertainty $XD_{i(t)}$ is bounded, the Lipschitz semi-norm $\|(N_{i+}\triangle N_{i)}\|$ is finite. Finally, this can prove that the above local RRCF control system is stable.

Based on the RRCF controller designed for robust stability, a PI-type tracking controller (PI-RRCF), as proposed in [16], was investigated. Though integration could eliminate static differences and improve control accuracy, it may cause a large deviation in the system output during the start-up or in face of significant changes with respect to the set value, which would lead to the accumulation of integrations with the resulting overshoot or oscillation [32]. To solve these problems, therefore, an integral-separation PI tracking controller is proposed, which is called ISPI-RRCF algorithm; cf. Figure 6 for a sketch. Then, the tracking controller C_i in the j_{th} workstation is designed as

$$C_i(s(\cdot)) = C_i^0 \cdot s(\cdot) + \beta \cdot C_i^1 \cdot \int s(\cdot) \tag{19}$$

Where C_i^0 and C_i^1 are tracking parameters, β is the integral term selector switch coefficient, and ϵ is the threshold, i.e.,

$$\beta = \begin{cases} 0 & |s(\cdot)| > \epsilon \\ 1 & |s(\cdot)| \leq \epsilon \end{cases} \tag{20}$$

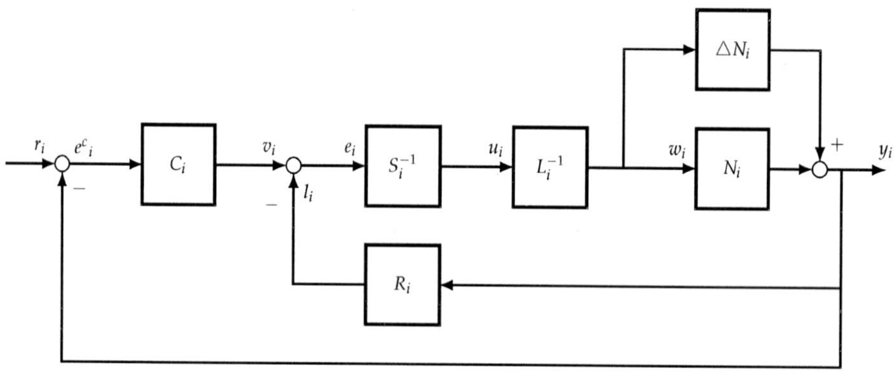

Figure 6. Nonlinear feedback tracking control of the MIMO system.

From (19) and (20), it can be seen that the integration does not work in the case of overshoot when the deviation exceeds the given threshold, and conversely. the integration would be (re-)introduced to minimize the static error once the deviation falls into the threshold. Now, the ISPI-RRCF feedback tracking control system is discussed with the following theorem.

Theorem 4. *Given the bounded and disturbed MIMO system (4) and the tracking operator* C_i *in (19), the closed-loop system in Figure 6 is stable.*

Proof. When the system is at the initial zero state, as shown in Figure 6, it obtains $y_i = (N_i + \Delta N_i) C_i(e^c_i(\cdot))$ with

$$\begin{aligned} y_i(t) &= \int C_i^0(e_i^c)(t) + \beta C_i^1 \int (e_i^c)(\tau) d\tau dt + \int C_i^0(X_i^P)(t) + \beta C_i^1 \int (X_i^P)(\tau) d\tau dt \\ &= \int C_i^0(r_i - y_i)(t) + \beta C_i^1 \int (r_i - y_i)(\tau) d\tau dt + \int C_i^0(X_i^P)(t) + \beta C_i^1 \int (X_i^P)(\tau) d\tau dt. \end{aligned} \tag{21}$$

By calculating the Laplace transformation of (21), it can be represented with

$$\hat{Q} : Y_i(s) = \frac{C_i^0 s + \beta C_i^1}{s^2 + C_i^0 s + \beta C_i^1} \cdot (R_i(s) + D_i(s)).$$

Let $S_i(\cdot) = R_i(\cdot) + D_i(\cdot)$ then, the Lipschitz semi-norm is obtained via

$$\|\hat{Q}\| := \sup_{F\in(0,\infty)} \sup_{S\neq\hat{S}} \frac{\|[\hat{Q}(S)]_F - [\hat{Q}(\hat{S})]_F\|}{\|[S]_F - [\hat{S}]_F\|}$$
$$= \sup_{F\in(0,\infty)} \left| \frac{C_i^0 s + \beta C_i^1}{s^2 + C_i^0 s + \beta C_i^1} \right| \leq 1. \quad (22)$$

Hence, the above feedback tracking control system is stable.

To improve the tracking control performance in complex dynamic environments, the parameters of the PI-type control are usually adaptively tuned by metaheuristic algorithms [33]. In this paper, an artificial neural network (ANN) method was considered, and a single neuron was utilized to adaptively adjust the parameters of the tracking controllers [34] (i.e., C_i^0, C_i^1 in (19)). In this case, the inputs of the single neuron were defined as $x_{i0} = e_i^c - e_i^{cp}$ and $x_{i1} = e_i^c = r_i - y_i, i = 1, \cdots, n,$ where e^c_i is the error between the desired and current feedback of the system, and e_i^{cp} represents the previous error. By using the connection weights of x_{ij} in the single neuron, the relationship between the input x_{ij} and the i_{th} output v_i in the context of incremental PI control is given as

$$v_i = v_i^p + K_i \sum_{j=0}^{1} \hat{w}_{ij} x_{ij}^T \qquad \hat{w}_{ij} = w_{ij} / \left| \sum_{j=0}^{1} w_{ij} \right| \quad (23)$$

where w_{ij} is a weighting coefficient, and $K_{i>0}$ is the proportional coefficient of the neuron. Concerning the self-adaptive learning rules, the supervised Hebb learning algorithm was adopted; this included the learning rate $\xi_{ij>0}$ and the correlative functions of input x_{ij}, output v_i, and output error e^c_i of the neuron, i.e.,

$$w_{ij} := w_{ij} + \xi_{ij} e_i^c v_i x_{ij}^T \quad (24)$$

With the update of the w_{ij} iteration, the parameters of the tracking controllers $C_{ij,j=0,1}$ for all workstations would be changed, and satisfactory tracking performance could be guaranteed in the presence of disturbances and delays.

Overall, the adaptive integral separation PI combined with the RRCF (ISPI-RRCF) method for WIP tracking control via RMTs is outlined in Algorithm 1.

Algorithm 1 Framework of the adaptive ISPI-RRCF
Require: Given the MIMO system with disturbances $Q^{-}(N+\Delta N)\circ D^{-1}$; 1: Transfer the MIMO system into a set number of SISO systems via decoupling controllers Z and G; 2: Design RRCF controllers R and S for each decoupled SISO system (workstation) to guarantee stability in the presence of uncertainty and delays. 3: Adopt ISPI controllers C for WIP tracking while decreasing overshoot; 4: Optimize the parameters of the C-based single neuron to improve the transient and robustness performance; Ensure: Converged WIP level (output) for each workstation within a given prescribed threshold through the assignment of RMTs (input).

NUMERICAL SIMULATION

In this paper, a job shop manufacturing process with four workstations and $n^{R=10}$ RMTs for three products [31] is considered. The flow probabilities between the workstations were dynamically changed with volatile demands for three different types of products. The system settings and simulation results are given below.

Simulation Settings

The demands for the products were bounded and normally distributed in the form of the randi ([45, 56]) function, which was the uncertainty of the system. In terms of parameter adjustments on the tracking controllers, the initial values of the weight and learning rate of the single neuron were identical for both the PI-RRCF and ISPI-RRCF control systems. The threshold in the ISPI-RRCF system was set to ϵ=[90909090]. The practical stability region concerning the converged WIP level was set to $\pm 3 * v_j^{RMT}$. The reconfiguration delay of the RMTs was 2 h, and the transportation delay between each workstation was 1 h. With these settings, together with those in Table 2, a performance analysis and a comparison of both control systems are given in the following.

Table 2. Simulation settings of the case study [35]

Workstation	1	2	3	4
Initial WIP level	400	400	300	200
Referred WIP level	240	400	400	240
Number of DMTs	4	2	2	4
Output rate of DMTs	20	40	40	20
Output rate of RMTs	10	20	20	10

Dynamic Performance Analysis

The dynamic performance of each workstation and product in both the PI-RRCF and ISPI-RRCF capacity control systems while facing stochastic demands are shown in Figure 7, Figure 8, Figure 9 and Figure 10. The dynamic optimization values of both the PI and ISPI tracking control parameters with the single neuron are given in Figure 9.

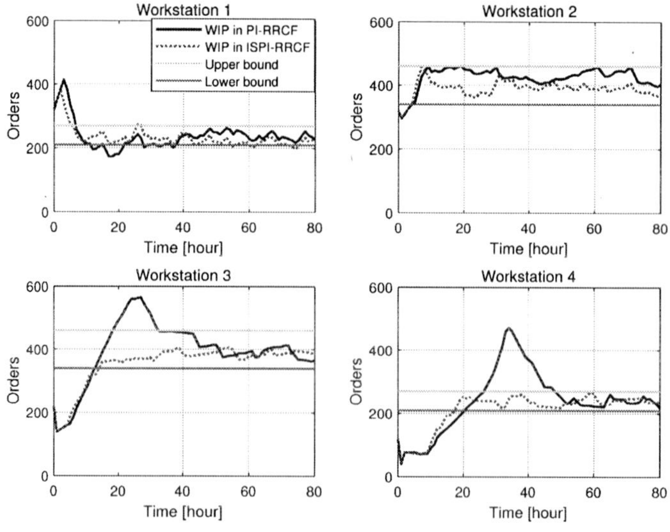

Figure 7. WIP levels of workstations for stochastic demands.

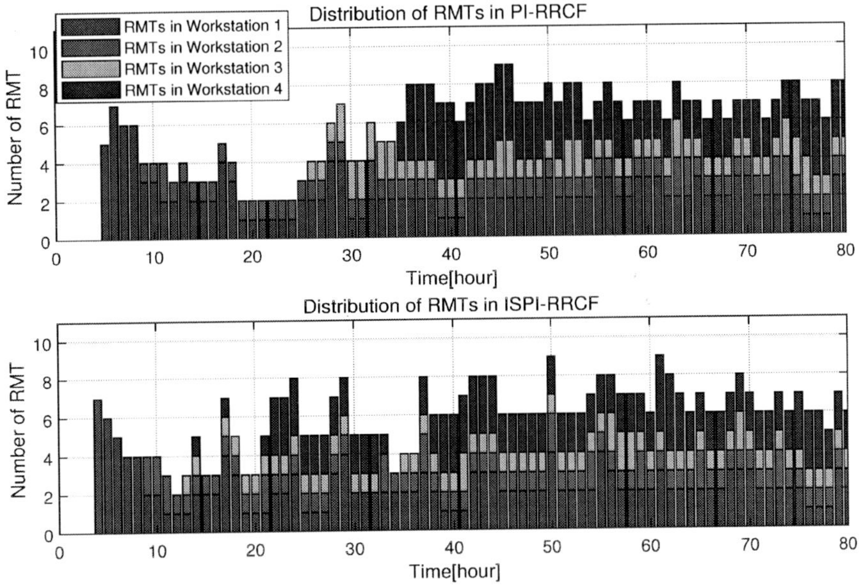

Figure 8. Distribution of RMTs for stochastic demands.

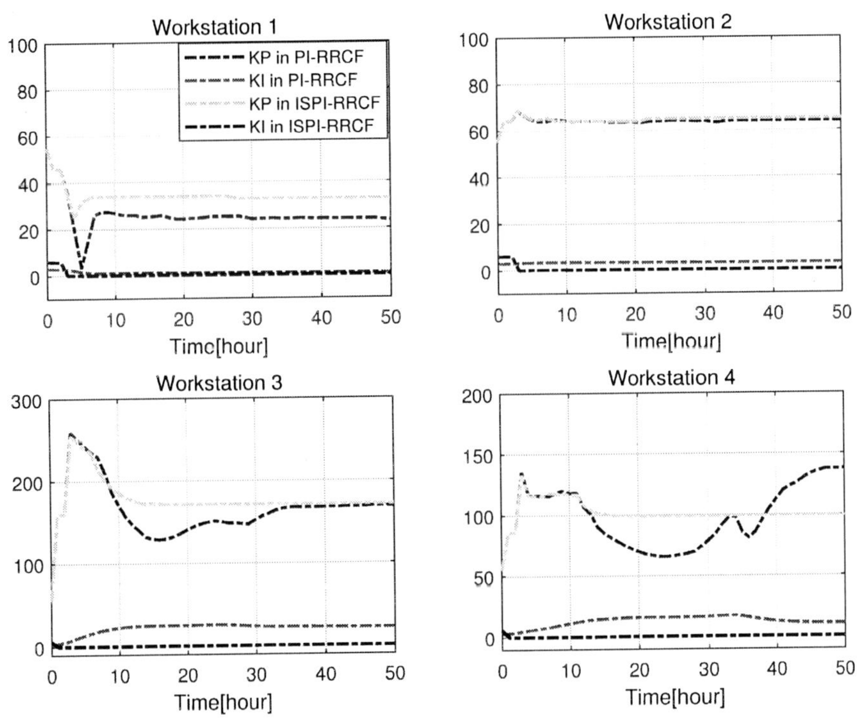

Figure 9. Value of the tracking controller's parameters.

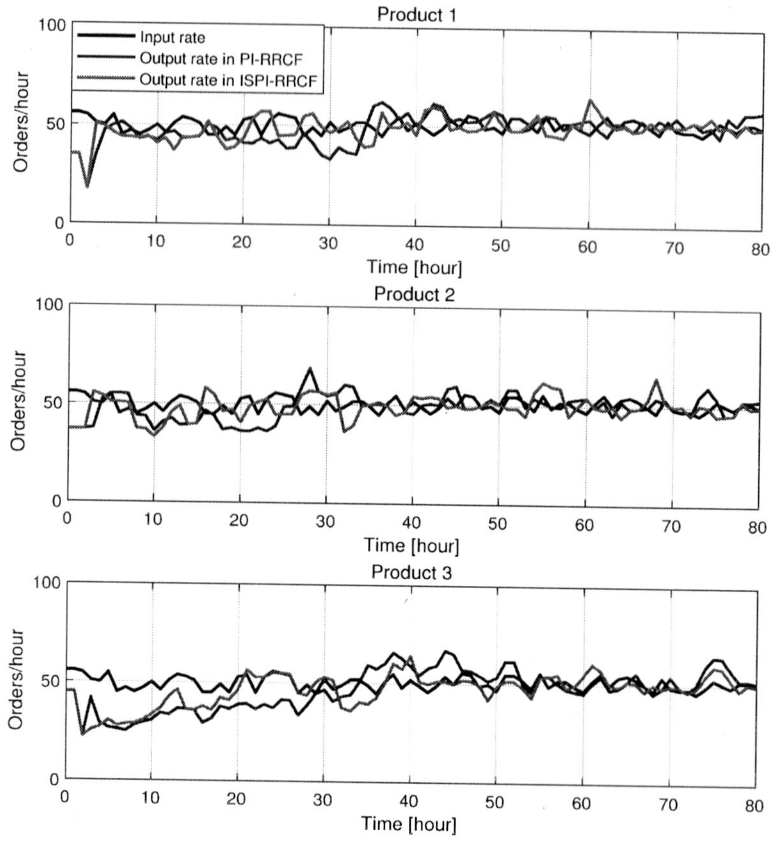

Figure 10. Dynamic performance of the products.

In Figure 7, the blue and red lines represent the WIP levels controlled by PI-RRCF and ISPI-RRC, respectively. In workstation 1, the initial WIP constantly increased with the orders flowing into the workstation at the initial stage, which could cause a bottleneck. This phenomenon can be explained—in the first few hours, the RMTs were not completely reconfigured and assigned to workstations due to reconfiguration delays and transportation delays (cf. Figure 8). However, the ISPI-RRCF control system showed a quicker response than that of the PI-RRCF system in terms of assigning RMTs to the workstation in the case of a bottleneck. After 20 h, the WIP levels were kept in the vicinity of the planned values for both the ISPI-RRCF and PI-RRCF control systems. Nonetheless, the former showed better dynamic performance with lower overshoots and shorter settling times. In contrast to workstation 1, the initial WIP levels in the other workstations were lower than or equal to their respective planned values. As the order outputs were higher than the input rates, the WIP levels decreased in the first few hours. Later, with more orders flowing through these workstations, the WIP started to increase and approach the planned levels. However, due to the lag effect caused by delays and the accumulation of integration, PI-RRCF had a higher overshoot and longer settling times. This indicated that, compared with the previous PI-RRCF, the proposed ISPI-RRCF could effectively improve the transient performance to avoid a high overshoot, which represented the bottleneck level and unbalanced capacity distribution. This greatly improved the productivity and decreased the production costs. Figure 8 shows the distribution of RMTs of each workstation in the capacity control processes, which shows that the response in the ISPI-RRCF control system was quicker than that of the PI-RRCF system in the assignment of RMTs to the required workstations. With the orders flowing to the next workstations, two RMTs, one RMT, and one RMT were, respectively, assigned to workstations 2, 3, and 4 at the 9th, 14th, and 15th hours, respectively. However, in the PI-RRCF system, five RMTs, one RMT, one RMT, and one RMT were, respectively, assigned to workstations 1, 2, 3, and 4 at the 5th, 9th, 27th, and 35th hours, respectively. Additionally, the ISPI-RRCF showed a bit less utilization of RMTs while facing quickly changing customer demand, which could reduce the production costs from the machine tools. Therefore, this indicates that the ISPI-RRCF could predict possible bottlenecks and assign enough RMTs to balance the capacity distribution by using the customized flexibility of RMTs. This further illustrates the quicker response in the ISPI-RRCF control system for effectively deducing high overshoots and avoiding bottleneck problems, which highly decreased the production costs and improved the dynamic performance.

For the tracking control parameter values, Figure 9 shows the dynamic optimization results obtained by using the single neuron in both the PI-RRCF and ISPI-RRCF capacity control processes. With the decoupling control, each workstation was an independent SISO system. Therefore, the parameter optimization was relatively independent in both the PI-RRCF and ISPI-RRCF systems. However, compared with Figure 8, the curves for the KP (i.e., C_i^0) and KI (i.e., C_i^1) in ISPI-RRCF showed relatively stable behaviors after 10 h, while the PI-RRCF took a longer time. The KI values in all workstations went toward 0 to avoid high overshoots when the error was over set threshold in the ISPI-RRCF control system. However, the KI values were not zeros in the PI-RRCF system, which explained one of the reasons for the high overshoots. From the overall settings, these values had relatively quicker updating in ISPI-RRCF in order to solve bottlenecks, and they had relatively stable settings when facing bounded stochastic input rates. This illustrated the effectiveness of the proposed adaptive algorithm based on a single neuron with supervised Hebb learning. On the other hand, this could also imply the better dynamic and robust performances in the ISPI-RRCF control system.

Unlike the performance analysis in the workstations, the input and output rates of each product were not independent, which caused dynamic changes in the workstations' productivity. When facing stochastic demands, the input rates of each product were the same in both control systems, as shown with the black lines in Figure 10. The blue and red lines represent the product output rates in the PI-RRCF and ISPI-RRCF control systems. Products 1, 2, and 3 were produced starting from the first, second, and first workstations and were finished at the third, fourth, and fourth workstations, respectively. The output rate of each product was produced by the DMTs at the beginning. With the additional RMTs assigned to the later two workstations, the output rates were quickly increased around the input rate in 20 h in the ISPI-RRCF system. However, the PI-RRCF system took a longer time. Additionally, the output rates in ISPI-RRCF were around the input rate for most of the time, which showed that there was greater customer satisfaction in this system. In summary, when facing stochastic customer demands, both control systems were able to provide the required output products, while the proposed ISPI-RRCF system still showed better dynamic performance with a quicker response for satisfying customers' stochastic demands. Considering the transient performance in the above figures, it was concluded that both control systems could deal with stochastic demands to guarantee that the WIP of workstations was kept in the vicinity of the desired level and that the output rate of the products was kept close to the input rates. However, the proposed adaptive ISPI-RRCF tracking capacity control system showed better behaviors with a quicker response and lower overshoot. This indicated that the control system could significantly avoid serious bottlenecks and quickly balance the capacity distribution to improve the productivity and decrease the inventory and production costs, which also illustrated the effectiveness of the proposed ISPI-RRCF method.

Robustness Analysis

Stochastic customer demands and different types of products were considered when measuring and analyzing the robustness of the capacity control systems. In this part, robustness was defined as the mean and standard deviation of the output variables. The distribution of the error between the planned and current WIP at each workstation is given in Figure 11. The blue and red error bars are the distributions of errors in the PI-RRCF and ISPI-RRCF capacity control systems. These showed that the distributions in the red bars of all workstations were highly concentrated, with smaller mean values and standard deviations than those of the blue bars, which indicated that the WIP values of the workstations were distributed closer to the desired levels in the ISPI-RRCF system, with a higher robustness. Additionally, the red error bars were distributed over zero, which meant that the WIP levels of the workstations were lower than the planned level in most cases. This illustrated the lower possibility of bottleneck occurrence in this control system.

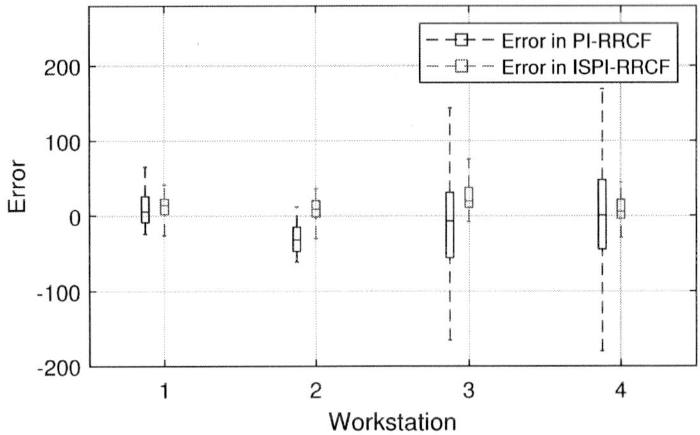

Figure 11. Error distributions between the planned and current WIP of the workstations.

Figure 12 shows the distribution of products while considering the input and output rates. The black error bars present the distribution of order input rates. The blue and red error bars in the PI-RRCF and ISPI-RRCF were relatively broad, but the latter distribution was still relatively concentrated. This showed that the robustness when considering the order output rate of products in the ISPI-RRCF system was still higher than that in the PI-RRCF system.

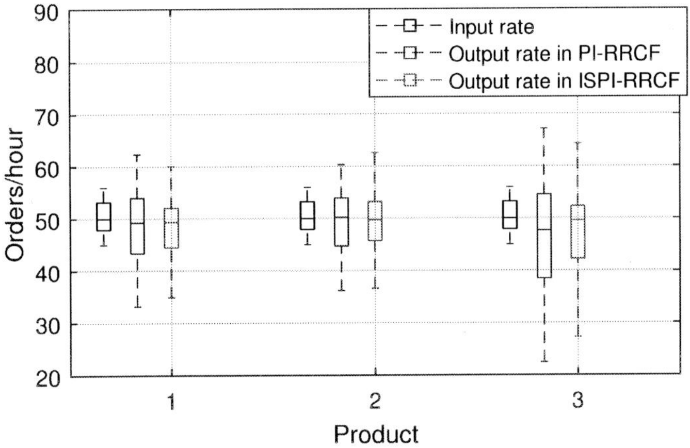

Figure 12. Input and output rate distributions of the products.

The overall statistics of the transient and robustness performance in both the ISPI-RRCF and PI-RRCF control systems are summarized in Table 3. The mean number of RMTs (MRMT) and standard deviation of RMTs (SDRMT) at each workstation were close in the ISPI-RRCF and PI-RRCF control systems. Nonetheless, the mean value of the absolute error (MAE) between the desired and actual WIP, as well as the standard deviation of the absolute error (SDAE), were smaller in the ISPI-RRCF system, which further indicated the higher robustness of this capacity control system. The transient performance when considering the overshoot and settling times of these two control systems was also collected. This further showed that the dynamic performance in the ISPI-RRCF system was better than that in the PI-RRCF system, with smaller overshoots and shorter settling times.

Table 3. Statistics of the capacity control systems

Number of the Workstation	**1**	**2**	**3**	**4**
MRMT in PI-RRCF	2.22	0.99	0.87	1.65
MRMT in ISPI-RRCF	2.23	1.01	0.87	1.66
SDRMT in PI-RRCF	1.22	0.41	0.69	1.52
SDRMT in ISPI-RRCF	1.17	0.52	0.49	1.11
MAE in PI-RRCF	18.85	34.62	51.97	60.90
MAE in ISPI-RRCF	17.24	13.25	26.65	21.55
SDAE in PI-RRCF	16.28	16.37	49.79	65.72
SDAE in ISPI-RRCF	10.43	10.46	28.89	34.74
Overshoots in PI-RRCF	0.72	0.15	0.41	0.96
Overshoots in ISPI-RRCF	0.60	0.14	0.02	0.12
Setting time in PI-RRCF	21	5	32	48
Setting time in ISPI-RRCF	6	5	13	18

In summary, for the capacity control of the complex job shop system with transportation delays, reconfiguration delays, and stochastic demand, the key system performance indexes and control performance indexes are discussed. The system performance indexes were represented by the WIP of the workstations and the output rate of the products, while the control performance indexes were represented by the transients and robustness. The performance of the proposed adaptive ISPI-RRCF and PI-RRCF control systems is compared and analyzed in this section. The system performance indexes showed that both control systems could keep the WIP and product output rate at the desired value to ensure productivity and satisfy customer demands. However, ISPI-RRCF had better transient and robustness performance in terms of its lower overshoots, shorter settling times, and smaller means and standard deviations. This indicated that the proposed algorithm could greatly improve the performance to avoid serious bottlenecks and balance the capacity distribution for high productivity, low costs, and high customer satisfaction.

CONCLUSIONS

This paper focused on the adaptive tracking capacity control of complex job shops. Considering stochastic customer demands, an improved ISPI-RRCF adaptive capacity control method was proposed to enhance the transient and robustness performance. Considering the customized flexibility of RMTs and the complexity of job shops, including stochastic customer demands, reconfiguration delays of RMTs, and transportation delays between workstations, a funnel-based mathematical model was introduced for the capacity controller design. Based on this model, an operator-based capacity controller was designed, which included a decoupling controller for the MIMO system and, later, a local ISPI-RRCF capacity controller for decoupled SISO systems. In particular, the local ISPI-RRCF controller was designed by including an RRCF controller and ISPI tracking controller, where the parameters were dynamically optimized by a single neuron based on the supervised Hebb learning algorithm. The stability of the closed-loop system was theoretically proven based on the Lipschitz norm. Finally, a case study for the capacity control of a job shop system was implemented in a simulation. The transient and robustness performance of the proposed ISPI-RRCF control system was analyzed and compared with that of a previous PI-RRCF control system. The results showed that when considering the system performance indexes, both the proposed ISPI-RRCF and the previous PI-RRCF capacity control systems could keep the WIP of all workstations in the vicinity of the planned levels and could keep the output rate of the products close to the input rates. However, for the control performance indexes, the proposed ISPI-RRCF system had a better transient performance with smaller overshoots and shorter settling times, as well as better robustness, with a smaller MAE and SDAE. Therefore, the effectiveness of the proposed adaptive ISPI-RRCF capacity control algorithm could be proven due to the avoidance of serious bottlenecks and the balancing of capacity distribution problems. This research also provides new opportunities for manufacturers for higher productivity, lower costs, and greater customer satisfaction when facing challenges from quickly changing markets, new technological revolutions, and sustainable manufacturing.

Author Contributions

Conceptualization, P.L.; methodology, P.L.; software, P.L.; validation, P.L. and Q.Z.; investigation, P.L., A.W. and J.P.; writing—original draft preparation, P.L. and Q.Z.; writing—review and editing, S.W.; visualization, A.W.; supervision, J.P.; project administration, P.L. All authors have read and agreed to the published version of the manuscript.

REFERENCES

1. Scholz-Reiter, B.; Freitag, M.; Schmieder, A. Modelling and control of production systems based on nonlinear dynamics theory. CIRP Ann. 2002, 51, 375–378.
2. Alkan, B.; Vera, D.A.; Ahmad, M.; Ahmad, B.; Harrison, R. Complexity in manufacturing systems and its measures: A literature review. Eur. J. Ind. Eng. 2018, 12, 116–150.
3. Thürer, M.; Stevenson, M.; Land, M.J.; Fredendall, L.D. On the combined effect of due date setting, order release, and output control: An assessment by simulation. Int. J. Prod. Res. 2019, 57, 1741–1755.
4. Stastny, J.; Skorpil, V.; Balogh, Z.; Klein, R. Job Shop Scheduling Problem Optimization by Means of Graph-Based Algorithm. Appl. Sci. 2021, 11, 1921.
5. Liu, P.; Zhang, Q.; Pannek, J. Development of operator theory in the capacity adjustment of job shop manufacturing systems. Appl. Sci. 2019, 9, 2249.
6. Zhang, Q.; Liu, P.; Chen, Y.; Deng, Q.; Pannek, J. An improved event-triggered predictive control for capacity adjustment in reconfigurable job-shops. Int. J. Prod. Res. 2022, 1–18.
7. Karimi, H.R.; Duffie, N.A.; Dashkovskiy, S. Local capacity h_∞ control for production networks of autonomous work systems with time-varying delays. IEEE Trans. Autom. Sci. Eng. 2010, 7, 849–857.
8. Landers, R.G.; Min, B.K.; Koren, Y. Reconfigurable machine tools. CIRP Ann. Manuf. Technol. 2001, 50, 269–274.
9. Scholz-Reiter, B.; Lappe, D.; Grundstein, S. Capacity adjustment based on reconfigurable machine tools–Harmonising throughput time in job-shop manufacturing. CIRP Ann. 2015, 64, 403–406.
10. Zhang, Q.; Liu, P.; Pannek, J. Modeling and predictive capacity adjustment for job shop systems with RMTs. In Proceedings of the 25th Mediterranean Conference on Control and Automation (MED), Valletta, Malta, 3–6 July 2017.
11. Zhong, R.Y.; Xu, X.; Klotz, E.; Newman, S.T. Intelligent manufacturing in the context of industry 4.0: A review. Engineering 2017, 3, 616–630.
12. Kim, J.H.; Duffie, N.A. Backlog control design for a closed loop PPC system. CIRP Ann. 2004, 53, 357–360.
13. Kim, J.H.; Duffie, N.A. Performance of coupled closed-loop workstation capacity controls in a multi-workstation production system. CIRP Ann. 2006, 55, 449–452.
14. Ang, K.H.; Chong, G.; Li, Y. PID control system analysis, design, and technology. IEEE Trans. Control Syst. Technol. 2005, 13, 559–576.
15. Chen, G.; Han, Z. Robust right coprime factorization and robust stabilization of nonlinear feedback control systems. IEEE Trans. Automat. Control 1998, 43, 1505–1509.
16. Deng, M.; Inoue, A.; Ishikawa, K. Operator-based nonlinear feedback control design using robust right coprime factorization. IEEE Trans. Autom. Control. 2006, 51, 645–648.
17. Xu, Y.; Deng, M. Particle Filter Design for Robust Nonlinear Control System of Uncertain Heat Exchange Process with Sensor Noise and Communication Time Delay. Appl. Sci. 2022, 12, 2495.
18. Bi, S.; Deng, M.; Xiao, Y. Robust stability and tracking for operator-based nonlinear uncertain systems. IEEE Trans. Autom. Sci. Eng. 2014, 12, 1059–1066.
19. Deng, M.; Wang, A. Robust non-linear control design to an ionic polymer metal composite with hysteresis using operator-based approach. IET Control Theory Appl. 2012, 6, 2667–2675.

20. Bu, N.; Pang, J.; Deng, M. Robust fault tolerant tracking control for the multi-joint manipulator based on operator theory. J. Frankl. Inst. 2020, 357, 2696–2714.

21. Wen, S.; Deng, M.; Bi, S.; Wang, D. Operator-based robust nonlinear control and its realization for a multi-tank process by using a distributed control system. Trans. Inst. Meas. Control 2012, 34, 891–902.

22. Gharib, M.R.; Koochi, A.; Ghorbani, M. Path tracking control of electromechanical micro-positioner by considering control effort of the system. Proc. Inst. Mech. Eng. Part I J. Syst. Control. Eng. 2021, 235, 984–991.

23. Salehi Kolahi, M.R.; Gharib, M.R.; Heydari, A. Design of a non-singular fast terminal sliding mode control for second-order nonlinear systems with compound disturbance. Proc. Inst. Mech. Eng. Part C J. Mech. Eng. Sci. 2021, 235, 7343–7352.

24. Nguyen, M.H.; Dao, H.V.; Ahn, K.K. Adaptive robust position control of Electro-Hydraulic servo systems with large uncertainties and disturbances. Appl. Sci. 2022, 12, 794.

25. Ruan, W.; Dong, Q.; Zhang, X.; Li, Z. Friction compensation control of electromechanical actuator based on Neural Network Adaptive Sliding Mode. Sensors 2021, 21, 1508.

26. Sidhu, A.S.; Singh, S.; Kumar, R.; Pimenov, D.Y.; Giasin, K. Prioritizing energy-intensive machining operations and gauging the influence of electric parameters: An industrial case study. Energies 2021, 14, 4761.

27. Lödding, H. A manufacturing control model. Int. J. Prod. Res. 2012, 50, 6311–6328.

28. Zhang, Q.; Freitag, M.; Pannek, J. Stability of Predictive Control in Job Shop System with Reconfigurable Machine Tools for Capacity Adjustment. Logist. Res. 2019, 12, 3.

29. Zhang, Q.; Liu, P.; Pannek, J. Combining MPC and integer operators for capacity adjustment in job-shop systems with RMTs. Int. J. Prod. Res. 2019, 57, 2498–2513.

30. Liu, P.; Zhang, Q.; Pannek, J. Evaluation of Control Approaches for Capacity Adjustment in Job Shop Systems. IFAC-PapersOnLine 2019, 52, 1966–1971.

31. Liu, P.; Zhang, Q.; Wang, A.; Song, J.; Li, D.; Yan, Y.; Yang, L. Machinery-oriented Capacity Control for Complex Industrial Manufacturing Processes. In Proceedings of the 2021 International Conference on Advanced Mechatronic Systems (ICAMechS), Tokyo, Japan, 9–12 December 2021.

32. Xiang, Z.; Shao, X.; Wu, H.; Ji, D.; Yu, F.; Li, Y. An adaptive integral separated proportional–integral controller based strategy for particle swarm optimization. Knowl.-Based Syst. 2020, 195, 105696.

33. Joseph, S.B.; Dada, E.G.; Abidemi, A.; Oyewola, D.O.; Khammas, B.M. Metaheuristic algorithms for PID controller parameters tuning: Review, approaches and open problems. Heliyon 2022, 8, e09399.

34. Li, W.; Hori, Y. Vibration suppression using single neuron-based PI fuzzy controller and fractional-order disturbance observer. IEEE Trans. Ind. Electron. 2007, 54, 117–126.

35. Liu, P.; Chinges, U.; Zhang, Q.; Pannek, J. Capacity control in disturbed and time-delayed job shop manufacturing systems with RMTs. IFAC-PapersOnLine 2018, 51, 807–812.

INDEX

T

U

V

W

X